Wil[...] of North Florida

by
Jim Stevenson

To Beth —
Enjoy our local animals!
Merry Christmas —
Jim Stevenson

VanJus Press

CONTRIBUTORS

Editors	Richard and Joy Gilcrease
Photographs	Jim Stevenson
Cover Design and Layout	Justine Gilcrease
Illustrated Color Plates	Photoshop work by Justine Gilcrease. Picture of Brown Water Snake on Plate 2 was contributed by Bill Love of Blue Chameleon Ventures. The background for Plate 14 was donated by Tom Kilty. All other pictures by Jim Stevenson.

ISBN 0-9666438-2-8

1618 23rd St., Galveston, TX 77550

(409) 762-2333, FAX (409) 762-0411

CONTENTS

ILLUSTRATED PLATES

■ **Plate 1. Lizards** *1. Broad-headed Skink (male) 2. Eastern Glass Lizard 3. Slender Glass Lizard 4. Green Anole (green) 5. Green Anole (brown) 6. Five-lined Skinks - (a) female (b) young (c) male 7. Ground Skink 8. Six-lined Racerunner 9. Fence Lizard* ■ **Plate 2. Snakes** *1. Ringneck Snake 2. Gray Rat Snake 3. Yellow Rat Snake 4. Cottonmouth 5. Garter Snake 6. Eastern Hognosed Snake 7. Rough Earth Snake 8. Green Water Snake 9. Corn Snake 10. Brown Water Snake 11. Bluestripe Ribbon Snake 12. Florida Brown Snake 13. Mole Kingsnake 14. Mud Snake 15. Rough Green Snake 16. Redbelly Water Snake 17. Eastern Kingsnake 18. Rainbow Snake 19. Scarlet Kingsnake 20. Eastern Coral Snake* ■ **Plate 3. Arthropods** *1. Tiger Swallowtails (five) 2. Golden Orb Weaver 3. Robber Fly 4. Monarch 5. Katydid 6. Gray-mantled Grasshopper 7. Garden Orb Weaver 8. Canopy Millipede 9. Lubber Grasshopper 10. Skipper Butterfly 11. Cutworm 12. Spider Wasp 13. Pill Bug 14. Bartel's Wolf Spider* ■ **Plate 4. Amphibians** *1. Red-spotted Newt 2. Mud Salamander (belly) 3. Two-lined Salamander 4. Tiger Salamander 5. Bullfrog (male) 6. Leopard Frog 7. Green Treefrog 8. Bronze Frog 9. Pig Frog 10. River Frog 11. Spotted Salamander 12. Squirrel Treefrog 13. Red Salamander 14. Bullfrog (female) 15. Three-lined Salamander 16. Gray Treefrog 17. Marbled Salamander 18. Dwarf Salamander* ■ **Plate 5. Mammals** *1. Eastern Fox Squirrel 2. White-tailed Deer fawns 3. Red Fox 4. Coyote 5. Raccoon 6. White-tailed Deer doe 7. Bobcat 8. Red Wolf 9. Eastern Cottontail 10. Gray Squirrel 11. Gray Fox 12. Armadillo 13. Gray Squirrel albino 14. Opossum* ■ **Plate 6. White Waders** *1. Cattle Egret 2. Snowy Egret (a) flying (b) standing 3. Great Egret 4. Wood Stork 5. White Ibis 6. Roseate Spoonbill* ■ **Plate 7. Dark Waders** *1. Yellow-crowned Night-heron 2. Limpkin 3. Reddish Egret 4. Tricolored Heron 5. Great Blue Heron 6. Green Heron 7. White Ibis (immature) 8. Black-crowned Night-heron 9. Virginia Rail 10. Least Bittern 11. American Bittern 12. Purple Gallinule 13. Little Blue Heron 14. Common Moorhen 15. Sora* ■ **Plate 8. Male Ducks** *1. Red-breasted Mergansers 2. Mottled Duck 3. Wood Duck 4. Northern Shoveler 5. Canvasback 6. Green-winged Teal 7. Hooded Merganser 8.*

Bufflehead 9. Ring-necked Duck 10. Redhead 11. Blue-winged Teal 12. Lesser Scaup 13. American Wigeon 14. Ruddy Duck 15. Mallard 16. Greater Scaup 17. Northern Pintail 18. Common Goldeneye 19. Gadwall
■ **Plate 9. *Large Shorebirds*** *1. Willet 2. Black-necked Stilt 3. American Oystercatcher 4. American Avocet 5. Marbled Godwit 6. Long-billed Curlew 7. Whimbrel 8. Greater Yellowlegs 9. Lesser Yellowlegs*
■ **Plate 10. Small Shorebirds** *1. Wilson's Phalarope 2. Red Knot 3. Ruddy Turnstone 4. Wilson's Plover 5. Solitary Sandpiper 6. Pectoral Sandpiper 7. Least Sandpiper 8. Piping Plover 9. Snowy Plover 10. Semipalmated Sandpiper 11. Dunlin 12. Spotted Sandpiper 13. Western Sandpiper 14. Semipalmated Plover 15. Short-billed Dowitcher 16. White-rumped Sandpiper* ■ **Plate 11. Birds of Prey** *1. Swallow-tailed Kite 2. Northern Harrier 3. Merlin 4. Bald Eagle 5. Red-shouldered Hawk 6. American Kestrel (female) 7. Peregrine 8. Broad-winged Hawk 9. Mississippi Kite 10. Red-tailed Hawk 11. Black Vulture 12. Turkey Vulture* ■ **Plate 12. Woodpeckers and Flycatchers** *1. Eastern Wood-pewee 2. Hairy Woodpecker 3. Redbellied Woodpecker 4. Yellow-bellied Sapsucker 5. Acadian Flycatcher 6. Great-crested Flycatcher 7. Red-cockaded Woodpecker 8. Pileated Woodpecker 9. Vermilion Flycatcher 10. Western Kingbird 11. Red-headed Woodpecker 12. Downy Woodpecker 13. Northern Flicker 14. Eastern Kingbird 15. Eastern Phoebe 16. Scissor-tailed Flycatcher* ■ **Plate 13. Miscellaneous Landbirds** *1. Red-breasted Nuthatch 2. Blue-headed Vireo 3. Brown Creeper 4. Golden-crowned Kinglet 5. Cedar Waxwing 6. Blue-gray Gnatcatcher 7. Eastern Meadowlark 8. Ruby-crowned Kinglet 9. American Pipit 10. Common Nighthawk 11. Chuck-will's-widow 12. Sedge Wren 13. Savannah Sparrow 14. House Wren 15. Chipping Sparrow 16. White-throated Sparrow* ■ **Plate 14. Colorful Songbirds** *1. Blue Jay 2. Baltimore Oriole (f) 3. Baltimore Oriole (m) 4. Indigo Bunting (m) 5. Indigo Bunting (f) 6. Blue Grosbeak (m) 7. Blue Grosbeak (f) 8. Orchard Oriole (f) 9. Orchard Oriole (m) 10. Painted Bunting (m) 11. Painted Bunting (f) 12. Scarlet Tanager (m) 13 Scarlet Tanager (f) 14. Northern Cardinal (m) 15. Northern Cardinal (f) 16. American Goldfinch (m) 17. American Goldfinch (f) 18. Summer Tanager (m) 19. Summer Tanager (f) 20. Rose-breasted Grosbeak (m) 21. Rose-breasted Grosbeak (f)* ■ **Plate 15. Warblers I** *1. Kentucky Warbler 2. Connecticut Warbler 3. Yellow Warbler 4. Canada Warbler 5. Nashville Warbler 6. Swainson's Warbler 7. Yellow-rumped Warbler (winter) 8. Cerulean Warbler 9. Blackburnian Warbler 10. Northern Parula 11. Common Yellowthroat 12. Blue-winged Warbler 13. Prairie Warbler 14. Golden-winged Warbler 15. Hooded Warbler 16. Magnolia Warbler 17. Chestnut-sided Warbler 18. Prothonotary Warbler 19. Black-throated Green Warbler* ■ **Plate 16. Warblers II** *1. Ovenbird 2. Yellow-throated Warbler 3. Black-throated Blue Warbler 4. Mourning Warbler 5. Pine Warbler 6. Black-and-white Warbler 7. Blackpoll Warbler 8. Wilson's Warbler 9. Northern Waterthrush 10. Yellow-breasted Chat 11. Worm-eating Warbler 12. Bay-breasted Warbler 13. Tennessee Warbler 14. American Redstart 15. Louisiana Waterthrush 16. Palm Warbler 17. Orange-crowned Warbler 18. Cape May Warbler* ■ **Plate 17. Thrushes and Mimic Thrushes** *1. Gray-cheeked Thrush 2. Eastern Bluebird 3. Brown Thrasher 4. American Robin 5. Northern Mockingbird 6. Gray Catbird 7. Hermit Thrush 8. Swainson's Thrush 9. Veery 10. Wood Thrush* ■

Paradise Found

About an hour from Tallahassee, a pleasant Sunday afternoon's drive, is a monument that makes me smile but also carries with it a poignant truth that sums up much of this book. It is found by heading out Highway 20 (Pensacola Street) from Tallahassee and driving to the sleepy town of Bristol, Florida. As you enter, take State Road 12 to the right and continue north for a couple of miles. Watch for a lovely dirt road angling off to your left, and there amongst the trees is a sign:

That testimonial about the Garden of Eden was meant in quite a literal sense. There are many in that neck of the woods who believe the area around Liberty County, with its superb steephead ravines, actually is the land on which God planted Adam and Eve millennia ago. I can remember smirking years ago at letters written to the editor by E. E. Callaway proclaiming this the original Garden of Eden. And, though I have no knowledge from the heavens about the exact location the apple fell (actually, I suspect it might have been a pomegranate), had I been an aspiring taxonomist like Adam, the pine forest and canyonland north of Bristol would have been a terrific spot to settle down with my arranged bride.

FUN FOR THE YOUNG (AT HEART)

My dear students always used to ask me if I thought these acres along the Apalachicola River really were those depicted in Genesis. I usually took the opportunity to explain that people often attach religious or sensational meaning to phenomena of extreme beauty: Angel Falls, Devil's Canyon and so forth. And I never missed the chance to remark that it wasn't the apple in the tree, but the pair on the ground . . . . But unless I miss my guess, there are many things in this world with wonderful figurative meaning that in religion, our narrow literal interpretations preclude us from seeing. And no phrase or adjective in my thesaurus describes this diverse and wondrous ecosystem of North Florida better than a Garden of Eden.

Author slogs out of a marsh with his Green Water Snake

As a child raised by a field biologist, I romped this garden from one end to the other. I loved hunting the ferocious Green Water Snakes (our answer to South America's anacondas) in Lake Jackson north of Tallahassee, diving headlong into the lily pads to grab these mean-spirited leviathans. There was no greater joy and feeling of accomplishment than launching my torso almost blindly toward the ghostly greenish-gray reptiles, and feeling my fingers clamp down on the slick posterior (great training for a future life at third base). Believe me, there was no

Stand of Longleaf Pines-standing for the fight for our natural heritage

greater pain than having the beast inevitably turn on me and sink those huge, needle-like teeth deep within my knuckles. Bleeding like a stuck pig, I would sit there in the shallows admiring my non-venomous catch, elated to have something in life I was really good at.

Thankfully, as an adult and scientist, the joy and appreciation I feel toward places like Lake Jackson has not been lost. Sure, I understand intellectually about Karrst Plain topography and the geophysical forces that sculpted this sprawling lake, but our minds should never eclipse the childlike wonder and excitement splendid places such as Lake Jackson brings us. Through the years I have used this marshy lake to catch some of my largest bass, teach some of my best field classes and shoot my limit of low-flying ducks on foggy January mornings. Lake Jackson will always be near and dear to my heart and bring back the fondest of memories.

The amazing thing is, it's just one of a multitude of heart-stopping locations for admiring life and appreciating the wonders of North Florida. If you're tired of the open spaces, try walking through a floodplain along the banks of the Econfina River to watch Pileated Woodpeckers hammer away at ancient Bald Cypress. If you long for marine animals, take a drive to the coast and snorkel a Turtle Grass bed. If you desire a field full of beauty, head to a savannah in the Longleaf Pine community, and check out the orchids, pitcher plants and dozens of other radiant flowers glistening in the sun.

Indeed, North Florida is a Garden of Eden—and of wonder, magic and beauty. It is a boundless collection of diversity, owing to the vast assemblage of differing communities. It is a confluence of huge ecosystems, such as the

Like the timber industry, wise use of natural resources means taking some and leaving some

southern limit of the Appalachian influence, unique peninsular habitats such as the palm/hydric community, and of, course, the edge of the Gulf of Mexico. It's a menagerie of the Creator's plans, all stuck together and neatly woven like a jigsaw puzzle. The final product is a sportsman's paradise, an outdoor kid's playground and a smorgasbord for biologists. Families may enjoy areas from Wakulla Springs to the Blackwater River State Park, and hikers will find the Florida Trail among the best paths to nature in the country.

TIED TO THE SEA

So walk with me through North Florida. Learn of the way soil and water have created serial and climax communities and how plants and animals have responded to them. See for yourself the tremendous diversity of creatures that hop in the night, burrow in the mud, and fly into the trees. Then you will know that our gift was as special as Adam's, and you will find just cause to be a wise steward of all we have.

Geologic History of North Florida

There is a tremendous list of forces and events in the abiotic (nonliving) environment which sculpt ecosystems. Some of these like plate tectonics (continental drift) are almost too slow for the mind to comprehend, others like ice ages happen at a slightly less deliberate pace, while events such as volcanos and collisions with comets and meteors turn the earth on its celestial ear overnight.

Each of these epochs and events in history have had their impact on our state, making it both unique and varied, as we pan across North Florida from Jacksonville to Pensacola. Our purpose here is to lay the groundwork for understanding the geologic frame on which our plants and animals have been distributed.

It almost goes without saying that the earth is not the same planet it was at nearly any point in its past. Three billion years ago, life was just dawning with microbes floating around in the primeval soup. Well less than one billion years ago these cells organized themselves into colonies which brought us such primitive life forms as sponges, and later jellyfish.

During this time, the sandstone under Florida was being laid down, while Florida was connected to the present day African continent. Later, during the Jurassic, shelled animals such as mollusks began forming limestone as their car-

bonate shells sunk to the bottom. This explains why there are fossil shells found between pulses of sand and clay throughout Florida's earth.

Limestone showing marine life which began accumu-lating since Mesozoic times

Patiently lying buried on a sea floor without similarity to present ocean configurations, Florida sat watching one phylum of invertebrate life after another appear and radiate in the less salty, warm waters that covered our future state. Following the sponges and jellyfish came worms, the first to move with much purpose in life's great watery birthing ground. Echinoderms with their spiny skin and hard-shelled mollusks followed, lending much calcium carbonate to the ocean floor, and beginning to create Florida's future crust. Arthropods in the form of trilobites, which gave rise to our living fossils, the horseshoe crabs, dropped their polysaccharide chitinous shells into the depths nearly a half-billion years ago, to join remains of earlier fallen creatures. All these organic contributions were nothing compared to the later shells that built up to form the magic rock that underlies our flowery state: limestone.

LIVING STONES

Limestone will will be seen throughout this text to be one of the chief ingredients of Florida's wonder, and a regular Gaia example, as the abiotic environment was sculpted by the once-living. This limestone remained buried and growing well past the great extinctions at the end of Mesozoic time, where new life perched on the edge of life's stage.

Our heroes, the Chordates, slipped into the late Paleozoic seas as Devonian fish, and stepped to the forefront of ecological balance with players like Placoderms, the giant, plated sharks. The fish at the end of the Paleozoic also paved the way for land animals, with amphibians acting in the transitional role (as they always have) of living in the gray twilight between aquatic and terrestrial ecosystems. Their reptilian children sat poised, at the beginning of the great Mesozoic, to rule for eons that make the Roman Empire an eye's blink. First, all life on earth witnessed one of the two great extinctions our planet has known. The K-1 boundary, roughly 235,000,000 years ago, depicts a time when utter destruction of many marine creatures occurred, and some land animals as well. Explanations for this terrible event come hard, but many experts look to possible atmospheric changes as hypotheses.

Then in marched the Mesozoic, and all during the famous "Age of Reptiles," with heat and humidity favoring the mighty dinosaurs, Florida continued to form as a huge, unborn child in its creator's salty womb. For almost two hundred million years, scaly monsters roared and roamed across the terra firma, leaving their bones in about every corner of the globe imaginable—except reluctant Florida. First, all land was congregated into massive Pangea (Triassic), then while the real Jurassic Park was being played in, it was broken into two mighty supercontinents, Laurasia and Gondwana. Finally, after their reign of terror, the mightiest of earth's inhabitants fell like sheep to the extraterrestrial blow of an impacting meteor. Striking near present-day Yucatan, this last great extinction of the K-2 boundary 65,000,000 years ago altered the balance of power ecologically like we have never witnessed before or since. And, still, Florida lay asleep.

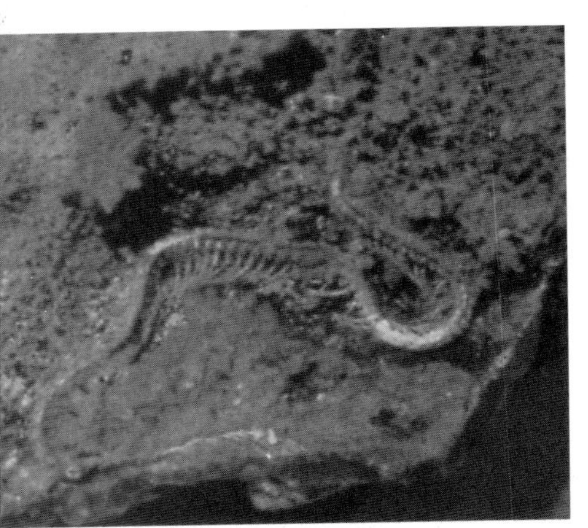

LEFTOVERS FROM THE DINOSAURS

A snake preserved in limestone shows its ribs and vertebral column exposed in the rock

The Cenozoic, or "Age of Mammals," would be Florida's era, but only at the eleventh hour. In the beginning, the punctuated equilibrium of evolution at its highest rate saw plants and animals replacing earth's losses at tremendous speeds. Ocean levels were so high, the entire Deep South was under water, save the Appalachians. Then, in the Eocene, a massive ice age (due to a warm ocean current being deflected to the Antarctic) crept up from the South Pole and forever changed the faces of Gondwana's three children, Africa, South America and Australia. But Florida never got so much as a sleepy chill.

By the Miocene, when the world supported about 20,000 species of birds (the other warm-blooded class to benefit from the dinosaur's disappearance), a tiny portion of the Sunshine State rose above the waves like a huge periscope on a mammoth submarine. And, of course, it was part of North Florida. Ocean levels fluctuated during the Miocene, but the stage was set for our state to rise above the ocean more and more in the millions of years to come.

There is a drop in the land there we call "Cody Scarp" (escarpment) that may be seen all across North Florida. The soil type changes from the red clay on the north side to the sand of the southern portion in many places, evidence of the lack of ocean above the scarp during much of the Cenozoic. To witness Cody Scarp, one need only drive U.S. 27 between Tallahassee and Perry, and observe the downhill ride from northwest to southeast. This was the edge of the ocean for quite some time around the middle of the Cenozoic. That fact explains why there is such a build up of sand in some locations, especially around rivers.

It was at about this time, however, that a seemingly insignificant geologic episode took place, but one that would change the course of Florida forever. In the ongoing saga of plate tectonics, mountains formed between South and Central America due to folding and faulting and created one very long, contiguous land mass. This deflected an ocean current, which had rushed between them east to west, in a northward direction. All the warm moist air from this tropical current was then carried up the widening Atlantic Ocean and to the North Polar region. You guessed it, the temperature started dropping.

By the beginning of the Pliocene, about 5,000,000 years ago, the Northern Hemisphere began to cool significantly, and ocean levels were dropping as ice began to form in the arctic. Without the land mass at the North Pole, there were millions of years of freezing before the actual ice age was upon us, but there was another abiotic factor that played into the puzzle.

Earth's orbit around the sun got knocked a little lopsided, so we went through periods when it was colder than at other times, called ice ages. Cycles lasted many thousands of years, and we are currently coming out of one that peaked about 18,000 years ago. So from about five to about two

SABRE-TOOTHED CAT

million years ago, temperatures dropped and Florida stood higher and higher.

By the Pleistocene, less than two million years ago, ice was forced out of the Arctic Sea and began expanding the only direction it could—south. It scraped over the areas of the far North like a giant plow, leveling the land we now know as coastal tundra. Down it came through the middle of the North American continent, scraping wounds in the earth we now call the "Great Lakes." In this time before us, there have been five major Pleistocene glaciations, each named for one of the Midwestern states ravaged by sheets of ice a mile thick.

During this time, the climate of present day "United States" was like that of the North tundra today. The Appalachians were bitter cold, and even Florida was pretty frigid, with scattered forests and windswept grasslands. Freshwater ecosystems stood hard as iron in the grip of each glacial onslaught, and extinction was everywhere. Even birds with their warm blood, had their worldwide diversity more than cut in half. But there was sure one group that was having a great time—the Great Pleistocene Mammals.

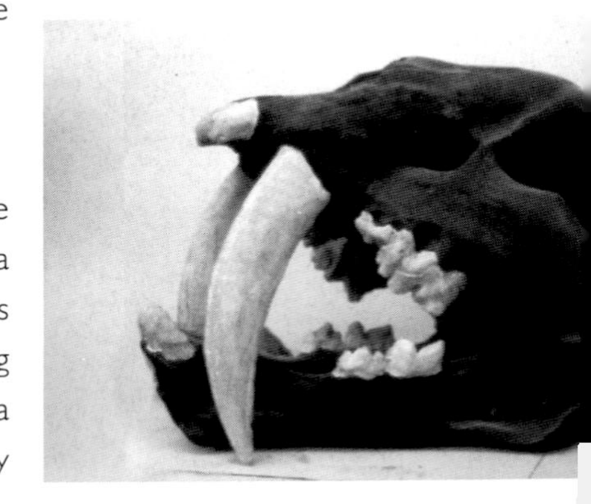

The Sabre-toothed Cat slit the jugular of larger mammals a few thousand years ago

The beasts were Asian in origin, but a land bridge was formed at the Bering Strait between Asia and Alaska. Here they came—lions, ground sloths, camels, sabre-toothed cats, buffalo, wolves eight feet long, and five-foot armadillos (who thankfully went extinct before the advent of cars). But the real behemoths were elephant-like Mastodons and Wooly Mammoths. The former was a browser, feeding on leaves like deer today. Mammoths were grazers, munching the tundra across North America with no natural enemies and a lot of space. Today, ten thousand years after the last one disappeared, their teeth can still be found in North Florida rivers. Mastodons, with cone-shapes on their teeth (thus the name "breast tooth") to reflect their browsing habits (think of deer teeth) and the grazing Mammoths with teeth like giant horses' teeth abound underwater.

There is a prejudice against Florida fossil collecting by some (ignorant) people, because we lack things like dinosaur bones, but the remnants of the Great Pleistocene Mammals are everywhere, if you know where to look. Moreover, though, the build up of marine animals during Florida's interminable gestation makes for fantastic fossiling of arthropods, echinoderms, and especially mollusks. Plus, the soft sediments make extracting their shells terribly easy, and some, such as aragonite, can even be removed by hand!

The last of the ice ages was the Wisconsin, which peaked about 18,000 years ago (be sure not to get Pentagonitis and confuse millions with thousands). Now that it has waned, the earth would be in a warming mode naturally, but apparently this is being exacerbated by artificial "global warming" at the hands of you-know-who. During the peak of the Wisconsin, the shoreline of the Gulf of Mexico south of North Florida was about a hundred miles farther out than today, and we can bet that it will continue to rise appreciably with each passing decade. I am not suggesting that we all build an ark, or move to

the mountains, but I'd be a little apprehensive about buying beach front property!

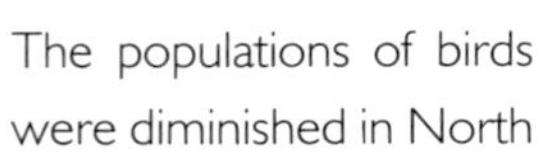

Ice ages have done much more than just create the heating oil business. Bird migration is the result of seasons, which were probably greatly reduced before the cooling in the Pliocene. The populations of birds were diminished in North America during the height of the Wisconsin, but with each passing decade, birds are still inching their breeding ranges farther Northward. In my home in Texas, we are getting almost one new tropical visitor (or nester) a year up from Mexico, and when I was near Inuvik, Canada, well inside the Arctic circle, I found breeding Barn Swallows, and even robins nesting in sparse spruce trees.

Ice ages have also acted as great instruments of destruction and extinction. As one who loves reptiles and amphibians, I often dream about living at a time dominated by cold-blooded animals and sorrow at the fact that we now have, instead of the sixteen orders of reptiles in the Mesozoic,

SHORELINE

just three orders today, plus the Tuatara. Birds, obviously another love, have significantly taken a plunge in diversity and population as well.

But there is something to be said about the indomitable nature of, well, nature. Scientists figure that at any point in earth's past since the Cambrian Explosion (beginning of multicellular life) nearly a billion years ago, there have been about two million species of animals on earth. We have been through a series of massive extinctions, including mind-boggling ones at the end of the Paleozoic and Mesozoic (K-1 and K-2 boundaries). So as the nutty mathematician said in Jurassic Park, "Life finds a way."

Stumps along the shoreline show that ocean levels are rising and killing coastal trees

This gastropod and bivalve fossil was quickly unearthed at Four-mile Creek

One thing is for sure. Natural selection is a brilliant strategy for organisms that live on a planet with ice ages, meteor collisions (K-2), superheating and poisoning of the atmosphere (end of the Cretaceous), radiational bombardment (end of the Paleozoic, K-1) and global flooding (due to ocean level rise). Had life been created in fixed, immutable patterns, genetically unable to adapt and mutate, life would be history. Aliens from the stars would one day find out about life on earth through fossils, but it

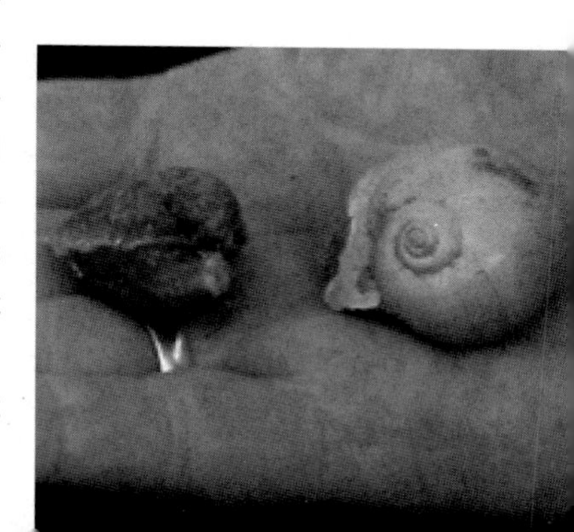

wouldn't include ours. (I am often mystified that some of the very people who profess the greatest admiration for the Creator completely miss the beauty, wisdom and wondrous methodology of the creation.)

In the pages to come, you will read about the beautiful climax communities of North Florida, and the wealth of creatures that roam this great ecosystem, but at every turn we will see how forces from thousands—and even millions—of years past laid the groundwork (literally and figuratively) for the habitat diversity we enjoy today. This book will help you understand these habitats and all that crawls within them. It is my hope that you will steer the course of the newest force on earth—humans—to protect, rather than destroy, what we have been so richly blessed with.

Longleaf Pine Forest Community

COTTON FIELD

Typical serial community planted by humans for our purposes

North Florida is divided into many *communities,* where certain abiotic (nonliving) factors exist. These are conditions such as soil type and moisture availability that determine which plants are found and in what abundance. The plants, in turn, have much to do with animalian population and distribution. In this chapter we will examine the terrestrial communities and see what to expect in which areas.

Communities may be either *serial* or *climax.* Climax communities are those where little or no change is taking place. Plant succession has ground to a near halt, causing an area to look about the same as it looked fifteen years before. Species of animals, likewise, are essentially constant in climax communities, making them stable patches of nature.

In climax communities, the production (plants making sugar) is roughly equal to the respiration (sugar used by plants for growth and repair). When sugar made by plants through photosynthesis is used by the plants, there is little excess energy for change. This is what causes climax areas to remain static. Some have used the formula $p=r$ to express the production of plants equaling that of their collective respiration.

LONGLEAF

Serial communities are quite different. They may be symbolized as $p>r$, as they are producing more sugar than they are using for their own purposes. This excess energy is utilized for change, and serial communities, therefore, undergo succession. Humans create serial communities through their agriculture and use this excess energy for food. Wheat, corn and rice fields, to name just three, are extremely productive ecosystems, and literally feed the world. Most of the serial communities we see in North Florida are the result of human interference, such as fields that lie unused and then begin growing shrubs, bushes, and later small trees. Even lawns are serial, as succession begins happening quickly, much to our dismay, if they are ignored. Incidentally, this is called *secondary* succession, where change is emanating from areas already having vegetation.

There are other differences between serial and climax communities that are worth mentioning. A serial

ᑭINE FOREST

community usually receives a bounty of sunlight, obviously needed for the amount of photosynthesis that occurs. That is why we have agricultural *fields,* instead of deep forests for growing our food. Even orchards, such as apple and pear, are spaced so each tree receives plenty of sunlight for sugar production. Thick, dark forests have significantly fewer animals, owing to the paucity of excess energy available. A short walk through one of North Florida's great Live Oak forests will reveal a few Blue Jays, Gray Squirrels and other creatures, but nothing compared to communities receiving more sunlight.

Somewhat sparse with dead "lightning rod" trees

Whereas there are many serial communities without particular designations, from abandoned fields to second-growth forest and even residential lots, there are readily recognizable climax communities with specific characteristics and organisms. This chapter is devoted to Longleaf Pine forests, which comprise a unique community in North Florida.

Longleaf communities are actually neither serial nor climax, rather having characteristics of both. If left alone, in the absence of fire, Longleafs cease reproducing properly and are overtaken eventually by oaks. But fire has long been a force keeping the succession of oaks from advancing, and, therefore, the Longleafs have remained. They (and the other naturally occurring plants in the Longleaf community) not only tolerate fire, they seem to thrive on it. So they are a community where the production is actually greater than the respiration, but succession is retarded because of the periodic fires. We then call the Longleaf communities (and others like it elsewhere) fire disclimax. You can now see why it is so unique in our area.

Dry soil is called *xeric* and is produced by low rainfall and large grains. These grains have cracks between them allowing water to percolate through and dry the soil. This sand is left over from the fluctuation of the ocean's shoreline through the ages and is found from the Delmarva area near our Nation's Capital to North Florida, and out to East Texas. This *coastal plain* is home to the famous Longleaf Pine, valued by conservationists and the timber industry alike.

There was a time Longleaf Pines stretched for millions of acres across the gulf coastal plain and up the Atlantic seaboard. Firmly rooted in the dry, sandy soil with its massive tap root, these great trees were the keystone species of a marvelous ecosystem that housed some of the terribly interesting creatures and fascinating plants in our country.

Across the Deep South, we have lost around 98% of the old-growth Longleafs because of timber interests, urban sprawl and other forest-clearing practices. Consequently, many of the animals which thrived in these special communities have been on the decline, and several are listed species. Perhaps the most famous is the Red-cockaded Woodpecker, an endangered creature that many compare to the Spotted Owl of the Pacific Northwest in its plight.

In North Florida, much of the Longleaf acreage left is in the Apalachicola National Forest and a few other government holdings. Management of these areas has been the topic of great controversy over the years. Not only does the timber industry want every last remaining Longleaf, the practices of the National Forest executives in the past have been suspect and outdated.

One of the chief problems with the management of this splendid forest type was the practice of planting Slash Pines rather than Longleafs. The former is not the native species of the Longleaf Pine forest but thrives in the Florida peninsula instead. Animals living in the forest have evolved with (and because of) Longleafs and disappear when Slash Pines replace those beautiful Longleafs. The scarcity of Red-cockaded Woodpeckers is just the beginning of the full-scale wildlife alteration and extirpation that results from changing the keystone species of an entire ecosystem. I must say that it is inconceivable that this practice—at the taxpayer's expense—was visited on such a beautiful and thriving ecosystem and cost us such a huge portion of our natural heritage.

It was the timber and paper interests that dictated the replacing of Longleafs with Slash Pines and other species. This lust for money destroying our natural resources is an old theme, but as long as our society places a greater value on the dollar than we do on this heritage, it'll be played out time and time again. But in this case, much of the problem was based on misinformation.

Slash Pines were chosen for their quick growth spurt the first few years. Longleaf Pines start out almost like a grass stage, and take years to start any kind of a growth spurt. But when they do, they easily outdistance the diminutive Slash Pines, and soar into the heavens with their majestic trunks and sprawling limbs. The problem here—besides ignorance—is the quick turnover of the dollar. Had we replanted Longleafs and been patient, we would have had more timber for the industries and preserved the only home many species of animals ever knew.

The choice of Slash Pines over Longleafs precipitated the absence of fires through control burns in the National Forest. In fairness, the advantages of prescribed burns were just becoming known to us (thanks to institutions like Tall Timbers Research Station), despite their being used effectively by "natives" in other continents for forty thousand years. Slash Pines are not a fire-tolerant species, and therefore the timber interests vetoed any thought of such activities in "their" forest. There was truly reason for misunderstanding about fires as well.

In a cruel twist of irony, though Longleaf forests need fire to survive the ages, rampant wild fires actually killed Longleafs and other plant species. This precipitated the Smokey the Bear advertisements some of us remember years ago proclaiming, "Only you can prevent forest fires." Actually, I think politics, greed and ignorance prevented quite a few.

For untold millennia, before our species graced the American landscape, fires swept through the Longleafs every three or four years. Mostly fueled by leaf litter and small limbs deposited on the forest floor, these fires were not terribly hot and had little effect on the trunks of the Longleafs. They also did little to retard the growth of dozens of species of fire-tolerant plants that coexist with Longleafs. Our heroes had little more than charred bark to show for the periodic burns.

The problem came when we showed up

(now that's an old theme) and endeavored to halt these fires from taking place. Our roads acted as fire breaks and any natural fire started by lightning (as had happened for thousands of years) was either soon extinguished or burned out in a small area. Historically, fires probably burned for many miles, possibly covering areas equal to present-day counties. In the subsequent absence of fire, huge masses of debris built up on the forest floor. Then, when the forest did catch fire, a towering inferno took place, and when flames torched the tops of the Longleafs (crown fire) they were destroyed. So fires were bad, but only because we hadn't had regular burns to control litter on the forest floor.

The solution Tall Timbers came up with was to mimic precolonial days and have controlled, periodic burns every several years. This theory was put into practice on Tall Timbers land north of Tallahassee, in the Red Hills near the Georgia border. As suspected, it returned large tracts of Longleafs to a healthy state, and species of animals which were diminishing in the national forest maintained solid populations on this experimental plot.

The results of this work were taken to National Forest officials so that these management practices could be implemented throughout the Apalachicola National Forest. Sadly, though, change takes place at a painfully lethargic pace, and these radical ideas were all but rejected for many years. Meanwhile, our (and I do mean "our") Longleafs were being clear cut and replaced by ecologically worthless Slash Pines. Our National Forest was being used for everything from deer hunting to logging but with no thought of biodiversity and proper management practices.

CLEAR CUTTING

A sad sight, an unnecessary waste of biomass where alternatives exist

But again, there was ignorance about why fire was so important to the Longleaf community. First, it kills invasive species such as various oaks, thus eliminating the Longleaf's competition. This is also true for many naturally occurring shrubs and smaller plants like palmetto. Many would have their tops seared by the flames, but their roots sprouted almost immediately upon the fire passing. I can think of no more beautiful sight in nature than new growth pushing its healthy, luscious sprouts out of a charred forest floor.

Also, though, this open ground becomes a perfect place for the seeds of the next generation. It receives a bounty of sunlight, and the nutrients from old limbs and leaf litter have been recycled into the black layer of nutrition that awaits all potential plants. Fires, in fact, should not be viewed as agents of death, but rather that which brings new life!

Nowhere is this more true than with the Longleafs themselves. It is the heat of lower flames that causes the cones to open, and within a few days, disperse all over this fertile ground. Therefore, you can see that fire is essential to a healthy Longleaf Pine forest, and the keystone species can't reproduce without it. They actually encourage fire themselves, with the inner mass of the old, dead ones filled with extremely combustible "lighter pine," making them function as one huge lightning rod. When struck, they can almost explode with fire, sending sparks and small flames all over the forest floor. Often, these flames land on the ubiquitous Wire Grass, which can al-

Prescribed control burn in a healthy Longleaf forest

most be burst into flames by staring at it. Indeed, the Longleaf community begs to burn!

We all looked on with horror at the terrible blaze that destroyed much of Yellowstone National Park in the late 1980's. Every effort was made to contain this inferno, but it scorched every acre it approached. There was nothing we could do. In a few hellish weeks, we and the animals of this huge park reaped the reward of years of mismanagement, and much of it literally went up in smoke. All across America, ecologists took a long look and saw that in many natural areas, fire is not the enemy. Fire is often a necessary part of the natural environment and the very force that ensures the survival and reproduction of our most cherished species.

HOLY SMOKE!!!

So let's say we agree to use prescribed burning as a management tool for the Apalachicola National Forest. That still doesn't solve the problem of logging, and especially clear-cutting in these public lands. Do we continue to allow timber interests to ravage large tracts of Longleafs, or is there another solution? Indeed, there is.

CROWN FIRE

Longleafs have been killed by fire entering tree tops

Some countries, such as the Philippines (which I trust is not more technologically advanced than we are) have started practicing selective cutting, rather than traditional clear cutting. They pick out certain trees within a forest to take and cut them down. The trees are removed with a helicopter and taken to mills for processing.

There is no money spent on trucks, or to maintain logging roads. Think of the savings! And the remaining trees spread their seeds over the areas opened by the tree's removal, and no money is spent on replanting. The ecosystem is virtually untouched as humans and nature are living in harmony with each other. Yes, it would take a lot of money to change logging methods, and, yes, it would take a different philosophy, but this is our natural heritage we are talking about.

Some may wonder what it is about Longleaf Pines that make them so special. I find them to be an especially majestic tree. They grow quite tall, and their thick, gnarled branches form a lovely canopy against the blue Florida

Different sizes of Longleafs showing natural seeding

sky. The elegant, long needles add to their beauty, as do the long, slender cones. Longleafs are told from Slash Pines easily by their limbs, as Slash have thin, straight branches with shorter needles. Longleafs are not salt tolerant, so they are replaced near the coast with Loblollies (which have short fat branches and smaller cones). Also on the coast are Sand Pines, a smaller species with short, fragrant needles and interesting bark. This species can't reproduce in the absence of fire, as its serotenous cones need the heat to open. We need to save the acreage of Sand Pines that grows naturally along the coast, but hopefully the experiments the paper companies conducted planting them inland will cease. Never have I seen a place more devoid of animal life than planted Sand Pine communities.

HEALTHY FOREST

It is the entire Longleaf community that really makes them special. A healthy forest has a great deal of open space from the shrubs and palmettos up to the canopy at the treetops. This makes for a bright forest, with the sunlight encouraging a tremendous bounty of flowers and berries. The periodic fires keep shrubs and bushes from interrupting the open space and makes viewing the abundant

Bachman's Sparrow

Eastern Towhee

animal life all the easier. We will now look at the animal life. Proper names of vertebrate species will be boldfaced at their first mention; classes will be boldfaced and underlined. Since many invertebrate names represent multiple species, their names are not boldfaced in this book.

Birds are usually the first creatures one encounters in Longleafs. In almost every direction echo songs of the , a steady, one-pitched trill high in the canopy. Never far away, the song of the local **Bachman's Sparrow** whistles across the pines, showing that this listed species still has a home in the National Forest. Listen for one sustained whistle followed by what sounds like someone whistling for his dog. But don't be fooled by the song of the **Eastern Towhee,** often accompanied by their whistled *towhee.* **Carolina Wrens** join the chorus near wet areas with their *teakettle teakettle teakettle* breaking the morning peace, often followed by their harsh scolds. Other warblers join the fray, including the stunning **Yellow-throated** in the canopy as well as the **Common Yellowthroat** issuing their *wichita wichita wichita* from the undergrowth.

Less musical cries of birds in the distance may include phoebes (winter), **Eastern Wood-pewees** (summer), **Blue Jays**, **American Crows**, fussing of the ubiquitous **House Wren** in winter, several woodpeckers both calling loudly or hammering, the constant chatter of **Ruby-crowned Kinglets** in winter, bluebirds calling plaintively, the odd squeaking of **Brown-**

BUDDIES

headed Nuthatches and the obnoxious chatter of female **Brown-headed Cowbirds**.

The most famous birds, the aforementioned **Red-cockaded Woodpeckers**, may be found in small roving bands, issuing their kingfisher-like rattle and flying from tree to tree. The white cheek is diagnostic, as is their "candle trees," where they have caused sap to ease down all over the tree in which they nest. This gooey covering (like wax) discourages predators like arboreal snakes and makes their nest site an unmistakable monument in the forest.

Species found commonly or exclusively in Longleafs

Red-cockaded Woodpecker

Brown-headed Nuthatch

These woodpeckers, **Bachman's Sparrows** and **Brown-headed Nuthatches** constitute three avian species found principally in our Longleafs, and they point to the value of the community, as well as our responsibility to sustain these forests for all creatures and for our natural heritage. They are not, however, the only creatures indigenous to the Longleafs that are seldom or never found elsewhere. There are many other notable vertebrates in this community, and we will now take them class by class.

LONGLEAF

The other group of "warm-blooded" vertebrates is the **mammals**, and they are well represented in areas like the Apalachicola National Forest. First, there are many burrowing mammals in this area because the soil is sandy and easily dug through. **Eastern Moles** are abundant, as they blindly bore their way smelling for worms and other invertebrates. Just as interesting is the **Southeastern Pocket Gopher** (not to be confused with a tortoise), which digs holes and leaves small piles of sand in open piney areas. The principal food of the Florida Pine Snake (another listed species), gophers create habitat for many small animals and are an important member of the Longleaf community's ecology. Their "pockets" are actually loose skin on their cheeks where they store food for short periods of time as they forage.

The common bat of the Longleafs is the **Red Bat**, a beetle eater and relatively small creature. In the warm months this permanent resident may be seen fairly high, about the level of the canopy, swooping acrobatically through the summer evening. They are about the same size as **Seminole Bats**, but ecologically separated, as the latter prefers hardwood forests. **Yellow Bats** are slightly larger and seen more in the migration.

Black Bear and **Bobcat** are fairly common in pine woods but are shy and retiring. Bear are most commonly seen in May and early

ENEMIES

June feasting on blackberries along the roadside, while Bobcat are usually seen very early in the morning walking along old roads. There are no other bears or large cats in our area.

A Canebrake Rattlesnake (top) . . .

The **Gray Fox** is a common hunter in the Longleafs, frequently seen crossing country highways at night. Told from escaped Red Foxes by the absence of black legs, their gray and red coat and long, full tail (without the white tip of the **Red Fox**) is diagnostic and beautiful. **Gray Squirrels** are sometimes seen in hardwood patches of pine forest, but breathtaking **Eastern Fox Squirrels** are frequently seen bounding across roads and open areas.

There are four species of rats in the Big Bend, though some originally came from Europe. **Black** and **Norway Rats** are introduced and have wide ranges. However, they are not normally seen in natural areas, opting for houses, barns, and other artificial structures (like many of the introduced creatures in America). They have long, scaly tails, with the more southerly Black Rat's tail being even longer than their head/body length. The **Eastern Woodrat** is present in wild areas but is found in hardwoods more than pine forests. However, **Cotton Rats** are all over pine forests, with their short tails and grizzled fur. They are an extremely valuable food source for many predators and should not be considered the pest toward man that Norway and Black Rats are.

. . . and what could be his snack: a Golden Mouse (lower left)

O**possums** and **Nine-banded Armadillos** are also common in the pine woods, with the former working the nights and the latter the days. Both are omnivores and are quite approachable. Armadillos arose around sixty million years ago and developed the horny shell that protects them against most predators. Opossums are very ancient, evolving when Tyrannosaurs ruled the earth, and making their way from Australia when various continents articulated in the world's oceans. The **Striped Skunk** is found in fairly modest numbers here in the pine wood's sandy soil as well.

C**ottontails** are common in the pine woods, easily recognized by their large ears, light brown coat and white tail. Living in warmer areas than the **Marsh Rabbit**, cottontails have larger ears for heat loss. They constitute an important food source for Red-tailed Hawks, Bobcats and foxes, with rattlesnakes eating their young. They are subject to population dynamics, with numbers rising and falling sharply over the years.

And speaking of white tails, deer are amazingly abundant in the Longleafs, as evidenced by the hordes of hunters in the National Forest by late fall. The **White-tailed Deer** are excellent examples of seasonal change, with summer specimens quite rich brown and winter deer grayish. In the absence of historical predators such as wolf and panther, deer face uphill battles against hunger, disease and space resulting from their burgeoning population. Though hard for many to swallow, deer hunters may serve an important, albeit artificial function in deer ecology.

R**eptiles**, by their ability to adapt to dry conditions, are abundant and diverse in the Longleafs. Snakes are easily found along National Forest roads by driving them on late spring and early summer mornings. When the weather really gets hot, snakes become more active at night and are harder to catch. It should be noted that many of the following species have become scarce, and my advice, for the good of the snake population, is to secure pets through stores that sell them as a result of captive breeding, rather than taking them from the wild. Virtually every snake in Florida, especially terrestrial ones, have undergone serious declines in the past twenty-five years, and need to be preserved along with the rest of our natural heritage.

Rattlesnakes of two species may be found commonly in the pine woods, with big **Eastern Diamondbacks** easily being the heaviest snake in the country. Diamondbacks are unmistakable with their yellow ground color, diamonds and loud buzzing rattle when alarmed. Though it prefers to slither away to safety, this is an extremely powerful, dangerous creature which many have unfortunately underestimated. Admire it from a distance, and please don't kill this magnificent animal!

P**igmy Rattlesnakes** are sometimes seen as well, but their size and protective coloration on the road make them easily overlooked. The dark spots on the gray ground color cause them to resemble harmless snakes such as hog-noses, so caution is again warranted. Though never fatal, I can attest to their unforgiving nature, as well as the pain of their bite. Carelessly saving one from oncoming traffic proved to me once again that no good deed goes unpunished.

Found mostly in the Lake City area, **Timber (Canebrake) Rattlesnakes** seem to prefer wetter areas, being especially common in the lower reaches of the Okefenokee. These beautiful snakes are not as dangerous as diamondbacks but should be given a healthy respect.

A

Cottonmouths, though essentially an aquatic creature, are amazingly abundant in pine woods, residing in the ditches and (especially) culverts along logging roads. They eat fish trapped in drying water holes, frogs, and sometimes even their competitors the Banded Water Snakes that dare to share their denizen. "Water moccasins" (as the locals call them) are stout brown snakes with some black toward the rear and irregular bands. But the best field mark to separate them from all water snakes (nonpoisonous) is the dark horizontal mask through the eye across the side of the face. A good confirmation on cornered specimens is their habit of opening the mouth and vibrating the tail (which a few terrestrial, slender, harmless snakes also do). Moccasins may be the scum suckers of the serpent world (they'd get my vote), but they should be treated with respect and great care. Yup, I also know how that one feels . . . .

The **Eastern Coral Snake** is the last venomous snake of the Longleafs and is about the last snake you will encounter these days. This "strikingly" beautiful snake has all but disappeared over the past twenty years, primarily from automobile mortalities. The "red touch yellow, kill a fellow" is a useful rhyme, but I suggest you simply remember the Coral Snake is the one with the black nose (black is the sign of death . . .).

Their incredible mimic, the **Scarlet Kingsnake**, is only slightly more common in the pine woods, being more abundant in damp habitats described later. However, the similar **Scarlet Snake** is still present in good numbers here,

SAD LOSS

although they are secretive. They also have the red, black and yellow rings of the kingsnake, but have white bellies and tiny pointed noses. They may be seen on dry summer nights on the paved highways that border the National Forest, an hour or so after dark. They eat lizards and small eggs, and make lousy pets—but at least they don't bite!

Beautiful "Blotched" Kingsnakes have virtually disappeared from their home in the Apalachicola River Valley

One of the tragic stories in herpetology is what happened to our **Blotched Kingsnakes**. Once a fairly common snake in the Apalachicola National Forest, but being a highly prized creature by snake fanciers, it has just about been exterminated in the wild by snake hunters. This snake, the same species as the Eastern "chain" Kingsnake, is dark with a white dot on each scale, giving it a salt-and-pepper appearance. Sometimes called "pied" kingsnake by locals (pied means black and white), they were easily found in the sixties and seventies in their restricted range, which included Tate's Hell Swamp near Carrabelle and adjacent pine forests.

I must say, as fine an organization as is Florida's Game Commission, it must move to protect varieties of snakes in trouble at a pace faster than frozen molasses. Even the regular **Eastern Kingsnake** has all but vanished in North Florida, and my efforts to get them looked at in a serious way were virtually ignored. Admittedly, cars are still their greatest enemy and hard to regulate, but pretending the problem doesn't exist until a species becomes as scarce as Indigo Snakes have is irresponsible and negligent.

Somewhat related to kingsnakes are rat snakes. The **Gray Rat Snake** is occasionally seen ambling across the road near stands of oaks. Their amazing cryptic coloration blends with oak bark as well as any snake camouflage I know. But the more abundant rat snake of the Longleafs is the **Corn Snake**, a splendid rusty creature with darker blotches. These handsome animals are still seen regularly in the National Forest, though in more modest numbers. Once again, obtaining them from licenced pet dealers yields better snakes and makes good ecological sense.

The muscular Florida Pine Snake lives off Pocket Gophers, constricting them with little effort

The crown jewel of the Longleafs is the **Florida Pine Snake**. Huge powerful constrictors, they eat pocket gophers and rats, while taking only the occasional bird. Closely related to the gopher and bull snakes of the American West, they show their affinity to these kin with their grayish color becoming reddish toward the tail. This is a rare animal now, and finally protected!

Racers and coachwhips still survive in the pine woods and are occasionally seen zipping across the road or appearing as a streak in the grass. A very local racer of the Apalachicola National Forest is the **Brownchin**, but it is quite black like the racer of the rest of North Florida. Large coachwhips have attained lengths of over 100 inches and have the

distinction of being darker in front and lighter toward the tail. Both of these snakes are poor eaters in captivity and bite eagerly. Avoid the temptation to keep one so they may be admired from a distance.

The Black Racer moves through Longleafs with amazing speed

R**ough Green Snakes** are pencil-thin, dainty guys with green backs and yellowish bellies. Like the last several snakes, they are largely diurnal, and have cars as their greatest enemy. Anyone driving in the pine forest should watch carefully for snakes and view them from a safe distance. However, green snakes never bite and have the interesting habit of eating grasshoppers and other invertebrate life. They are also poor pets and major escape artists.

Hog-nosed snakes may be found in the pine woods, although the **Southern Hog-nosed Snake** is quite rare. The **Eastern Hog-nosed Snake** is still occasionally encountered, and the joy is all ours. They will hiss, puff up, spread their neck, and eventually roll over and play dead, defecating all over themselves (probably face issues of self-esteem). This act itself is enough to ward off most would-be attackers and amaze the human bystander.

SPEEDSTER

Though hog-noses will never bite, they are actually armed with rear fangs and mild venom. This is used to subdue their quarry of toads, with the fangs serving to give the puffed up toad a deflating experience. These "puff adders" are also trichromatic, being found in any of three color forms. They may be coal black, yellow and black, or red, yellow and black mottled. In any color, they are the king of the showboats.

Southern Hognosed Snakes like this fat fellow are hanging onto a precarious existence in sandy soils like Longleaf 's

Other snakes may be found in the National Forest by virtue of streams and other wet areas. They will be discussed in later sections, since this summary concerns dry land species. I have, however, probably seen another dozen species crossing roads from one wet area to another in my days in the National Forest.

Lizards are even better adapted for dry conditions than snakes, and several really neat species may be found in the Longleafs. They are seen scurrying across the road, sitting on logs or woodpiles where humans have worked, or on the sides of trees soaking up sun. They are easily told from each other, and, unlike snakes, there is no penalty for misidentifications.

RARE FIND

The Fence Lizard lives on pines and oaks in sandy soil across North Florida

My personal favorite is the **Fence Lizard**. At home in pines or scrub oaks, these guys have some of the world's most amazing camouflage on their backs. Their dorsum is rough, like bark, and is the color of the tree's surface as well. When approached they scurry around to the back side, but are not hard to catch. When captured, you must admire the bluish bellies (especially the males) and be sure to rub their tummies and make them go to sleep while on their back. I am not kidding here. Lastly, the males do "push-ups" on logs to mark their territories. Cool critter!

Moving at the speed of light is the **Six-lined Racerunner** (the only member of its genus in the East), which can actually elevate and run on its hind legs. They are slightly blue underneath but are easy to distinguish from the preceding species by their stripes. While foraging they move in a herky-jerky fashion but can take off like a starship when chased.

The **Green Anole** is common throughout North Florida, and certainly in the pine woods. Turning alternately green or brown to match its surroundings, it is often erroneously called "chameleon" by locals. The male's red throat fan is a territorial display to discourage other creatures from foraging on its territory.

The incredibly abundant **Ground Skink** is found everywhere in the Big Bend as well, scurrying along the ground from one shelter to another. Sleek brown lizards, these are sometimes thought of as salamanders, but a captured one easily shows its reptilian scales and claws. This is one reptile that is completely at home in every terrestrial habitat, including your back yard.

There is a complex of three skinks that are very similar. Males are brown with reddish heads, females are all brown with stripes and the young have blue tails. This genus Eumeces has many members elsewhere around the country, but the common representative in the Longleafs is the **Southeastern Five-lined Skink.** They are most easily seen on wood piles or found under logs.

A truly amazing lizard group is the legless lizards. The **Slender Glass Lizard** is common in the Longleafs, as is the **Eastern** (which often prefers more damp locations). The former is light tan with dark stripes running down the torso, while the latter is greener with barring on the sides. But young Easterns look much like Slenders, so consult a field guide for help. Glass lizards are diurnal like other lizards, but behave like snakes in many ways. They may accept insects like grasshoppers in captivity, but those not eating should be turned loose quickly.

Excluding aquatic species, turtles have two members found in the dry regions of pine woods.

GOPHER TORTOISE BURROV

The **Gopher Tortoise** is a remarkable creature, somewhat depressed for life in burrows. Their front feet are adapted for digging and offer some protection when placed in front of the head. In our area, this species has greatly declined and has some protection under the law. It is also the keystone species in the mini-ecosystem created by its burrows, which provide homes for snakes, mammals, frogs and many invertebrates. The hideous practice of "gassing" gopher holes should have been stopped years ago, and one hopes we move away from deeds like this as a society. The resulting wholesale slaughter of innocent creatures is staggering and incredibly wasteful.

Pictures show the hole above ground as well as the den below, with a rattler and Gopher Tortoise (top) and Gopher Frog (right)

Eastern Box Turtles are seen on many morning drives through the pine woods in the warm season. They have been reduced through the pet trade, as they do thrive in captivity. But between this and road casualties, their numbers have also plummeted in recent years. Several races of the box turtle come together in North Florida, and genes flow through various communities freely. They may be told easily from gophers by their high shell and ability to close up with their hinged plastron.

A**mphibians** are more abundant and diverse in this dry community than one might expect. This is due to their low nutritional needs and ability to remain dormant in cold or dry weather. There are toads, frogs, treefrogs and salamanders all through the Longleafs, from burrowing creatures to those found high in the canopy.

Clearly an inhabitant is the **Pine Woods Treefrog**, a dark species with bright yellow coloration on the back of the thigh. Their voice has been likened to Morse code, but I find descriptions fall short. **Squirrel Treefrogs** also inhabit the pines (and about everywhere else), named for their squirrel-like scoldings. This species may be green, gray or brown, but lacks the dorsolateral line that is so conspicuous in **Green Treefrogs**. A few of the latter, with some **Barking Treefrogs**, may be found in wetter areas, but are scarce. **Gray** and **Bird-voiced Treefrogs** may also be found in the pines, though the second is more of a swamp frog.

The dry conditions of the Longleafs plays right into the hands of toads. The species found all over North Florida is the **Southern Toad**, which is as abundant in pine woods as anywhere. They are our only common toad of any size and are generally light grayish on sandy soil. They do change color, however, and specimens migrating to wet, dark areas will turn dark gray or brown. Less variable is the tiny **Oak Toad**, found in open areas of pine woods. They are light gray with a yellowish stripe down the center of the back. Their call is a sustained, high-pitched whistle, while that of the preceding species is a trill, several seconds in duration.

Oak Toad

TOADS

Narrow-mouthed Toad

All of these Toads are found in Longleaf forests

Two creatures bearing the toad name but not their typical appearance are the **Narrow-mouthed Toad** and the **Eastern Spadefoot Toad**. Both seem partial to sandy soil and spend vast amounts of time underground. The former emerges after heavy summer rains and issues a nasal call note that can be described as a Norelco razor or sheep crying. They are less than an inch in length and have a head so small, it could hardly make anything but a nasal sound! Growing as large as Southerns is the Spadefoot, identified by the two light mirror-image lines down its back. Both these toads have smooth skin, unlike the warty covering of those in the last paragraph. Only found in the western Panhandle is the **Fowler's Toad**.

Spadefoot Toad

True frogs (genus *Rana*) are not as common as the toads and treefrog in Longleafs, as most require more water. But the **Leopard Frog**, omnipresent in North Florida, abounds in wet areas, especially with grassy borders. Their spots and pointed snouts make them easy to identify, and there are few others to confuse with them in this habitat. However, in scattered localities there exists the truly unique **Florida Gopher Frog**. Subterranean and often in the holes of tortoises, it emerges to breed in late spring with heavy rains. Their call sounds like snoring, and their color is much like other pine-woods species like Pigmy Rattlers, with dark spots on gray ground color.

The Mole Salamander Burrows into the forest floor waiting for winter rains to fill up ephemeral ponds for their breeding

Two off-beat frogs that may be incredibly abundant in the pine woods at certain times are the **Southern Cricket Frog** and the **Little Grass Frog.** The former gets its name from its call, which is heard around most grassy lakes through the forest. The latter may be abundant right along the roadside, and its extremely high-pitched ascending whistles are almost ear-splitting. Grass frogs have a black stripe dorsolaterally, and cricket frogs have one on the back of their thighs. Crickets average just less than an inch in length, while grass frogs may be half that!

Salamanders are less well represented in pine woods, but there are some interesting exceptions. Whereas the huge family of Woodland Salamanders (Plethodontidae) is virtually absent, there are two representatives of the Mole Salamander family (Ambystomatidae). The first carries the name of the family, as the **Mole Salamander.** It is a chunky, dark amphibian that varies between black and grayish-brown, and has light dandruff-like flakes as markings. These may be seen in large numbers all over North Florida, including pine forests, crossing the road during heavy winter rains.

The rare **Flatwoods Salamander,** now a listed species, still survives in a few pine woods. I have discovered this slender, "frosted" species more than once just east of the visitor's center on Lighthouse Road (St. Mark's Refuge) on rainy winter evenings. Lastly, contrary to the information in field guides, uncommon **Central Newts** are sometimes found in ephemeral ponds in Longleaf habitat (such as on Highway 61 south of Lake Munson).

The presence of some reptiles and many amphibians in the Longleaf community is owing to wet areas within the forest. This is created by various soil conditions where water becomes trapped at the surface and alters significantly the species composition of both plants and animals.

There are within pines places where tannic acid builds up from decaying plants and their leaves and eventually eats through the limestone underneath. This leaves acidic ponds with very dark water and little plant growth. This is where species like Mole Salamanders reproduce, and some other amphibians and reptiles congregate. Their value to avian and mammalian species has not been studied, but it surely aids these creatures by quenching their thirsts.

These isolated water sources are home to yet two more amphibians, the **Lesser Siren**, and the **Southern Dusky Salamander.** Sirens are very ancient creatures with one pair of (front) legs, a compressed tail and external gills. They may be a foot or more in length and live out their adult lives in water with gills (*neoteny*). The dusky salamander is about three inches long and returns to the water from its hiding places to breed.

Southern Dusky Salamanders hide under wet leaves in swamps watching for morsels of tiny invertebrate life

Between these acid wetland bogs and the Longleafs is a transitional area known as a Shrub Bog. The soil is not *hydric* like in the former bog, but neither is it xeric like around the Longleafs. This soil is *mesic* or damp, but not saturated. Species of shrubs growing in this soil include Buckeye and Ti ti. Certain species within the National Forest are shrub-bog species, and, in fact, it very likely was home at one time to the now-extinct Bachman's Warbler. When fires rage through the Longleafs, they burn right down to the shrub bogs, but stop there. Any soil other than xeric is too moist for their plants to burn, except under the most serious drought conditions.

LITTLE HABITAT

In some places in pine forests, the soil is too wet and soft to support trees, so various grasses are the predominant plants. These are called *savannahs* and are lovely assemblages of grasses, some insectivorous plants such as the Trumpet Pitcher Plant, and great assortments of flowers. There are also a few animals unique to these wonderful habitats, such as the Mole Kingsnake. There is a lovely savannah a few miles

north of Sumatra on Highway 65. In this and other savannahs, the family of orchids flourish, contributing to the floral paradise.

In many places, soil is very poor, due to nutrients percolating down through sand grains and being lost as potential plant food. Very often, plants supplement their photosynthetic diet by capturing insects through a number of ingenious strategies. The body of the poor bug is digested extracellularly (despite the chitinous exoskeleton) and absorbed. Some bogs may have several of the following groups of insectivorous plants.

ON THE PRAIRIE

This acid wetland stands alone on a lovely prairie just north of Sumatra

The most conspicuous insectivorous plants are pitcher plants, genus *Saracinia.* The widespread Trumpet has a yellow top and attains a height of well over a foot. Found in the Sumatra area are Parrot and Purple Pitchers and the rare White-capped Pitcher may be found in a number of bogs in the middle of the Panhandle. Two less common species are rare and local. Venus Flytraps, planted unscrupulously years ago, thrive in a bog also filled with White-capped Pitcher plants just west of Hosford on Highway 20.

Another plant strategy for insect capture is employed by the sun dew (genus *Drosera*). Squatty Red Sun Dews and thin, green Thread Sun Dews are abundant over much of the western Big Bend. They are recognized by their dew-looking sweet, sticky substance, in which tiny bugs become stuck to the plants and are also digested extracellularly.

Even in the water, plants feed on insects. Looking like a mass of frog eggs, Bladderwort grows just under the surface, sucking unsuspecting aquatic insects into its bladders. This is found in the same bog near Hosford, along with both sun dews. Other lesser-known insectivorous plant groups do exist, and are covered in more detailed literature.

Sphagnum bogs also may be found in North Florida, heavily laden with this primitive moss. In some sphagnum amphibians abound, such as the larval salamanders in certain areas. Sphagnum, like ferns, practices alternation of generations and needs the moisture to reproduce. The moss itself appears almost like a shag carpet lying over parts of the bog. Very primitive vascular plants,called Bryophytes, mosses and ferns developed to live with amphibians in the gray twilight between water and terrestrial environments.

It should be obvious now that a Longleaf Pine forest is more than just a bunch of pine trees. It is a dynamic ecosystem, full of diverse habitats and myriads of animals. It has endangered species, unique birds, tremendous reptile and amphibian populations, and the loveliest plants in the South. Clearly, this is an extremely important part of our natural heritage, and should be preserved and properly managed at all costs. If you are not convinced, take a drive through the Apalachicola National Forest and see what conservationists have been fighting so hard to protect for the last twenty-five years. You will agree it is a wondrous ecosystem with amazing secrets and fascinating animals.

Beech/Magnolia Forest to Floodplains

Longleaf Pine forests, remember, are products of dry (xeric) soil. But when the soil is damp, the forest type changes radically. Scores of plant species that survive better in wetter soil and more shade fight for supremacy in a forest known for two of its more prominent members—Beech and Magnolia trees.

Beech (don't call me Birch) trees have whitish bark and their leaves have serrate edges. They are one of the few deciduous trees in this forest type, as winter finds a surprising number of evergreens, both conifers and angiosperms, spreading their green throughout the forest. Magnolias need little introduction to Southerners, as their broad leaves and huge white blossoms decorate many yards with shade and color.

Thousands of acres of Beech/Magnolia forest have been semi-cleared to make residential areas, and we often see the leftovers like American Holly growing in neighborhoods. Most of these forests were high enough to resist flooding and offered plenty of shade and nice trees for good homes and gardens.

Beech/Magnolia forests do not have nearly as many endangered and threatened species as some other communities discussed in this book, so they haven't gotten the notoriety of other forest types. They are lovely woodlands, though, and a vast assortment of plant and animal species may be found easily. The best Beech/Magnolia forest I know is around Wakulla Springs, and I highly recommend the trails near this grand old retreat. Those of the steephead ravines are also exquisite and offer glimpses at unique creatures, as well as our geologic past. Some ravines of West Florida are well stocked with this forest type.

One conifer is quite common in this forest type—the Spruce Pine. Some grow to majestic size and tower out of hardwood forests like skyscrapers in the city. Their dark, small-squared bark is diagnostic and crushing their fragrant needles provides aroma from the gods. If this isn't enough to identify them, notice that their cones are tiny, compared to Longleafs. Like many pines, their needles discourage plant growth in a perimeter around them, often leaving bare ground.

The *canopy* effect is well-known to most of us. This is a thick forest insulating its understory against heating and drying from outside air. A walk into a Beech/Magnolia forest on a summer day will find the drop in temperature refreshing. Possibly imperceptible to us (in the North Florida sauna) will also be a slight rise in humidity, as moisture is contained in the absence of direct sunlight and hot air. Therefore, the thick trees of the Beech/Magnolia forest create a cooler, drier abiotic environment for animals and other organisms.

The "other organisms" refers to the fact that many species of diminutive plants thrive in more damp soil, where desiccation is not a problem. This may be harder to see in neighborhood Beech/Magnolia remnants, but in healthy examples, the forest floor is strewn with luscious, dark-green, wide-leafed plants. Ferns, mosses, monocots galore and some beautiful dicots all may be found within a few feet of each other. Speaking of cool, damp environments, the entire kingdom of Fungi seems to be invited to the lower portion of Beech/Magnolia forests, with brilliant oranges, yellows, reds, and a few unbelievably radiant surprises. As in Chapter 2 we will look at various groups of animals in these communities and boldface the proper species names when first introduced, plus underlining classes, also boldfaced.

Our topic here is the wildlife, which is found in multitudes. Some large taxa of animals crave this type of abiotic condition and are thus well represented. **Amphibians**, always seeming to live in the gray twilight between water and land, are lurking underneath logs, rocks and debris for nightfall, insects or rain. I have often wondered just how many eyes are actually trained on me while slipping through the woods, and I'll bet a lot of frogs and salamanders are following my size thirteens down the wooded paths of moist forests.

The **Slimy Salamander**, now about a dozen species separated mostly geographically, scurries through the damp leaf litter in search of a wide range of invertebrates. Black with white flakes, they have a sticky, mucous covering on their skin that not only repels the drying influence of the air, but also must surely taste about like a terrestrial slug. One of the zillion woodland salamanders, Slimies also breathe through their moist skin (until and if it dries) and pose no threat to humans, unless we unwittingly put our fingers in orifices after handling them (and that is a really dumb idea). Their most amazing characteristic, though, is that they reproduce through direct transformation. Unlike most amphibians, Slimies lay their eggs in moist places like under logs, and the larvae transform within the egg. Upon hatching, the gill stage is over, and the precocial young are free to roam the detritus in search of their first meal. Our species, the **Southeastern Slimy Salamander**, is widespread and sometimes quite abundant.

Another amphibian that is invading Beech/Magnolia forests and has been abundant for decades in border grass around residences is the **Greenhouse Frog**. Members of a huge tropical genus, they probably arrived in potted plants (like our common earthworm, *Lumbricus terrestrius*) and have made a killing in *Leriope* and other yard plants. They are occasionally uncovered when we lift up boards and other debris around the yard, and discover these tiny, brownish-red animals. But we have all heard them hundreds of times, as their chirping fills the summer evenings with music. Of great interest, though, is the fact that they practice a similar direct transformation like the Slimy Salamanders discussed in the previous paragraph. The only difference is that these females lay their eggs on their back and carry them around while developing.

Many of the treefrogs discussed in the Longleaf Pine section may also be found in mesic forests, but the **Squirrel Treefrog** is by far the most abundant. In residential areas, this species is seen so frequently in warm, damp weather, it has earned the nickname "rain frog." This is not to be confused with the genus name of true frogs like the bullfrog, which is *Rana.* True frogs are not common in Beech/Magnolia forests, although **Bronze Frogs** are found along streams and other water sources.

Burrowing amphibians have a tougher time in the mesic soil of the Beech/Magnolia forest, and this likely diminishes the species composition. It is ironic that there are actually more species of amphibians in dry, Longleaf Pine forests than in this damp woodland. This may well account for why the only really common salamander here has such a noxious skin mucous. In the absence of burrows or streams to dart into, Slimy Salamanders are left "high and dry."

Beech/Magnolia forests are great places for insects and their arthropod cousins. The moderated air temperature and conditions less favorable to desiccation cause arthropods to do quite well. We all think of mosquitoes when we say "insects," and, indeed, they may be abundant at times. With half the animal species in the world, the diversity of insects is staggering. I feel certain that these forests have the top species density of any community at our latitude (though far from the greatest concentration of mosquitoes).

Spiders are abundant **arachnida** and diverse in moist forests. Humidity keeps these hunters, quite exposed, from drying up in the summer air. The masses of lowerstory limbs give options for web building in many prime spots. These arachnids must have quite a smorgasbord with the plethora of diurnal and nocturnal insects sailing through the lower canopy. Perhaps the most sensational in North Florida is the Golden Orb Weaver, commonly called "banana spider" by many locals. Their golden strands are incredibly strong, and both my father and I have separately found birds stuck in their webs. I am almost hesitant to state the rather unbelievable fact that it was the same species of bird both times—a Yellow-breasted Chat!

Aside from the spiders with webs, which sometimes get annoying when hiking trails, there are oodles of wolf spiders on the forest floor as well. These rather benign hunters are detected easily at night with a flashlight, as their eyes give off a blue "eye shine" when one holds light near their face, but pointing toward the ground. It is a testament to the number of insects that must traverse the leaf litter under the cloak of darkness.

I am pleased to say that the worst of the spiders are not found in Beech/Magnolia forests, but in drier soil types. Also in sandy soils are scorpions (especially near the coast), one of the few poisonous animals never to have nailed me. What these damp forests do have in the arachnid world is ticks. Early summer you can almost hear the rumble driving past. Powdered sulfur on lower pant legs with strings tied tightly around them is a good deterrent. Their arachnid partners in crime, the chiggers, are somewhat discouraged by this scheme as well. But I am unaware of anything that controls the hordes of biting flies (genus *Tabana*) that fill the early summer air, except maybe our friends the spiders and Great-crested Flycatchers.

ALIKE

M**illipedes** and **centipedes** make their way along the ground at various speeds, and only resemble each other in very superficial ways. The former has a thick shell on top, two pairs of legs under each *somite* (body section), and make extremely slow progress on their "thousands" of legs that move like a wave. Millipedes protect themselves by rolling up into a ball and also by emitting a profoundly nasty liquid from the *repugnatorial* gland. They eat rotting vegetation on the forest floor and are absolutely no danger to humans.

Centipedes are quite another story. They scurry quickly after tiny invertebrates, which they kill with the poi-

Centipedes and millipedes resemble each other superficially and in name, but that's where it stops

BUT DIFFERENT

son fangs on their anterior end. With one pair of legs sticking out from each somite and no armor like their cumbersome cousins of the preceding paragraph, they are the terror of the tiny world beneath our feet. And don't ever try to catch one with your fingers! They are quite difficult to pin down and secure behind the head and the price you pay for a slip is hardly worth the feeling of accomplishment from catching a centipede—for heaven's sakes! The red centipede of the Beech/Magnolia forest issues a nasty little bite (yes, that happened to me in front of my former science club officers at Alum Bluff), but the big gray species that lives in the Longleafs will absolutely light up your whole day with its venom. Ignore the temptation.

The moist woodlands of the Beech/Magnolia forest offers a plethora of **birds** to feed on the aforementioned insects. Not surprising, some of these are flycatchers. The **Great-crested**, a handsome species with a brown back, reddish tail and yellow belly, feeds in the upper canopy on *Tabana* flies, and issues a loud, whistling *WHEEP!* to all within ear shot. They are famous for using the shed skins of snakes for their nests and for being heard a lot easier than seen. Great-crests are members of the large and confusing tropical genus *Myiarchus,* but God was good to Eastern birders by placing only one species of this menagerie east of Texas.

DESERVING

Speaking of difficult complexes of birds, the other common flycatcher in the Beech/Magnolia forest is a member of the *Empidonax* genus, undoubtedly the most confusing group of birds in North America. The **Acadian Flycatcher** is a small, greenish bird with a very sharp, high-pitched chip, which penetrates the forest for several hundred yards. Further evidence of divine blessing, no other *Empidonax* breeds in North Florida, or is even common in migration. Both species of the above flycatchers arrive in early spring, nest in early summer, and depart by early fall.

A tremendously diverse insectivorous bird family is the warblers, the crown jewels of the avian world. Several species nest in our Beech/Magnolia forests, such as the incomparable **Hooded Warbler**. Like the flycatchers above, and most birds of the dense forest, they have sharp, piercing calls and/or songs. Joining the Hooded is the superficially similar **Kentucky**, and the **Northern Parula** (whose orange and blue colors have never impressed this Seminole positively).

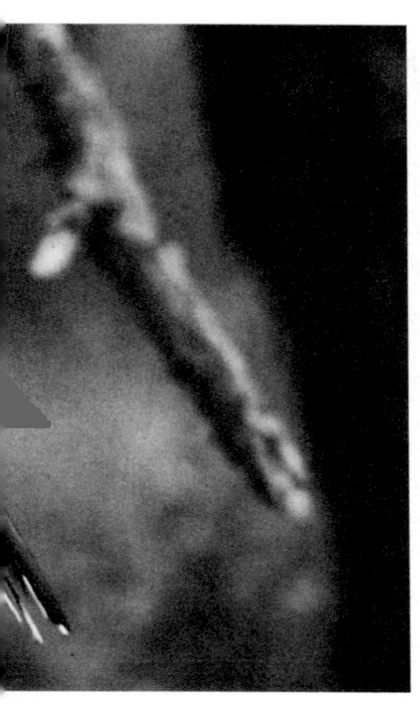

OF ITS NAME

The cuckoo clucks in the distant canopy eating its fill of caterpillars

Vireos are often confused with warblers but have hooks on the end of their beaks, which allow them to pull caterpillars out of bark crevices. This forest contains the **Red-eyed** and **White-eyed Vireo**, with the first in the upper canopy and the latter in lower, scrubbier areas. The beautiful **Yellow-throated Vireo** prefers the tallest of trees, where it seems to show off its bright yellow patch and echos its raspy song throughout its neighborhood.

Several interesting non-songbirds also live in the Beech/Magnolia forest. **Yellow-billed Cuckoos**, or "rain crows," proclaim their descending "yuk yuk yuk..." over the moist woodlands spring to fall, and eat everything from insects to lizards and treefrogs. But they build their nests near the ubiquitous tent caterpillar nests, making food-gathering for the chicks an easy task.

The comments about being spared the confusion of myriads of *Myiarchus* or endless *Empidonax* may be made about hummingbirds as well. With over three hundred species in the New World, the only species breeding in the Eastern United States is quite at home in our damp forests. The **Ruby-throated Hummingbird** is named for its ruby throat, but "squeakingbird" describes how it sounds as it streaks through the canopy like a giant bug. Quite fond of feeders, this bird generally shows up in March and stays well into the fall before heading south. Winter hummingbirds, rarely seen, are normally one of the western species, such as the **Rufous**.

HARDLY GIVING A HOOT

Great Horned Owl

A number of birds of prey are found in this forest as well. At night, the **Barred Owl** may be heard giving its *whoooo-ahh* in the distance, adding color and flavor to a dark evening. **Screech Owls** and **Great Horned** are occasionally heard as well, especially in winter, but are more common in huge stands of oaks or the Longleaf community. They seem to feed better over the open ground, rather than in the dense undergrowth often associated with Beech/Magnolia forests.

Eastern Screech Owl

By day, **Red-shouldered Hawks**, who never saw a forest they couldn't live in, may be found perched high along open breaks (often road sides) watching for cold-blooded prey such as frogs and snakes. In summer they are joined by the similar (but whiter underneath) **Broad-winged**, which is more exclusively loyal to the Beech/Magnolia community. They both have descending, high-pitch whistles, the latter somewhat like a wood-pewee. Issuing a similar call, but being much grayer and far more

Barn Owl

Owls, such as this Barred Owl, sit quiely by day waiting for their nocturnal raids

slender, the **Mississippi Kite** prefers dense hardwoods while it nests in our area. They love lizards, and apparently snatch a lot of **Broad-headed Skinks** and anoles while sailing past the canopy.

Accipiters are long-tailed, bird-eating hawks with short, rounded wings and lightning-fast moves. Adults are blue-gray on the back and reddish barred (not unlike a Red-shouldered) underneath. Like many hawks, immatures are brown on top with streaks below. Both species are canopy feeders, picking out a hapless songbird and matching it move for move through the limbs until they quickly overtake them. The **Sharp-shinned Hawk** is hardly larger than a robin, and regular in forests in winter. **Cooper's Hawks** are very similar but larger and nest in Beech/Magnolias. These "blue darters" are seldom heard and generally not seen well.

Sharp-shins have a smorgasbord in winter as roving bands of songbirds move through heavy forests eating hardy insects and plucking berries. Winter flocks are comprised of zillions of **Yellow-rumped Warblers**, **Blue-headed Vireos**, a few **Orange-crowned** and **Black-and-white Warblers**, resident **Carolina Chickadees** and **Tufted Titmice,** chatty **Ruby-crowned Kinglets**, and a few others. On the forest floor, **House Wrens**, **Hermit Thrushes** and **White-throated Sparrows** poke around looking for treats. In the migration, excellent flocks of warblers and their seasonal friends congregate in the canopy in search of groceries and a cool place to rest, nap and drink. Birding can be quite good at any season and is often done in scenic, peaceful locations.

DEER TO OUR HEARTS

White-tails rest in their autumn haunt

M**ammals**, who disdain heat, seem to be drawn to the Beech/Magnolia forest. Many well-known species such as **Raccoons**, **Opossums** and **Gray Squirrels** may be found here, as well as mice and wood-rats as food items for many creatures. Much of the mammalian activity revolves around the nuts and fruit that fall from the canopy and on munching on the tender shoots that slip up through the ground in warm, moist conditions. Hanging in the canopy by day is the abundant **Seminole Bat**, a mahogany-colored smallish insectivore found all over North Florida.

Some larger mammals may be found in Beech/Magnolia forests, but few have enough acreage to support creatures like **Gray Fox** and **Black Bear**. Our **White-tailed Deer** do not seem especially drawn to this forest type like they are to the Longleafs, but are occasionally found here.

The Box Turtle ponderously plods through the North Florida undergrowth

The **reptiles** did not fail to notice all the small birds, mammals and amphibians busily tending to their chores in the Beech/Magnolia forest. Providing shade enough to make mammals happy may dismay some of our scaly friends, but there are still plenty of reptiles in this dense forest. Probably the most abundant are the secretive **Ground Skinks**, looking more like brown salamanders than a lizard. Perfectly camouflaged in the brown detritus, these guys seldom miss a small "bug."

CARRYING ITS HOUSE ON ITS BACK

Larger and more formidable is the **Broad-headed Skink**. Males are brownish with a red head, females are brown with wide streaks down the back and young ones have a bright blue tail. This tail contains a neurotoxin quite dangerous to animals like cats, but the blue color makes chasing it irresistible. This takes attention away from the vulnerable body, and remember the blue tail is made to break off. The quickness of the lizard, coupled with the effect of the poison, assures the youngster of escaping, while the attacker who ate the tail reels in pain. Cute trick.

There are also plenty of **Green Anoles** in this forest type, as there are virtually all over North Florida. Not a climber, however, is the **Eastern Glass Lizard**, a robust creature with gaudy colors and excellent quickness. These guys eat plenty of grasshoppers and other substantial arthropods but will also take small snakes and lizards.

Box Turtles are at home in moist forests, eating succulent plants and small animals like worms. Few other turtles grace this area normally, but in warm months, some aquatic turtles do rise from their watery homes and seek places to lay their eggs. Most commonly seen are various of the sliders and cooters, with occasional mud and musk turtles found.

The predominant large snake of the moist forest is the **Gray Rat Snake**. Quite the color of oak bark, with many individuals easily obtaining six feet in length, this creature plays a significant role in controlling rats and mice, as well as taking some of our avian friends. They are often called "white oak snakes" and seem especially fond of oaks, but easily accept any broadleaf forest in North Florida. Some have called them the rather nonspecific "chicken" snake, and on a number of occasions when picking out their small teeth from my hands, I made up a few new epithets for this species as well.

Young rat snakes have a surprisingly different diet from the adults, eating treefrogs and lizards. They also look quite unlike adults, with strongly patterned top sides and well-marked heads. The closely related **Corn Snakes**, sometimes found in Beech/Magnolia as well, have young with more red in their pattern. Racers and coachwhips, found in dry areas, also have strongly patterned young. This is a far cry from the notion that baby reptiles are tiny replicas of their parents.

There are several small species of snakes found in moist forests, the most famous of which is the **Ringneck Snake**. Shiny black on the top and bright yellow/orange underneath, its head actually resembles a Coral Snake with the black nose and yellow ring behind the head. These are completely inoffensive beasts, save the musking on your hands, and make interesting pets for short periods of time. Their principal food is invertebrates (somewhat unusual for snakes), but I have actually coaxed several into constricting (!) anoles.

Even smaller than the **Ringneck Snake** is the **Rough Earth Snake**. They aren't much on looks, as they are plain brown with a slightly darker, cone-shaped head. This is a very abundant snake, often found under trash piles and the like, looking for various invertebrate food as well as shelter. These are told from the **Smooth Earth Snake** of the pine woods by their more pointed snout and fine keels on each back scale. Smooths often have tiny black dots on their backs, too.

The **Redbelly Snake** is another dwarf of our broadleaf forest, normally seen early morning or at night. They, too, have a pattern just behind the head, but the reddish underside is a giveaway. Usually found in somewhat wetter habitat is the **Midland Brown Snake**, also with a telltale light area behind the head. Contrary to much literature, the Pine Woods Snake simply isn't found in the Big Bend.

The Pigmy Rattler has a temper as bad as their venom

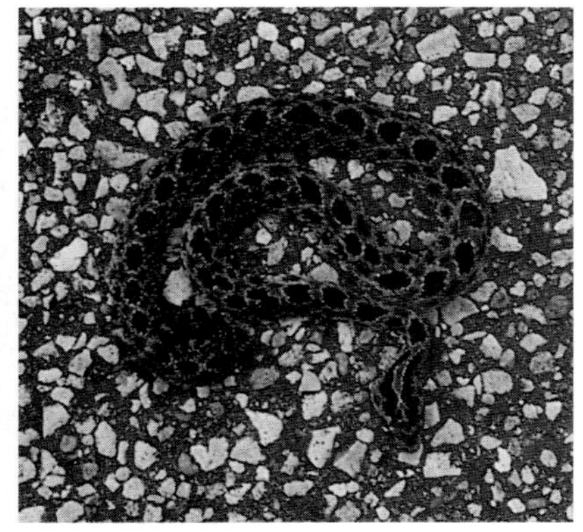

Another thing that makes Beech/Magnolia forests nice places for hiking, etc., is the virtual lack of poisonous snakes. This is not to say you will never see one, but most species either like it wetter or drier, with just the occasional **Pigmy Rattler** seen in Wakulla and Jefferson County forests. And you'd have to do something stupid to get a bite from one of those midgets.

DON'T LET THE SIZE FOOL YOU

The copperhead slips into the steepheads from its Appalachian range

The **Southern Copperhead** is the venomous snake of this medium-range forest, but this species is all but absent in our state. There are a few records in Liberty County, especially in the steepheads, but even there it is almost completely absent. But with its abundance farther north, coupled with peoples' bent toward making every snake story about a poisonous variety, I have heard more than my share of copperhead encounters. Checking on virtually all of them, I have found more dead Banded Watersnakes, young Cottonmouths, and sadly, even Corn Snakes. The copperhead has perfectly symmetrical hourglass bands, no bold facial markings, elliptical pupils and a yellow tail tip on the young. In all the years my father and I begged for substantiation of a copperhead record in the Tallahassee area, we never got the first nibble.

Speaking of Liberty County, there are very special Beech/Magnolia forests found along the Ochlockonee and Apalachicola Rivers that vary in many ways from those in the rest of North Florida in two ways. First, there is much relief in these forests, with steep canyon walls, unlike the rather flat forests of much of North Florida. Second, there's a strong Appalachian influence with the plants and animals in these unique ravines, owing to their geologic past.

A RARE VISITOR TO FLORIDA

We are talking about the marvelous steephead ravines, which inspired tales from Liberty County residents about the Garden of Eden and Adam's old stomping grounds. Never mind the tales, the real miracle is the fantastic biodiversity, heart-stopping scenery and organisms unique only to this locale.

To understand steephead ravines, we must start with the geology of the area in our mind's eye. It begins with over a hundred feet of sand piled on top of limestone, with a Longleaf Pine forest on top in the dry soil. The limestone, hopelessly buried underneath the sand, slants very slightly toward great rivers, such as the Apalachicola. The limestone was left over from Florida being under the sea, and the sand was deposited when the sea's shoreline was at certain places for long periods of time. Now, the geologic table is set, and the rest is up to time.

Over the eons, rain fell and percolated easily through the sand. Upon reaching the limestone, it gently flows in the direction of the river and is carried downstream. As the water exits the ground at river level (there are high banks of sand along the edges), it takes small amounts of sand with it, through a process called *steephead* erosion. Consequently, underground streams get started, invisible except for where they enter the river.

Over the millennia, though, these tiny underground streams take appreciable amounts of sand to the river, and the ground above the stream begins to sink slightly. The closer the stream gets to the river, the more erosion has taken place, so eventually there is a considerable valley formed over the underground stream near the river. The valley continues to enlarge and deepen until it reaches the limestone. By this time, it has become a pretty darn big valley.

Today, if you follow this stream up to the headwaters, you will find a small amount of water easing its way out of the sand just above the limestone. This place is called the amphitheatre, and the water has two characteristics. First, it is quite clean, as it has been percolating through the sand above for quite some time, being filtered as it drops. Second, the temperature is quite moderate, as it is essentially the temperature of the ground far below the surface. In winter, even if it's bitter cold, the water feels warmish compared to the air. In summer, when you may feel you missed the Garden of Eden and went down to you-know-where, the water is a refreshing temperature, and absolutely delicious to drink. And all that without chlorine.

Campers can't believe the scenery at Alum Bluff

CAN THIS BE FLORIDA?

The neat thing is, steephead formation never ceases. Not only does each steephead continue to grow larger and away from the river, smaller steepheads grow off the original. You can walk up a major steephead that empties into the river behind you and suddenly find one coming in from the side. And—you guessed it—over the thousands of years, these smaller steepheads create their own tributaries. So from the air, what the trained eye sees is a series of steepheads all feeding into one large one, and headed toward the parent river. At Alum Bluff, where many have hiked on The Nature

Conservancy land, one such major stream called Sweetwater Creek lies a few hundred yards upriver from the bluff. A short hike down to Sweetwater will add another place to anyone's list of Edens.

We all know that plant life is contingent upon the abiotic conditions at any site. Therefore, with damp soil on the valley sidewall of the canyon forged by the steephead stream, the Longleafs at the top remain right there. The forest type in the canyon is, in fact, Beech/Magnolia, and there are some earth-shattering Beech and Magnolia trees that sail far out of the canyon, along with towering Spruce Pines. But it's not just a Beech/Magnolia forest. . . .

During the last ice age, the Wisconsin, the Appalachians were frigid and almost lifeless. But the seeds from many plants washed down large rivers like the Apalachicola and lodged on the bank in present-day Florida. These plants found a home in the balmy water of the steephead streams and slowly spread into the canyons. Therefore, our steepheads are colonized with Appalachian plants as well as those of the typical Beech/Magnolia forest. A walk through a steephead reveals the fragrance of Star anise, and from early spring the Wild Azalea decorates the sunlit banks. All around is the smell, feel and look of the ancient mountains to the North.

Perhaps the most spectacular thing about these ravines is the animal life. For while plant seeds were making their way down the rivers, so were some key animals. To the herpetologist, these laboratories of evolution and history are as exciting as they are instructive. They are Florida's Galapagos, filled with species that exist nowhere else in the world.

During the Wisconsin Ice Age, between fifteen and twenty thousand years ago, many amphibians were forced down to North Florida. Needing a place during those bitter times, the moderated waters of the steepheads must have gotten their collective attention. Up they went into the valley, and niches were sorted out between several species. Today, thousands of years later, they remain in the oasis that saved their collective lives from certain death.

A slow and careful walk down the valley sidewall of the steephead ravine will reveal many logs on the slope. By rolling the wood gently, you will soon find the most widespread of the Beech/ Magnolia's salamanders, the **Slimy**. They will be toward the top, as they are the species that can tolerate the driest conditions. After admiring the creature, please replace the log as you found it.

Not far down the sidewall, the second of the salamanders will be found in the same manner—the beautiful **Two-lined Salamander**, a slender, bright yellow fellow with a dark dorsolateral line. It and the Slimy may be topped by the discovery of the awesome **Marbled Salamander**, one of the lunged Mole Salamander family. This jet black creature with white bands stays underground the majority of the time, but moves above in winter to breed.

Upon reaching the stream, kneel down and begin picking through the leaf litter in the stream. It will not take long to find the most abundant salamander around but the most important as well. Any small, dark figure will be the **Apalachicola Dusky Salamander**, an endemic in steepheads, found no place else on earth. They undoubtedly evolved from the **Northern Dusky**, marooned here so long ago. But they have done quite well and are in virtually every stream in the area. In some areas of West Florida, Northern Duskies are found, and separating them geographically is simple and safe. The ravines around the Blackwater River are loaded with them.

You will see many small duskies between one and two inches. These are the juveniles, and they breathe through their skin like the adults (as do all woodland salamanders). Soon, though, you will find a larger, brown specimen, which is the adult female. They are scattered all along the stream but more common in the upper reaches. Then, ease your way upstream to the amphitheater. Here you will find the hefty, wide-jawed male, a black creature with an attitude toward other salamanders. He hogs the area right where the sparkling water emerges from the ground and defends his territory against all comers. They hide under pieces of wood for protection against creatures like **Garter Snakes** and **Raccoons** and eat tiny invertebrates in the detritus.

My students at Leon High conducted ecological research for years on these salamanders, and we were curious, among other things, about what would happen when artificial structures were introduced into the amphitheater. The idea was suggested by Bruce Means, a long time friend and Director of Coastal Plains Institute. Essentially, we endeavored to find out how large an artificial structure we could place in the amphitheatre and have it defended by only one male. Plus, we were curious to learn if these artificial structures, by helping to protect the all-important males, would manipulate the population of duskies upward.

The results of the ten-year study were that

once the piece of plywood reached 18 x 24 inches, two males occasionally appeared. This was the case in five of fourteen steepheads studied, and at no point did we ever find an amphitheatre without artificial structures with more than one male. And though we did see a slight rise in the population of duskies in certain of the streams, I believe the results of the second portion would best be described as inconclusive. These data will not change the direction of American conservation, but gave literally hundreds of kids some hands-on science and a deep appreciation for steephead ravines. What that gave their teacher cannot be expressed in words.

One other somewhat interesting surprise was that the mammoth **Red Salamander**, which ate everything up to and including small snakes in captivity, coexisted nicely with duskies under the plywood. This robust woodland species is found regularly on the lower valley sidewalls and occasionally in the leaf litter.

Speaking of red, on rare occasions we would find the **Red-spotted Newt** in these streams, with the amazing ecology to be explained in Chapter 10. Finally, before moving to another color, the crayfish in some of the streams of the steepheads (especially near Torreya State Park) are honest-to-goodness red as well. This may be to match the changing soil color they exist in—I don't know.

Steephead streams have few snakes, as fish and frogs are not abundant. But the little-known **Queen Snake** may be found sunning on limbs in the warm season or hibernating under masses of litter down in the floodplain in the cooler months. Other snakes are pretty incidental, as are turtles, in this habitat of little food for carnivores.

One interesting lizard is found along these streams, and is not surprisingly a more northern species than what is normally found in North Florida. The **Five-lined Skink**, one of the troublesome three Eumeces, seems to be found along water courses far more than anywhere else in North Florida. I believe that it cannot compete with the larger Broad-headed, or the **Southeastern Five-lined** of the Longleaf community, and consequently stays along banks. This is not to say, however, that **Broad-headed** are never found near water.

These steephead streams eventually widen and often form floodplains before reaching rivers. For that reason, we shall, at this point, continue the discussion of steepheads, even though it involves a somewhat aquatic environment. The floodplains at the end of steephead streams are quite different from simple low areas along rivers, for several reasons. One is that the water level of floodplains in the steepheads doesn't fluctuate like other low ground near rivers, thus creating a more stable environment. But the major reason I see is the species composition. Fish get in the normal floodplains near rivers, making for fewer salamanders and possibly other amphibians, and are followed by turtles, snakes and the occasional **alligator**.

There are some salamanders in the floodplains below steephead streams, and one is remarkably like the endemic earlier discussed. The **Southern Dusky** lives in the muck of flood plains, as well as other wetlands across North Florida. Also, the handsome **Three-lined Salamander** is easily found under logs near the water and may be ridiculously common. Not so common, but regular with some looking, is the **Mud Salamander**. Muds look a lot like Reds, but are darker on the back.

One of the truly fantastic finds in the area, and a relative recent addition to our body of knowledge, is the **One-toed Amphiuma**. These fellows are little more than a foot long but are the top-level carnivore in the alluvial bogs in which they live. They are not rare in their local habitat but are secretive, and those of us who know how to catch them aren't telling. They could easily become over-collected, and some (ask the Blotched Kingsnakes) have no scruples about such things. It is interesting that in recent years, three new species of amphibians have been discovered, with two in this steephead system and one just west of here (**Bog Frog**). Indeed, there is much about the Florida Panhandle yet undiscovered and unstudied. With a history of few field vertebrate biologists/ecologists, the harvest is great and the harvesters are still few.

Frogs are everywhere in the floodplain. **River Frogs**, **Bronze Frogs**, and a few huge **Bullfrogs** are found throughout, while two unique treefrogs call the dark, wet forest home. **Spring Peepers** and the **Bird-voiced Treefrogs** liven up the swamp air—the former beginning its song in January! Any of three species of chorus frogs are possible in our floodplains, along with the omnipresent **Southern Toad**.

North Florida also has some wonderful, expansive floodplains as low areas along major rivers. Some rivers, such as the Apalachicola and Ochlockonee, move slowly east or west as they flow south. This causes them to cut into the bank as they dig one way, but they leave in the wake of this movement a low floodplain on the opposite side. These areas, strewn with potholes to ponds and oxbow lakes, may contain hordes of cold-blooded vertebrates from stranded fish to the turtles and snakes that endeavor to make a meal of them.

Floodplains are essentially swamps (wet areas with trees) found in low areas along rivers. The low light and frequent floods make for bare ground with little associated plant life. Great trees, fed by a nutrient smorgasbord and plenty of water, reach to the light above and create a lovely canopy with an almost eery look. Most are deciduous, so a dim sky broken up by scattered bare limbs forms almost a surreal roof over the floodplain in winter. Then in spring, the huge Swamp Tupelos, Bald Cypress, Sweet Gum and other monsters of the deep forest leaf out into dense foliage, replete with fruit, seeds and cover for small nesting birds.

Of **reptiles**, **Brown, Banded** and **Red-belly Water Snakes** (genus *Nerodia*) may all be found in floodplains, although the last is mostly in the western part of the Panhandle. **Banded Water Snakes** are actually not river snakes, but floodplains contain stagnant water. With much black, bands, and a stripe (albeit a diagonal one) through the eye, this species is most likely to be confused with a **Cottonmouth**. A big **Brown Water Snake**, though, is a mighty formidable looking creature and backs up the look with a bite from Hades. The

TOO OFTEN CONFUSED

latter, common on all area rivers, is light brown with dark brown squares—no black at all.

It is the saddest of all things that Water Snakes are so persecuted, especially by fishermen. Their only "crime" is that they eat sick and diseased fish, thereby making the fish population more healthy. They are in direct competition with Cottonmouths (*A. picivorous*=fish eater) and also improve the fishing. So what's the first thing fishermen do? Blow 'em away!

Cottonmouths (top) and Banded Water Snakes are hard for many Floridians to distinguish

Water Snakes are easy targets, lying out on limbs by day, sunning themselves. At night, they feed in their respective niches, before returning to limbs the next morning. When approached, they scoot off into the water, never to be seen again. Unfortunately, they are easy targets with shotguns from boats and are almost always judged "moccasins" by those who fish. Cottonmouths almost never lie out on limbs, preferring the solitude of tangles and roots along the shore.

Red-belly Water Snakes swim the rivers at night along the banks looking for frogs and fish in shallow water. Bandeds work the shallow puddles and inlets, often heading up on the bank for frogs and toads. Browns, confirmed fish eaters, lie on the bottom waiting for prey like a sucker or catfish to swim by. Water Snakes have large teeth to hold their piscine quarry but are not poisonous. They do bite painfully, though, and are not popular pets.

Being more creatures of dry areas, lizards are represented by the aforementioned **Five-lined Skink** and ubiquitous **Green Anole** as about the only common representatives in floodplains. Turtles are more in evidence, with **Box Turtles** joining about every aquatic group. Various of the sliders and cooters may be seen where sufficient water stands, and mud and musk turtles wander the wet forest floor to change feeding grounds. Soft-shelled turtles are also discovered on rare occasions, but often these are females looking for places to lay eggs. True snapping turtles are not commonly found anywhere, but floodplains have their share.

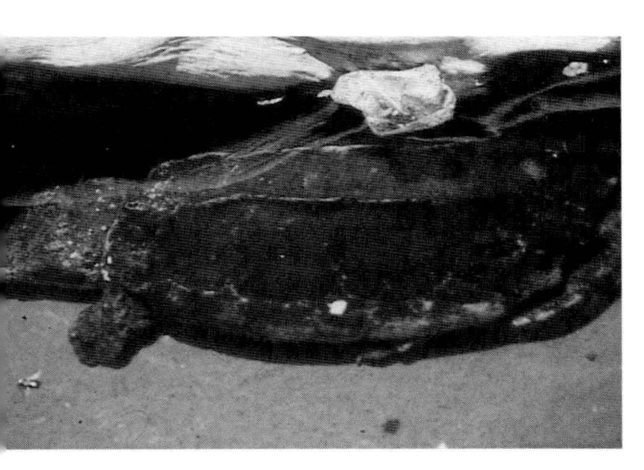

The Alligator Snapping Turtle (above) could be disarming to anyone unlucky enough to swim past one on the bottom

The **Common Snapping Turtle** is the species normally seen, and it is almost black with discernable ridges equally distributed on the back. The monstrous **Alligator Snapping Turtle**, a truly hideous beast, stays on the bottom of great lakes and rivers almost its entire life. I have encountered only two on land in my forty years of field work in Florida, and these were probably females looking to lay eggs. I do think, however, that many peoples' identifications of "snapping turtles" is about like that of poisonous snakes. It's somehow cooler to say you saw a snapping turtle, or a "moccasin," rather than a benign water snake or cooter. Moreover, when locals do find Common Snappers, certainly not a rare turtle, those somehow become Alligator Snapping Turtles. These monsters of the deep have three rows of very large keels running down the back of the shell and are normally brownish in color.

Snapping turtles of both species lie on the bottom with their mouths open. They wiggle their pink tongue as a lure, and unsuspecting fish come by for a look at the "worm" as the jaws of death come crashing down on them. Those encountered on land should be given a wide berth, but if you are strange like me, and must catch everything for closer examination, pick the snapper up by the tail with the head pointed away from your legs. 'Gator turtles have been known to snap boat paddles, so imagine what they could do to your kneecap.

Somewhat less sensational, mud and musk turtles will deliver a rousing bite and should not be trusted. Small blackish turtles, they resemble each other from the top, but the plastron reveals that muds have a hinged underside like a Box Turtle, while musk turtles have a smaller bottom shell. Musks make up for less armor with their pungent odor (*Kinosternum odoratus*), but both will bite the beejeebers out of anyone who carelessly handles them.

M**ammals** are not terribly well represented in floodplains, but **White-tailed Deer** certainly offer a lot of mammalian biomass. They are hunted extensively in the winter, and I am always a little reluctant to walk floodplains during that season. Buckshot and rifle slugs are very unforgiving and sustain a great velocity at long distances, compared to the bird shot of dove hunters.

G**ray Squirrels** are abundant in floodplains, although few of our hunting buddies seem to know that. **Raccoons** feed a fair amount here, too, and are joined by **Eastern Woodrats**, with their huge eyes peering out under debris. It has always surprised me that more mammals don't utilize floodplains, but perhaps the openness of it makes them want for places with brush to hide in.

Floodplains are excellent places for **birds** of many groups and at various seasons. Water birds may be

The Anhinga answers to a variety of North Florida names

found in tremendous concentrations when water levels are down and fish get trapped in drying up pools. **White Ibis**, egrets, herons and occasionally **Wood Storks** all flock together in a frenzy around low water, grabbing what they can before the rains return.

Wood **Ducks** breed in floodplains, with their numbers augmented in winter. In addition, there are woodcocks, night-herons, **Anhinga** in oxbow lakes and kingfishers rattling through the dense woodlands. Occasionally in this area one may find rookeries of water birds and the squawking in the distance is really strange to the ear. The importance of these nesting grounds for our wading birds cannot be overstated, and human interference should be kept to a minimum.

WATER TURKEY SNAKE BIRD

Many interesting land birds are common in season throughout the floodplain as well. **Barred Owls** are common in wooded portions along every river and are replaced by day with **Red-shouldered Hawks**. Many birds of moist woodlands (Beech/Magnolia forest) are also found in floodplains, including summer resident **Yellow-billed Cuckoo**, **Ruby-throated Hummingbird**, **Acadian Flycatcher**, **Northern Parula**, **Red-eyed Vireo** and the occasional **Wood Thrush** and **Swainson's Warbler**. Perhaps the poster bird of the floodplain is the golden **Prothonotary Warbler**, a very common nester throughout North Florida's river banks and swampy areas.

Resident birds found commonly in floodplains include **Pileated**, **Downy**, **Hairy** and **Red-bellied Woodpeckers**, **Carolina Chickadees** and **Tufted Titmice**, **Carolina Wren** and **Northern Cardinals**. In winter, though, quite a few interesting birds are easily found, including **Rusty Blackbird**, **American Goldfinch**, **Hermit Thrush**, **Blue-headed Vireo**, **Black-and-white** and **Orange-crowned Warbler**, **Eastern Phoebe**, **Whip-poor-will**, **White-throated** and **Swamp Sparrow**, and **Winter Wren**.

Gray Rat Snakes, thought of as a snake of the "high and dry," are abundant in the floodplains and draw a great crowd of many of the above-mentioned birds when they are on the prowl. Birds are also drawn to Barred Owls to fuss at them, and you may occasionally find yourself the target of such verbal abuse. One ploy that often attracts birds, especially in the breeding season, is "squeaking." Lick the fleshy back of your hand between the thumb and second finger bone and suck hard, making a sound that nesting birds seem to equate with their young. Birds of prey like Barred Owls are also drawn to it, possibly because they may "think" it is a food item. It can be a neat experience for the squeaker, but less so if there is deet on your hand.

BEAUTIFUL LAZY RIVER

A peaceful alluvial river meanders past its floodplain

When one visits a place like Alum Bluff, it is a remarkable and instructive experience to walk from the Longleafs on top downslope through the Beech/Magnolia community in the steepheads and into floodplains waiting below. I especially enjoy the transitional zones where one distinct forest type diffuses into another. Certainly, nature is organized in gradients, with recognizable areas of definition along the way. At dawn, the darkness slowly gives way to daylight, which is with us until it gives way to nightfall at dusk. Then finally, the dark "area of definition" gives way once again, and the circle—or cycle—is complete. This walk downslope brings into focus all the abiotic factors, the associated plants and the responding animals into one linear mosaic.

This book can pass along a few scientific facts and insights, but there is no substitute for a walk through nature, as it was in precolonial days. Watch the Fence Lizards scurry around the bark, smell the Star anise, gaze at the beauty of a Longleaf canopy, and watch the turtles plop off one log after another. This is where the real education is. So get your buddy, your sweetheart, or the entire family, pack some food and water, and head to the wonderland of nature's classroom.

Miscellaneous Terrestrial Communities

It should be quite obvious to each of us that our species has completely altered the forest types wherever our hands have touched. You would be hard pressed to drive across much of North Florida and recognize many places as good examples of Beech/Magnolia or Longleaf ecosystems. We may be able to tell what a forest used to be but most are now jumbles of assorted trees with no specific type or ecological plan. A tremendous amount of North Florida is planted pines for commercial purposes, such as Sand and Slash Pines. Though these are native in other parts of the state, they do little for the creatures of the inland Panhandle.

But there are animals in these "mongrel" communities, and the overall species composition of creatures is affected by "mixed up" assortments of trees. To understand this, one must see that there are two opposing strategies of animals on earth, and actually this is true of all organisms. One is the generalist, and the other is the specialist.

We know that generalists can live in many places and are very adaptable creatures. Some survive well around man and his edifices. **Green Anoles**, **Southern Toads**, **Opossums** and **Common Grackles** are examples of vertebrates which have always been in our area but take to neighborhoods quite well. Other creatures such as **House Sparrows**,

SEEN NO

European Starlings and two rat species were brought over, intentionally or unwittingly, by our founding fathers. Since they got their beginnings in civilization, they do quite well in cities.

But, adaptable animals are much more than just those that can survive in town. Some creatures have a wider diet, more methods of gathering food, varied options for reproduction, greater ability to withstand heat and cold, better defenses against diverse predators, and so forth. They are simply superior in a changing world, and this offers a lesson about earth's living history.

Throughout time, earth has gone through periods of immense change (Chapter 1). Creatures (and plants) that can adapt have a far better chance of surviving with the changing world than those which are specific to their niche. Change is the great exploiter of weakness. Dinosaurs seemed to have no weakness but zipped right into oblivion when the dust pall from the meteor collision shut down the plant community. Their weakness was that they were overconsumptive (I think about that every time I eat a seafood platter at Julia Mae's).

On a local level, Ivory-billed Woodpeckers were fairly common in some places in the South and were labeled "pesky" at Wakulla Springs by the late Dr. Herbert L. Stoddard. Their problem? They didn't like being around people. They were shy, retiring birds who took their population farther and farther into the floodplain until there was no place to go. Now they have taken their last journey, and are having fellowship with the dinosaurs.

But earth has had its stable periods as well. During these times, specialists become extremely success-

MORE
Ivory-billed Wood-peckers have vanished from our planet, due to the loss of the floodplains

ful and populate their niche with almost reckless abandon. They are closely tied to their abiotic environment, as well as the plant community in which they live. The inevitable will, however, happen—ice age, comet, raging fire, climatological change, or possibly a mutated virus. Then a period of change takes place, and the generalists are successful.

Evolutionists see the pace of change as "punctuated equilibrium." It simply speeds up or slows down with upheavals in the abiotic environment, and the plants, then animals, follow right along. Probably the greater the change in the nonliving environment, the faster and more pronounced the evolutionary period for organisms. These are the great periods of extinction, but also of new life.

When discussing extinctions, we have traditionally pointed to the K-1 and K-2 boundaries as the greatest extinctions in earth's history. These took place at the beginning and end of the dinosaur age, the Mesozoic. But amazingly, scientists have concluded that the rate of change—and extinction—in the world right now is greater than at either of these two periods in history. The activities of our species, *Homo sapiens*, are exterminating more creatures than the wholesale destruction that the comet visited upon us 65,000,000 years ago.

What is disappearing? The specialists. There are plenty of **Raccoons**, **American Crows**, **Ground Skinks** and **Greenhouse Frogs**. They can roll with all the punches we humans throw at them. But the **Southeastern Five-lined Skinks** in North Florida have to have a properly maintained Longleaf community. **Pig Frogs** require open, grassy lakes. And there are some kinds whose specifications are even narrower than these examples. For us not to be the agent of a mass extinction like the world has never known, we must preserve and properly maintain our climax communities as if the future of hundreds of species depend on it—because it does.

This is why Beech/Magnolia and Longleaf Pine forests are so critical. They are simply the only place many species can live and reflect what our country was like before we began altering the environment for our purposes. It is our natural heritage and losing it is like losing a part of ourselves. That is why people fought so hard to preserve and properly manage the Apalachicola National Forest and the steephead ravines. They realized what our government finally came to grips with: You cannot save species unless you save their habitat.

So what are all these "mutt" forests with random conglomerations of various species of trees? Well, they are not damaging North Florida, they just aren't helping the creatures who need help the most. Two species of birds, the **Orchard Oriole** and the **Indigo Bunting** are having a field day right now (no pun intended) with all the old-field, second-growth forest in Eastern North America. Their numbers have skyrocketed, and they line the coast in the migration, but these two have always been a stable population. All we have done is to make the generalists richer and the specialists poorer. These fragmented habitats have drawn **Red-tailed Hawks** to our area, common in winter and occasional breeders. These are abundant throughout much of the country, so we have done little to aid the overall biodiversity by giving a generalist yet one more place to call home.

Which generalists are in the mixed-up forests in North Forida? Well, good luck. Just as there is a jumble of plant types, the animals in evidence are always a surprise.

FAMILIAR

Honestly, sometimes I find creatures I never expect to unearth. Affixing a general species list to these forests would be like saying what breed of dog parented every mongrel dog that ever lived. The combinations are endless, and there is little value to the exercise.

This is not to say these forests have no value. They provide homes for animals, recreation areas to hunters and hikers, and are a dang sight more attractive than shopping malls and houses. There is no suggestion here to cut them down and grow Slash Pines. Please. Indeed, some maintain Longleaf species for a few years, and that's better than deforestation. But landowners do have an interesting alternative: habitat restoration.

Many people with the resources to do so are turning portions of their property back to nature and restoring it to a natural forest type. This is most common with dry-soil areas, where owners are planting Longleaf Pine seedlings, along with Wiregrass and other species from the Longleaf community. They even provide periodic burns, and some have seen creatures of the Longleafs almost magically appear out of thin air! I am convinced that, as I said in the last paragraph, some Longleaf species survive for a time in mixed forests. So it may well be that in areas where the Longleafs have been removed, forest restoration will bring home stranded animal populations waiting to disappear.

Those interested in reforestation should bear in mind that the removal of invasive plant species is as important as the reintroduction of those that belong there. Fire is an important tool in this quest with Longleaf restoration, as oaks

Chickadees and titmice live in our neighborhoods and come to our feeders like they own them

and slash pines (to name a couple) are eliminated with fire (if they are not too big). Their ash fertilizes the ground, and their absence in the canopy opens up the ground for small plants. If they are too big to kill with fire, the very chain saw that cost us our Longleaf forests can reduce invasive species to rotting logs in a hurry.

For more information on forest restoration, contact the Florida Forestry Service (850) 671-5332.

A climax, though unnatural, community in North Florida is the Live Oak forests. There have gotten to be quite a few areas with large tracts of Live Oaks, with some of it replacing pine woods. These trees are magnificent and may be centuries old. There are few creatures that require oak forests, but some interesting species are relatively common.

Given the acorns to be had, **mammals** like **Fox Squirrels** may be found in oak forests, as well as the abundant **Gray Squirrels**. Also though, the fascinating **Flying Squirrel** sails through the canopy at night escaping predators and searching for nuts. Their whistles may be heard from these forests on warm summer nights, adding to the enchantment of huge Live Oaks. **Deer** are common, drawn to the acorns, with many hunters making blinds in the oak trunks. **Bobcat** are surprisingly found in good numbers, with **Seminole Bats** flitting along early evening. Oddly, **Cottontails** are very common throughout oak forests, adding to the hunter's delight.

Birds like **Blue Jays**, **American Crows** and **Red-headed Woodpeckers** share the love for acorns, and may be joined by **Carolina Chickadees** and **Tufted Titmice**. **Great Horned Owls** are common in oak forests, and **Screech**

Owls often show up in winter, if not to breed. **Red-tailed Hawks** and the summering **Mississippi Kites** hunt here, with the latter having a love for **Broad-headed Skinks**. Songbirds like **Summer Tanagers** and **Blue Grosbeaks** add color to the canopy, and their songs (somewhat similar) echo through the forest.

Gray Rat Snakes probably change their diet to include mostly birds in this community, with a few rattlesnakes down below playing predator control (rat patrol?) on any rodents around. The swift **Black Racer** lives within this forest, tearing out after small vertebrates and ascending oak trees when confronted by faster predators. They may be joined by **Eastern Coachwhips**, but not to my experience. Few lizards live here, and even fewer turtles.

There are some lesser known naturally occurring terrestrial communities in North Florida. One that I have actually lived in down the Wakulla Beach Road is the palm/hydric community. This is a peninsula ecosystem found abundantly from around Perry down to the Everglades. Portions of it reach North Florida along the coast up the "Gulf hammock" area. The dominant tree is the Cabbage Palm, but various species like the massive Loblolly Pine seem to play an important role as well. Fire is not a natural part of the ecology, as the soil is too wet. Some have burned it in dry weather to open it up for deer hunting, but this destroys some forest species and upsets the natural balance within.

Deer are abundant in this community, with **Raccoon**, **Nine-banded Armadillo**, **Opossum**, **Gray Squirrel**, **Marsh Rabbit** (note the absence of a white tail), **Black Bear**, **Gray Fox**, **Eastern Woodrat**, and sadly, feral hogs. These introduced beasts wreak ecological havoc all over the community, both eating plants as well as animals such as salamanders and frogs. As much as I detest hunting on National Wildlife Refuges, I must support the killing of hogs on refuge land.

The palm/hydric community is not a hotbed of avifauna, although there are some interesting ornithological things happening there. **Bald Eagles** frequently nest in huge pines, and two pair raised their young quite near my former home on the Wakulla Beach Road. In addition, excellent winter flocks of songbirds roam the community, heavily laden with insects, bringing us exciting species such as **Brown Creeper**, **Golden-crowned Kinglet**, **Black-and-white** and **Yellow-throated Warbler**, **Blue-headed Vireo**, **Pine Siskin**, **Eastern Phoebe** and many more. Also in winter, tremendous flocks of **Tree Swallows** feed over the canopy on sand gnats (argh), and huge congregations of **American Robins** are everywhere. I have even found **Winter Wren** and **Lincoln's Sparrow** at this time.

A great area on the St. Marks Refuge. Bring your binoculars and bug spray

Excellent flocks of migrant songbirds may be found in the palm/hydric community, as they seek water, groceries and shelter either before or after crossing the expansive Gulf of Mexico. One of my best spots for migrants is the gated road just inside the refuge on the Wakulla Beach Road.

BUGS AND BIRDS

This community also seems to form the southern extent in North Florida of several species of insectivorous song birds, including **Acadian Flycatcher**, **Eastern Wood-pewee**, **Wood Thrush**, **Red-eyed** and **White-eyed Vireos**, **Hooded Warbler** and **Blue-gray Gnatcatcher**.

Snakes may be the top group of animals in this area, which, of course, had nothing to do with my living there. . . . **Pigmy Rattlers** are even more abundant than **Cottonmouths**, which, in such a wet community, is surprising. Even a few big **Eastern Diamondback Rattlesnakes** make their home down to the moist forests, probably to poke around in the dead palm trunks for woodrats. Those hiking in any area where palmetto are found should be exceedingly careful about what lies under palm fronds. Though seldom fatal today, a snake bite is a dreadful, life-changing experience.

Many nonpoisonous snakes are also found in the palm/hydric community. **Scarlet Kingsnakes**, everywhere else a rare animal, are actually fairly common here. I have often found them hiding under the bark of dead pine trees, seeking refuge from the daylight. Their larger cousins, the **Eastern Kingsnakes**, are present but disappearing rapidly.

Gray Rat Snakes are common members of this ecosystem, and in the Big Bend they begin looking like the "gulf-hammock rat snake." In the drier reaches of this area, **Corn Snakes** may be found regularly as well.

One of the truly fascinating examples of convergence in nature is exemplified with the **Garter** and **Ribbon Snakes** in this community. Convergent evolution occurs when two species develop a set of similar characteristics due to some commonality in their respective habitats. Though closely related (unlike many textbook examples), these two creatures have blue lines running down the back, making both their subspecies names *Bluestripe* (Ribbon or Garter Snake). Something in the environment selects for a bluish snake with this genus, and I am aware of no hypotheses for this. Real blue is, incidentally, an extremely rare color in snakes.

Banded Water Snakes are the only one of their genus that can survive in most palm/hydric systems. They can find fish and small frogs in ditches, tiny ponds, small streams and swamps. They are the generalists of the water snakes and can make a living about anywhere. There is another interesting aquatic snake, though, found sympatrically with Bandeds. **Glossy Crayfish Snakes** live in the great swamps of the South, part of a group of mild mannered, iridescent guys that eat primarily soft-shelled crayfish. None of these, including the **Queen Snake** in the streams of the Panhandle eat well in captivity, and they make poor pets.

Other snakes may be found in the palm/hydric community, but, frankly, there is little data from our area. Species that I encountered in my travels there, other than the preceding, include the **Rough Green Snake**, **Southern Ringneck Snake**, and **Eastern Hognosed Snake**. Others are likely, including some of the small, burrowing "ground" snakes, which are easily overlooked.

Lizards are not fond of wet areas, but one may find **Eastern Glass Lizards**, **Five-lined Skinks** (nearly their southern limit), and, of course, **Ground Skinks**. The **Green Anole** is as common here as in other communities, but observers need to watch for other species of anoles moving up from the peninsula, such as the **Brown Anole**.

RARE IN FLORIDA

This Spotted Turtle showed up on the St. Marks Refuge

Turtles roam all through the palm/hydric community, especially the **Box Turtle**. But one amazing find on the St. Mark's Refuge was a **Spotted Turtle**, long thought an inhabitant only of the farther Northeast. Its discovery only serves to underscore our lack of knowledge for this area, and demonstrates the need for much more field work. I am astounded at times at the lack of field work and field knowledge on the part of science teachers and even university professors. Armchair herpetology has no place in North Florida!

The genus *Pseudemys,* turtles called cooters and sliders, has been left out of this book to this point, although they are frequently seen crossing roads and basking along watercourses. However, they will be discussed at great length in the chapter on aquatic ecosystems. Suffice it to say, they may certainly be seen in this habitat as well, but these are essentially aquatic, albeit wandering creatures.

Numbers of **Amphibians** are high in the palm/hydric community, especially frogs. In some places, there seem to be **Leopard Frogs** everywhere, bouncing around in front of us hikers. They form the chief food for the **Bluestripe Ribbon** and **Garter Snakes**, as well as some other snakes, **Red-shouldered Hawk**, **Barred Owl**, several mammalian predators, and bass in the water. Their spots and narrow, pointed snout make identification easy, and they are the only true frog (genus *Rana*) that lives an appreciable amount of time out of and away from the water, except the rare **Gopher Frog**.

Southern **Cricket Frogs** also may be abundant, as well as **Narrow-mouthed Toads**, the little black guy that calls like a Norelco razor. Along with them are **Squirrel Treefrogs** by the oodles, **Gray Treefrogs** and the larger, handsome **Green Treefrogs** in larger ponds. **Greenhouse Frogs** also peep in the night, perhaps exploring a new habitat for its species. All these hungry frogs indicate large numbers of insects, and believe me, they have it. Along with mosquitoes are the beloved sand gnats, cleverly dubbed "no see 'ums" by the natives. Of course, we always notice the insects that bite and forget that there are multitudes of nonbiting bugs all over the damp forest floor being consumed by various spiders, frogs and toads, flycatchers, lizards and Lord knows what else. But the most evident "bug" of summer for people is the biting flies, family Tabanidae, like Deer, Dog, Horse and Yellow Flies. Early summer finds great swarms of them through this area, swarms which have been known to run a few hardy hikers plum out of the woods.

Speaking of insectivores, **Slimy Salamanders** are scattered through this area, hiding under pieces of palm log and other debris. Joining them are surprisingly common **Mole Salamanders**, which may disappear for three seasons and suddenly cover the roads on the first rainy night in midwinter. These nights they are joined by **Spadefoot Toads**, which, with the **Leopard Frogs**, prefer to breed in the spring. The virtual absence of reptilian predators at this time, the presence of a food source for their larvae that is less affected by the season, as well as the lack of competition as winter or early spring breeders make winter an ideal time for some amphibian reproduction.

When you are in the area along southern Wakulla County, you simply must take Highway 375 down to the beautiful little town of Spring Creek. Right at the end of the road is a small landing which is adjacent to a spring. In fact, the entire area is replete with dozens of springs, making this the real "world's largest spring," which you often hear associated with Wakulla. The tiny springs all through the main waterway are excellent **Sheephead** spots, where the fish are all too eager to take shrimp off your hook. Use a small hook and fish the edge of the water boils, where they hide in the limestone edges of the miniature springs.

Before leaving this little hamlet, make sure you are hungry. The Spring Creek Restaurant, owned by the Lovell family since fried trilobites were king, has some of the finest prepared seafood I've ever eaten (on six continents, by the way). Leo Lovell is a great guy whose business displays very interesting decorations like whale vertebrae and huge limestones in the wall replete with fossils.

Adjacent to the palm/hydric community is the coast, and an awful lot of salt marsh. This productive and interesting community will be covered in the marine ecosystem chapter, but just west down the coast from the last of the palm/hydric community is another climax system that we will mention briefly. It is the Sand Pine community. It stretches from about the mouth of the Ochlockonee River westward, along the Panhandle, and there's a very good reason why.

This river brings a lot of sand with it to the gulf, and much of it is fine, "sugar" sand. Anyone who ever tried to drive out on the tip of Bald Point—even in a four-wheel drive—knows only too well how treacherous the sand at the mouth of that river is. This fine sand is blown inland by strong southeasterly winds and deposited not far from the coast. In this sugar sand grows the only pine that can live here, the Sand Pine, and this is the only area where it grows naturally. Longleafs cannot tolerate salt, Loblollies are too huge for the light-weight, shifty sand, and Spruce Pines require far more water than this desert-like area offers. Like so many times in nature, a species lives in a harsh environment only because it can, when others cannot.

Sand Pines are lovely little trees, with bark that resembles Spruce Pines. The needles are quite fragrant when crushed, making it seem like, with pines, short needles have more aroma than long ones. Sand Pines have tiny cones that are extremely serotenous—they cannot open to drop seeds unless induced by fire. Therefore, in the absence of fire (historically discouraged by man), they have suffered from a lack of new seedlings in some places.

A few bushes and shrubs like Rosemary grow in this community, but the ground is quite open and the soil is amazingly dry. There are quite a few animals that live here that are often likened to those in deserts, because sand and salt are almost prerequisites to our definition of deserts. Most of these around the world are old oceans that have dried up, so it is no wonder deserts are sandy and salty. Obviously, this community of Sand Pines is quite similar in the abiotic characteristics and, therefore, shares many animals with "true" deserts.

Quite a common creature under debris along the coast is the Black Widow Spider. They may be identified by their glossy black, fat little bodies, and the red hourglass pattern on the abdomen. This is a very dangerous creature! People sticking their hands under trash along the coast run a big risk with the abundance of widows. Any bite will have serious consequences, and, depending on one's body chemistry, could result in death. Always wear gloves when doing yard work in sandy soil anywhere in North Florida, and do not even think of letting children around trash piles coastally.

A LOVING MOTHER?

This mama scorpion is covered with her young during their early stage

Joining the above menace is a potentially worse creature, the scorpion. As a rule of thumb, the larger a species of scorpion gets, the less poisonous it is. Unfortunately, ours is a small, nasty species . . . . It is tan brown with forward pincers and a long tail curving upward. When acquiring food or defending themselves, scorpions thrust their tail forward, over their bodies, and nail their targets with lethal accuracy. Avoid them at all costs.

Are you starting to relax? Well, consider the fact that all four species of poisonous snakes found regularly in the Big Bend are found in the Sand Pines and along the coast as commonly as they are anywhere in North Florida. Big diamondbacks hiding under palm fronds, **Pigmy Rattlers** in trash piles, **Cottonmouths** creeping away from local streams and ponds looking for lizards and birds, and even the brilliant **Coral Snake** foraging on warm evenings and summer mornings in lawns and bushy areas.

No longer like animals? Let's try some plants. This community is home to saw palmetto, which left a permanent scar on my right hand from when I was eleven. There are more stickers than unburned undergrowth in a Longleaf forest. Our only cactus, the Prickly Pear is abundant along the coast, and is made to break apart and stick to your shoes (a method of vegetative propagation). When you are pulling one out, be sure you don't hit the tiny hair-like needles at the base of the long spine that go into your skin easily (but don't ever seem to leave).

Speaking of seed dispersal, need we mention sand spurs? Nothing is more fun than stepping on these guys on the way to the water. Nothing cracks me up more than watching someone at the beach cursing sand spurs all the way back to his car or beach house, throwing them out into the dunes one by one. I can almost hear them saying, "Thank you, thank you, thank you." We could not do a better job of planting this loathsome scourge if we planned it.

The phantom menace plant of the Sand Pine/beach community surely is the Stinging Nettle though. A diminutive plant with pretty white flowers, it invites victims to try picking them (regrettably, children on many occasions) and delivers a sting like the fires from the place they were no doubt conceived. Upon closer inspection, you can see the tiny hair-like needles, which act as little hypodermic syringes to inject burning crystals under your skin. When your prayers are answered and the burning stops, expect itching like you have never known. A remedy few people have heard of is rubbing ether on the sting. It is unclear whether this actually reduces the pain or half knocks the patient out, but it seems to help in "ether" event.

Other than the poisonous snakes mentioned earlier, there are actually quite a few harmless ones. Our two swiftest and longest snakes are still found with some regularity in the Sand Pines along the coast. **Eastern Coachwhips** tear across the ground at amazing speeds, quite a lot like Black Mambas (a brownish snake) on the African savannah. Uniquely dark toward the front and lighter in the aft, coachwhips can outrun about any predator—except cars. Sadly, this tan-colored comet has all but vanished in many of its original locations.

Looking like a black coachwhip is the **Brownchin Racer**. Essentially a subspecies of the widespread **Black Racer**, but found in the Apalachicola River Valley, its genes flow along the coast eastward to about the Ochlockonee River. Once an abundant snake, this "black snake" is still seen crossing Highway 98, and falls victim to cars as well. Racers and coachwhips make bad pets, eating poorly (except fingers) and remaining agitated in captivity.

Other harmless species still found in this area include **Corn Snake**, **Ribbon Snake** (both races), **Garter Snake**, **Rough Green Snake**, **Scarlet Snake** and **Gray Rat Snakes** in coastal stands of hardwood. People who want to discourage snakes in their yards, as well as some of the arachnids described earlier, should keep their yards mowed and free of trash and other debris. No place this side of Australia has so many nasties in one ecosystem!

Two of the common lizards of the Longleafs are found along the coast—**Six-lined Racerunners** and **Fence Lizards**. Racerunners are especially abundant in loose sand and may occasionally be seen running on their hind legs! **Green Anoles** are their usual common selves, along with the **Ground Skink**, **Slender** and **Eastern Glass Lizards**, and **Five-lined Skinks** near wet areas.

NATURE'S HANDLE

The long, strong, rough tail of the common snapping turtle provides the only way to hoist one out of the swamp

One amazing turtle lives along the coast, the **Gulf Coast Giant Box Turtle**. Quite a bit larger than other box turtles, these big guys are still regular on old roads and often show up in yards. **Gopher Tortoise** used to live here, but have all but disappeared. **Eastern Mud Turtles** are common in roadside ditches, and are often seen in the road early mornings in summer. **Common Snapping Turtles** are surprisingly common in ditches as well, and best left there. Occasionally, various cooters and sliders show up on the beach, including a record of an **Alabama Redbelly Turtle** in my youth with my father. True sea turtles would normally beach themselves on barrier islands but occasionally come ashore along the mainland coast (see Chapter 6).

Birds are plentiful along the coast, though not especially so in stands of Sand Pines. In winter, **Golden-crowned Kinglets**, scarce elsewhere, are frequently found with the ubiquitous **Yellow-rumped Warbler**, **Eastern Towhee**, various sparrows, roving flocks of **American Goldfinches** with occasional **Pine Siskin**, **Blue-headed Vireo**, **House Wren**, and, very likely, the northern race of the **Blue Jay**.

In the migration, however, exciting little colorful birds may pile up along the coast, depending on the weather conditions. In spring, with inclement weather such as rain or an associated cold front (with north winds), songbirds on their way from the tropics to Canada or the northern U.S. may be abundant, giving a show with tremendous colors and diversity. Many species of warblers plus tanagers, orioles, buntings and grosbeaks fill the pines and scrub oaks with yellow, green, blue and orange. More drab families such as flycatchers and vireos join the fray and make the kind of birding days birders live for.

THE

Without these weather conditions, a few migrants may be seen, such as **Blackpoll** and **Cape May Warblers**, but most ride the predominant southerly wind for an hour or so inland. Even on the slow days, given the number of water birds around, birders can easily spot over a hundred kinds of birds on any spring day. The migration spans from about mid-March to mid-May and peaks in late April. St. George Island State Park, at Rattlesnake Hammock, is one of the top locations in the Panhandle to search for migrants in both spring and fall.

BOSS

A male Boat-tailed Grackle with a nearby harem rules the roost in this marsh

Fall is very different from spring, as the birds are quiet and dressed mostly in their drab colors. Interestingly enough, those same cold fronts that produced birds by "downing" them in spring also bring masses of birds in fall, but for the opposite reason. In September and October, birds migrate slowly, from tree to tree, in no hurry. Then, when a cold front sweeps across the South, they take full advantage of the northerly winds and fly hard to the Gulf shores.

These first few cold fronts in fall have always been my favorite birding days of the year (which could have something to do with my absence from school on brisk, cool, September days) and bring an excitement for me unparalleled in zoology. Zipping overhead by the dozens, headed around the coast to the peninsula, are **Barn Swallows**, **Eastern Kingbirds**, **Northern Flickers**, and **Palm Warblers**. Raptors, such as **Merlins**, **American Kestrels** and **Peregrines**, suddenly appear for the first time since April, and loads of song-birds feeding in the canopy excitedly make it hard to know which way to look. Mosquitoes, quiet for the first time since early spring, are beaten down by the refreshing winds, and the much sought "perfect day" is at hand. The only thing that tops this great day of birding is a stop at Julia Mae's for a plate of seafood!

With as great as the coastline is for bird-ing in the migration, summer brings a period of almost birdless days. **Laughing Gulls**, **Fish Crows** and **Boat-tailed Grackles** are common, but there is little diversity or excitement. There is a colony of **Black Skimmers** and **Least Terns** on the cause-way to St. George Island that is fun to watch as one drives past slowly, but my suggestion is to enjoy the water, fish, or go looking for snakes. Being on the southern end of the continent, Florida just doesn't have the birds in summer like it does the rest of the year.

M**ammals** are not well represented along the coastal Sand Pine community, but some species are quite common. **Raccoons** feed on the bounty of the low tide flats, where many groups of invertebrate marine life are stranded and "easy pickins." They are joined by Herring Gulls who know how to take creatures like scallops up high and drop them, opening the shells. Raccoons occasionally contract rabies, and any unusually tame 'coon should be reported to authorities and given a wide berth.

O**possums** and **Nine-banded Armadillos** are common along the coast, the latter for the ease of burrowing into sandy soil. Another burrower, the **Striped Skunk**, is abundant in the Sand Pines, and provides a food source for the **Great Horned Owl**, which completely lacks any sense of smell. Amazingly, we can smell horned owls that have been sprayed by hapless skunks when we get close enough to them!

M**arsh Rabbits** are common along the coast, as are the **Bobcat** who eat them. **Deer** are secretive in most places coastally but are occasionally seen. In the air, **Yellow Bats** seem to be the species found most often. Largely a migrant, this robust creature is seen from about March through the end of the fall. A few **Red Bats** and **Seminole Bats** are also witnessed around dusk.

GRACE AND BEAUTY

Just north of the best Sand Pine forest, between Carrabelle and East Point, lies an area known as Tate's Hell Swamp. Not a swamp at all, it was once possibly the largest shrub bog in the world. Much of it was ditched, drained, and the owners, Buckeye Cellulose, planted Slash Pines from about the Franklin/Liberty County line southward to the coast. This put a serious dent in it as a natural area, but the place remains development-free, and has been bought by the State of Florida as a wildlife corridor. This expansive area is interesting to drive through and offers glimpses at hard-to-find creatures like **Black Bear** and **Bobcat**.

Stunning Swallow-tailed Kites nest in rising numbers across North Florida

Breeding birds in Tate's Hell include **Swallow-tailed Kite**, **Swainson's**, **Hooded**, **Prothonotary** and **Pine Warblers**, **White-eyed Vireo**, **Red-shouldered Hawk**, **Green** and **Little Blue Heron**, **Yellow-crowned Night-heron**, **Mississippi Kite**, **American Woodcock**, **Barred** and **Great Horned Owls**, **Chuck-will's-widow**, **Ruby-throated Hummingbird**, **Acadian** and **Great-crested Flycatcher**,

Barn Swallow, **Wood Thrush**, **Brown Thrasher**, **Orchard Oriole**, **Yellow-breasted Chat** and many less interesting birds.

R**eptiles** are plentiful with **Cottonmouths** as dense as I've ever seen them. Both rattlesnakes are frequently seen, making this a pit viper paradise. Nonvenomous snakes include **Rough Green Snake**, **Glossy Crayfish Snake**, **Banded** and **Brown Water Snakes**, **Garter Snake** (with bright red tongues), **Ribbon Snake**, **Gray Rat Snake**, **Corn Snake**, **Eastern Coachwhip**, **Brownchin Racer**, and the disappearing **Blotched Kingsnake**.

Lizards are an interesting mix between the shrub bog relics and the planted pine woods fellows. **Fence Lizards** and **Six-lined Racerunners** represent dry land habitat, while **Five-lined Skinks**, **Eastern Glass Lizards** and **Green Anoles** are most likely leftovers from the wetlands. I found the **Mimic Glass Lizard**, brand new to science, in this area, as well as in the Apalachicola National Forest adjacent to the north.

C**ommon Snapping Turtles** and **Eastern Mud Turtles** are all through Tate's Hell, lumbering across the road, going from ditch to ditch. Fish are abundant in these ditches, including some specialties such as **Dollar Sunfish** and **Pygmy Sunfish**. Cooters and sliders are not common in Tate's Hell because they are not a bog genus, but **Box Turtles** are more abundant here even than in the National Forest.

Some **amphibians** are found in great numbers in Tate's Hell Swamp. **Bullfrog**, **Leopard** and **River Frogs** are all easily seen, heard and captured. **Barking**, **Squirrel**, **Green**, **Bird-voiced** and **Gray Treefrogs** all call their lungs out in season, and **Southern Toads** hop across the dirt roads in good numbers. **Two-toed Amphiumas**, a throwback to days well before there were any reptiles on earth, slither through the ditches, sucking up hapless fish and tadpoles. Fishermen who catch these on their cane poles need to beware; amphiuma have well developed teeth and know quite well how to use them!

One of the great surprises in Tate's Hell one rainy June night was ponds full of breeding **Florida Gopher Frogs**. To check on this location, take the main road in from the old Buckeye Plant in Carrabelle, stay to the right where the main dirt road forks, and take the first right after you cross the small bridge over a tributary of the Carrabelle River. In less than a mile, you will see some odd, dug-out ponds on your right, and that's where they bred in 1992. Between a few alligators in the area, as well as some "bream" being placed in these ponds, it is hoped the tadpoles survived and are continuing the population of these rare frogs.

Well off to the northeast is another jumbo shrub bog, known as Bradwell Bay. Located in the Apalachicola National Forest, this bog is due east of Crawfordville, easily found by taking the forest road west out of town and watching for the sign on the left. There is a circular drive of National Forest roads that is terribly interesting and offers excellent views of many groups of wildlife. In addition, there are some good insectivorous bogs along the west side of Bradwell Bay right on the road by borrow pits. Several species of pitcher plants, both sun dews and other species of the insectivorous zone are easily located right on the shoulder of the road.

Part of the famous Florida Trail runs right through the bay, and offers breathtaking experiences with an untouched ecosystem. Bring bug spray, pack water, wear boots and get a good night's sleep—this is not a hike for the faint of heart. Be sure to get maps from the forestry service, and make arrangements with others to pick you up on the east side. And for heavens sake, watch the red glazes on the trees so you don't wind up spending the month wandering Bradwell Bay!

Although there are always variations of ecotones, this concludes the major mixed forest types across North Florida from the Jacksonville area to Pensacola.

Aquatic Ecosystems

North Florida is replete with fresh water. Rivers run all over the area, lakes dot the map on all corners, swamps and marshes cover thousands of acres and even unique systems like bogs and sink holes are easily found. As one might expect, there is a tremendous diversity of fresh water animals in these varied ecosystems, and that is the topic of this chapter.

Fresh water entities can be easily divided into those which move (lotic) and those which are stagnant (lentic). Lotic bodies are, of course, rivers and streams, while lentic refers to a vast array of lakes, ponds, marshes, swamps, sink holes and the like. There is a close relationship between lentic and lotic areas, as the latter often leads to the former, and many animals move back and forth between the two. In this chapter we will separate them as much as possible and investigate the types of animals that live in each.

The difference between rivers and streams is about the same as between lakes and ponds—size. A stream is simply a small lotic community, while a river is larger. Sometimes it seems a creek is somewhere between the two, but this is not an exacting science. Econfina Creek is larger than the Econfina River, and nobody really cares.

One river is not the same as another, by any means. There are three kinds of rivers in the world, and amazingly enough, all three are plentiful in North Florida.

Globally, alluvial rivers are quite the majority, with some black water and spring-fed systems. Alluvial rivers are simple, the result of water flowing downhill, collecting into waterways, and finding its way into lakes and gulfs. The largest rivers in the world are alluvial, and of course, our largest river (the Apalachicola) is an alluvial (as is the mighty Mississippi).

The lovely Ochlockonee, shown here during low water, slips through the Panhandle on a lazy pace

ON THE WILLOWS

When water washes over the ground after rain falls, it takes topsoil and other goodies with it on its way to streams and rivers. This topsoil is called alluvium, and will have a profound impact on life in the river. Generally, rain rolls over the ground, makes its way to streams, and then to larger streams, and finally to real rivers. Water continues to flow downhill until it becomes part of a lentic water body. Of course, as we learned in school years ago, it then evaporates, is carried inland, and falls as rain again. So it is alluvial rivers that are most important to the water cycle.

Alluvial rivers change temperature throughout the year. By late winter, they are quite chilly, and life in them grinds slowly. In August, they reach their warmest, and are crawling with reptiles, amphibians, fish and warm-blooded vertebrates. They flow fastest at these two times as well, because these are the end of North Florida's two rainy seasons, winter and summer.

The water itself is dirty looking, owing to the fact it is carrying topsoil in large quantity. This topsoil is replaced by rotting vegetation, but what is taken by the river winds up in the future lentic body discussed in the next paragraph, the Gulf of Mexico. This has had a profound impact not only on the geology of the Panhandle, but also on its life and economy.

When the sand contained in the topsoil reaches the Gulf of Mexico, longshore currents carry it west along the shoreline, because of the Coreolis Effect. Sand from the Ochlockonee River has created Bald Point and Alligator Point, plus Dog and St. George Islands. Sand carried out from the Apalachicola River added to Little St. George, plus creating St. Vincent Island, Indian Pass, Cape San Blas, and the St. Joe Peninsula. This sand is actually ground up quartz from the north, mostly the Appalachians. If you take a look sometime at a world map, you can see the effect some of the world's larger rivers have had on the landscape near the river's mouth.

In this topsoil, besides sand, are the nutrients that give topsoil its fertile properties. This nutrient load washes out into the Gulf and becomes food for shrimp and filter feeders like oysters, which is why Apalachicola is the world's leading producer of oysters. These nutrients are at the bottom of

LIKE A RIVER OF TEA

a food chain that also supports Blue Crabs, oysters, mullet, and many other species of fish higher on the food chain. The fact that the seafood industry is based on alluvium carried by our rivers explains why some fought hard to keep dams off the Apalachicola. By the way, calcium is also carried by the alluvial rivers, and is necessary to mollusks like oysters for shell growth.

The Apalachicola and the Ochlockonee are the best examples of alluvial rivers in North Florida. The Suwanee, far to the east, is both alluvial and spring-fed, and the Wacissa and Wakulla are solely spring-fed rivers. The beautiful Blackwater River between Panama City and Pensacola is a classic black water variety, and there are plenty of smaller black water lotic bodies all across our area emanating from Panhandle bogs.

Black water rivers originate in bogs, with water carrying a great deal of tannic acid seeping out into small streams. These streams look stained, like tea, and appear quite different from alluvial water. Tannin is an acid found in most leaves that inhibits digestion by most herbivores. This is why humans can't eat leaves and digest them. The tannin lowers the pH of the water, since it is an acid. This acts as a limiting factor for some animals that might otherwise live in a black water stream in North Florida.

The Econfina provides many animals with a home, and great recreation for residents of Bay County

Black water streams carry neither much sand, nutrients, nor calcium. The absence of the latter is why there are **Queen Snakes** in black water streams. Calcium is required for crayfish shells, and the virtual absence of calcium causes crayfish shells to stay soft much longer when they shed. As Queen Snakes eat soft-shelled crayfish almost exclusively, there is a bounty of food in black water streams, as well as a bounty of Queen Snakes. They are also found in steephead streams, a variation of black water creeks, because the water coming out of the ground has no calcium.

Two-lined Salamanders are also found along many black water streams, possibly in the absence of larger, more competitive species. Other animals found in this habitat, but not confined to it, include **Cottonmouth**, **Brown Water Snake**, **River** and **Leopard Frogs**, **Five-lined Skink** and musk turtles. The streams may flow through Longleaf or Beech/Magnolia forests, and species composition is partly contingent upon what the terrestrial environment is like.

There is a very large genus of fish called *Notropis*, which is quite abundant and varied in black water streams. These creatures are one to two inches, have coppery tops, and a broad, black line down their sides. An interesting point to make about them is that these are the true "minnows" of the fish world, whereas most people call any small fish a minnow. Technically, "minnow" is a strict term for *Notropis*, just as "bream" are actually European fish. Those panfish we call bream are actually various species of sunfish. Vernacular names such as "moccasin" and "buzzard" often create problems with identification, and hopefully this book will straighten out some of that.

Alluvial river systems are loaded with life. The nutrients form a solid base for a food chain, and most groups of vertebrates are well represented. Sometimes alluvium piles up and forms bogs in which many creatures live. The recently discovered **One-toed Amphiuma** rules the roost in these muddy places, but many other amphibians and reptiles may be found here. Most of the creatures mentioned in the floodplain account toward the end of Chapter 3 are found along the edges of alluvial rivers, plus the following:

Brown Water Snakes are large, spirited fighters that love rivers. They feed by lying on the bottom and grabbing slow, dumb fish. Similar to the color of logs, they lay out on limbs and big stumps sunning themselves by day. By afternoon, they will generally move out of the direct sun but endeavor to stay dry for the health of their skin. They have no black, which contrasts to the venomous Cottonmouth. Also, the latter has bands, as opposed to the water snake's squares. As mentioned earlier, water snakes are not only in competition with Cottonmouths (who virtually never lie out on limbs), they also eat sick and diseased fish. Their value to the river's ecology, as well as their value to fishermen, cannot be overstated.

Redbelly Water Snakes are found on rivers in North Florida. They are coppery on the back and distinctively orange to reddish underneath, with no facial markings (as is also true of Brown Water Snakes). Redbellies work the shores at night for fish and frogs, and seem to prefer live willow limbs for a perch. They do not hesitate to follow the food source into the floodplain but seem more at home on lotic waters. Young of this species are mottled, and, unlike our other water snakes, bear no resemblance to their parents. Closer to

Pensacola, their red bellies become more yellow, as the range of the Yellowbelly Watersnake approaches.

Turtles love rivers. On the bottom of most lotic bodies lies the ferocious **Alligator Snapping Turtle**, lying in wait with its mouth open and pink, lure-like tongue dangling. Once in a while, one comes to the surface for air, and we see why we don't swim to the bottom of rivers. Also a fierce, but diminutive, species, the **Loggerhead Musk Turtle**, works the shallows and is often seen lying out on branches near the water.

One of the toughest complexes to sort out is the cooters and sliders. These are medium-sized aquatic turtles that lie out on logs or the bank by day and scoot off into the water at the slightest sign of trouble. There are three very confusing species in North Florida, and most people really don't care enough to learn to tell them apart. They sometimes interbreed, which makes it even worse. But there are field marks, as well as ecology, to help us sort them out.

Cooters normally live in lotic waters and are represented by two species. The **Eastern River Cooter** (concinna) has a fairly conspicuous "c" right in the middle of each side of the carapace that reminds scientists of their species scientific name, *Pseudemys concinna*. Superficially alike is the **Florida Cooter**, *Pseudemys floridana*, which may be found in company with concinna. However, floridana lacks the circle designs of concinna, substituting a more vertical bar-like pattern on the carapace. The third musketeer is the **Yellowbelly Slider**, which is in a different genus. It prefers lentic waters, and is easily told by a conspicuous yellow ear patch. However, when a river such as the Ochlockonee runs into a dam, like at Lake Talquin, all you-know-what breaks loose. I have seen turtles so mixed up in this artificial environment, they look like cast-off from Star Wars.

CATCHING SOME RAYS

A pancake-like Spiny Softshell sunbathes along a Florida river

Alluvial rivers have quite a few **Spiny Softshell Turtles**, which can often only be detected by observing their straw-like noses protruding above the water. They are quite rounded, but flat, like a pancake. If you should encounter one crossing the road, for example, to lay eggs, be wary. They are extremely fast biters and can be vicious with their beak. Whereas cooters and sliders will only bite if you put your finger in front of them, softshells have fantasies about biting fingers in their sleep.

M**ammals** are not well represented along alluvial rivers, but the occasional **River Otter** zips past like a miniature submarine. Strictly fish eaters, and quite shy of people, they have been known to attack swimming dogs with disastrous results. They are found mostly in less disturbed sections of rivers, both alluvial and spring-fed. See also the floodplain mammals in Chapter 3.

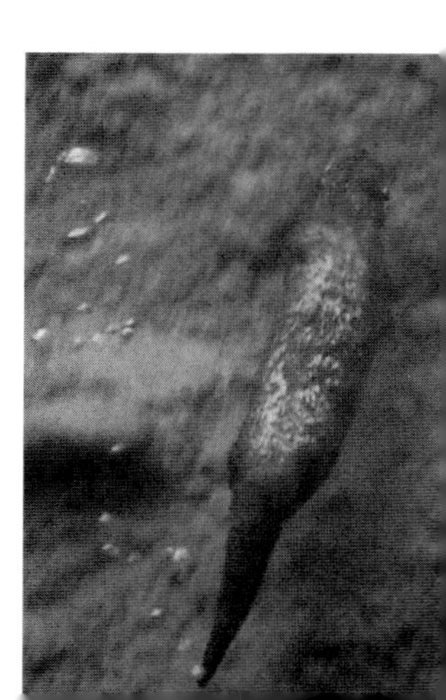

There are a good many **birds** along alluvial rivers, including most that were mentioned in our discussion about floodplains. Conspicuous birds seen along the river include **Red-shouldered Hawk**, **Prothonotary Warbler**, **Anhinga**, **Wood Duck**, **Double-crested Cormorant**, **Fish Crows** and **Spotted Sandpiper**. Two rare breeding warblers that should be looked for are the **Swainson's Warbler** and **Louisiana Waterthrush**.

The third kind of river, and certainly a big favorite in our area, are those that are spring-fed. There are quite a few springs in Forida, and the reason dates back to its geological roots. With limestone as the base to its ground formation, Florida becomes a prime candidate for springs. This is because tannic acid seeps down through the soil and eats holes in the limestone. Under the rock is a huge reservoir of water known as the Floridan aquifer. Under a great deal of pressure, water naturally eases out of the hole and flows downhill. This is the formation of the springs and the ensuing river. In the case of Wakulla Springs (allegedly the world's largest) the river is fed by one large spring primarily. Others, such as Wacissa Springs over in Jefferson County, have any number of smaller openings which combine to form the water flow.

HE OTTER SWIM FAST

Racing to chase down fish in a spring-fed river, the otter speeds through the water with few rivals

Obviously, spring-fed rivers are quite different from either of the first two varieties. Our first observation must be that the water is clear. This is not hard to understand, since it just came out of the ground, with no erosion, etc. Our second observation, as soon as we stick our big toe in, is that the water is significantly colder (on warm days) than other rivers in our area. These rivers do not have the temperature fluctuation of other rivers, because they are less affected by seasons. If the

Wakulla River is 66 degrees at some location in January, it won't be much higher there in July.

This brings about some interesting questions. For instance, do groups of cold-blooded animals that normally hibernate in alluvial situations do so in spring-fed rivers? If hibernation is a way of dealing with the cold temperatures of winter, but the water temperature hardly drops in winter in spring-fed rivers, do the animals still hibernate? Two creatures that have caused me to wonder are **Mud Snakes** and **Rainbow Snakes**. These two creatures live in various aquatic areas including, and especially, spring-fed rivers. They eat mostly large salamanders, like amphiuma and siren. But the snakes are extremely aquatic, seldom venturing from water. So, making the assumption that their food source stays active all year, these might be our only year-round snakes. I believe a study on how the lack of temperature fluctuation causes living systems to function differently than other river types would be a great dissertation topic for some budding biologist.

SNIPPING SNAILS FROM RIVER'S CATTAILS

The Limpkin eases along banks taking lunch as cargo

With water coming up from the aquifer and through limestone, spring-fed rivers have a great deal of calcium. This is used in the formation of mollusk shells, so one of the abundant animals in these rivers is the Apple Snail, genus *Pomacea*. Historically, these were food for the Snail (Everglade) Kite, but in their absence, plenty of the unique bird called the **Limpkin** make use of them. Limpkins are extremely loud wading birds, whose calls are heard all over spring-fed rivers (like on old Tarzan movies). Eating even more snails, though, are young alligators.

COMRADES ALONG THE RIVER

A lone Anghinga and several Suwanee Cooters log a few hours along the Wakulla River

Aside from Limpkins, there are quite a few birds on spring-fed rivers. Many of these are the same as on alluvial rivers. Some more unique to spring-fed would be **Common Moorhen**, **Pied-billed Grebe**, **Purple Gallinule**, **Anhinga**, **Green Heron and Swallow-tailed Kite**. In winter, a good many **American Wigeon** and **Lesser Scaup** decorate the rivers, and often cause the air to be filled with shotgun blasts. Other winter birds include **Eastern Phoebe**, **American Coot**, **Rusty Blackbird**, **Swamp Sparrow**, **Forster's Tern**, **Tree Swallow**, **American Goldfinch**, and droves of **Yellow-rumped Warblers**. Some years, two rare finches, the **Pine Siskin** and **Purple Finch** may be found, and I found **Red Crossbills** on one Christmas Bird Count on the Wakulla. The banks of these rivers can produce good numbers of migrants, especially in fall, but few people seem to take advantage of this area for that purpose.

R**eptiles**, other than those mentioned above, may be common and easily found along spring-fed rivers. The **Brown Water Snake** is ridiculously abundant in many areas along these rivers, and leave locals with the idea there are "moccasins" everywhere. The unique **Bluestripe Ribbon Snake** occasionally hangs out with them, and occasionally one finds a **Banded Water Snake** during drought.

C**ottonmouth** are rare along the limbs of rivers, but back in the floodplain they may be found in enormous size! The largest Cottonmouths (several) on record have been taken on the Wakulla River, with one measuring six feet two inches. That is an absolute leviathan! There appears to be a gene pool of Cottonmouth on the Wakulla and Wacissa systems that grow to be massive in comparison to other areas within their range. It might be due to the cold water and heat retention like Bergman's rule about warm-blooded animals being larger in colder climates, I don't know. But having run across several of these monsters in places like McBride's Slough, I can tell you they easily grow to sizes we usually associate with big rattlesnakes. They also seem to have sexual dimorphism, rare among snakes. The males have a fair amount of black in their bands while the huge females are more uniform tan brown. A bite from a creature this large could inflict serious tissue damage and even death. But they are also a unique population in danger of disappearing because of human encroachment. This is a prime candidate for the "leave it alone" edict and allowing them to live out their cycle of life undisturbed would say a lot about our species in terms of tolerance and wishing to live in peace with other creatures.

F**lorida Cooters**, and especially **Eastern River Cooters** line these rivers, becoming tame and trusting of humans. The latter has a wider yellow stripe leading down the neck from the eye area than the former, and also attains a larger size. These cooters are still hard to catch off their logs but underwater are somewhat dimwitted. They will eat in captivity, but pet rocks eat less, are more interesting, don't bite and you don't have to clean up after them. Joining the cooters on logs are both musk turtles and plenty of **Five-lined Skinks**.

This is a female Bullfrog, but still rules the shore

A<u>**mphibians**</u> on the river include some monster **Bullfrogs**, **Two-toed Amphiumas**, **Green** and **Squirrel Treefrogs**, **Mole** and **Slimy Salamanders**, and very dark **Southern Toads**. There is not much temporary water along these rivers for amphibian reproduction, so there is not nearly the species diversity found on alluvial rivers.

Although <u>**mammals**</u> are generally scarce in rivers, spring-fed communities boast two unique and interesting creatures. The **River Otter** is not uncommon, though shy, in both rivers, and often may be seen darting through the clear water. But the real attraction is the **Manatees**. These huge, gentle giants lie around in the warm months eating veggies off the bottom and giving swimmers the chance to be near original "mermaids." Looking more like banged up rollerball queens instead of the bewitching ladies of early paintings, their grotesque looks and blimp-like bodies bring comic relief to paddlers and swimmers alike. Clearly, if we can avoid killing such lovely creatures as huge Cottonmouths, we can at least turn down our power boat engines in manatee- infested waters to give them a fighting chance in the next century.

There are obviously a lot of fish in rivers, as figured by the number of fishermen in said power boats with their rods. Bass are one of their chief targets, a fine fighter and excellent on the plate. Sunfish (bream) are frequently caught as well, and are not called "panfish" for nothing. But one of the top fish for quality of meat and abundance is the mullet. They may be easily caught from some river bridges with worms or bread balls, and fresh mullet are just scrumptious. The freshwater catfish are more common on alluvial rivers, or large lakes, and when skinned, make a fine meal.

MARSH

A neat thing about fishing in rivers is the salt-water fish that enter them, and sometimes come very long distances upstream. There are also freshwater fish that have little trouble entering salt water, and it all has to do with how their bodies handle salt. But there are times, especially in the brief cold season, that **Speckled Trout** and **Redfish** spend a fair portion of time in the lower parts of rivers and are caught with shrimp, jigs, and "minnow" lures like rebels, mirrows, etc. Sharks and other salt-water fish also occasionally enter rivers, and as a boy, I even saw a sturgeon off the Upper Bridge of the Wakulla River!

Rivers are wondrously beautiful places where people can swim, boat, fish and hunt, or just float quietly down one portion gaining needed relief from life's stresses. But they are also hotbeds of biodiversity and contain many creatures unique to North Florida. We should do all we can to keep rivers as natural as possible, so that their wealth of nature may be enjoyed by all, as well as by future generations.

North Florida has a priceless lentic environment as well, with lakes, swamps, marshes and other wetlands adding untold wealth to our biodiversity. From the deep

dark swamps with towering cypress and tupelo, to bright, open lakes with lunker bass and lily pads, our lentic wetlands offer something for everyone, and every water-loving animal a home.

Lentic water sources are essentially depressions where more rain collects than is lost. Where there are trees, the shade cuts direct sunlight and therefore evaporation, but moisture is lost through evapotranspiration, the water vapor given off through photosynthesis. Open lakes lack much of this evapotranspiration, but sunlight and wind evaporate much water. The more water is lost to the air, the more it rains and fills the low areas.

BECOMES SWAMP

At the south end of Lake Miccosukee the marsh filters into a swamp

First, let's understand some terms. A swamp is a lentic water source with trees. It is a climax community (see Chapter 2), but may be slowly filling up with sediments which will eventually replace the water by raising the depression. There is little direct sunlight that reaches the swamp floor, so flowering plants are sparse and the lower level is open. Primary productivity in swamps is low, contributing to their being climax communities. Sound doesn't travel well, so many birds such as **Acadian Flycatchers** and **Prothonotary Warblers** have loud, sharp notes. Plants in swamps usually have broad leaves to absorb as much sunlight as possible, and many of the plants are herbaceous and annual. The water is very dark, owing to the build-up of tannic acid, and many animals are dark as well, some through natural selection, or some, like toads, changing color to match a dark environment. Floodplains are, for all practical purposes, swamps that run along the edges of rivers (river bottoms).

Marshes are similar to swamps in some ways, but have grasses instead of trees. They may have open areas of water in the middle, but the vast majority of acreage is weedy vegetation. Primary productivity, with so much sunlight added to the same nutrients and water as swamps, is off the scale. This leads to a bounty of available food, and marshes have many more times the animals of swamps. Flowers are everywhere in this bright community, though the water is a little dark with a fair amount of tannin accumulated. Like swamps, marshes are generally shallow.

Lakes are open bodies of water with little weeds or trees. The open water can provide huge microscopic algal blooms, and yield a large bottom to the food chain. Truly aquatic plants like lily pads live best in lakes, along with other floating vegetation. Many of our lakes are artificial and deep, created by dams, storm water drainage, and other human methods. But lakes are important as a watering hole for terrestrial animals, a stopover for migrating birds, a home for many aquatic creatures, and a great recreational area for our species.

It is very likely that there is a fair amount of secondary succession with these three aquatic systems. However lakes are formed, perhaps through a river taking an alternate route, they are filling up with sediments all the time. This makes them shallower and vegetation can grow from shore easier. Dead vegetation sinks to the bottom, and begins to fill in lakes. This process is called *eutrophication*, or the natural aging of a lake. As the lake fills in, vegetation becomes more preva-

Lake Jackson in northern Leon County draws bass fishermen from all over the South

lent, and the lake takes on more characteristics of a marsh. An example of this is happening in Lake Jackson, north of Tallahassee. With time, this serial community may evolve into a marsh, as its species composition changes over the decades. But fresh water marshes are also subject to change. They may continue to fill in, become firmer, and become invaded by trees. Some swamps may be, in fact, the end result of lakes and marshes. Here in North Florida, there are certainly some wet areas which exhibit some characteristics of both. Lakes Jackson, Iamonia and Miccosukee, all in Leon County, are quite shallow and marshy over much of their acreage. Similarly, marshes with scattered trees are frequent along some highways, so we may be seeing transitional zones with both these phenomena. A return trip to Earth in two centuries might reveal a swamp where we had left a marsh!

SPRAWLING LAKE

There are many sizes of lakes, and I don't discriminate in this work, except to say that "ponds" in my mind are small lakes. There is clearly a difference between life in large lakes and "ponds," although much remains the same as well. But we will begin with the large and splendid lakes I mentioned in the preceding paragraph, and work our way down.

The formation of lakes is often the action of depressions in the limestone, whether by the work of tannic acid or other forces. But some of these lakes in the Karrst Plain across the northern part of the state are enormous, covering several square miles. They can be seen from Highway 90 east of Tallahassee (Lake Miccosukee), Highway 27 north of Tallahassee (Lake Jackson), or south of S-12 (Lake Iamonia). A day on one of these lakes will yield many interesting wildlife sightings, excellent fishing, boating and skiing, or winter hunting.

Speaking of hunting, **birds** are certainly well-represented on these large lakes in winter by huge populations of diving ducks. Species include the ubiquitous **Ring-necked Duck**, **Ruddy Duck**, and several others that are heavy enough to swim to the bottom and eat mollusks. There are also six species of less abundant "puddle ducks" which taste better and are less filling. **Blue-winged Teal**, **Northern Shoveler**, **Northern Pintail**, **Mallard**, **Gadwall** and **American Wigeon** are all possibilities, but they are often more wary than the diving ducks. Despite the hunting pressures, these lakes are terribly important for wintering waterfowl. Some shorebirds winter around these large lakes as well, including **Common Snipe**, **Greater Yellowlegs**, **Killdeer**, both dowitchers and **Least Sandpipers**, to name the most abundant. Even the raptors get into the act with the **Bald Eagle** and **Osprey** taking fish off the surface of these great reservoirs.

Exposed mudflats are critically important to migrating shorebirds in spring and fall, turning out 15 to 20 species on good days. Oak hammocks along the edges of the lakes may also fill with songbirds of many varieties. In fall, when the migration is leisurely, warblers and their friends congregate in these dense forests with plenty of fruit and bugs, with water nearby. In spring, the songbirds usually fly over the coastline on their way north, and land well inland (unless there is inclement weather that day). Certain areas around these lakes can be most productive for these colorful gems that are literally here today and gone tomorrow.

Summer is a critical time for water birds like waders, as a great quantity of food is needed for their hungry chicks. Water levels are dropping throughout the spring, and it becomes easier to snare fish and other aquatic vertebrates. Even the endangered **Wood Stork** is a common breeder in North Florida, and these huge lakes are prime sites for them. This species works the muddy water, swishing its bill sideways, and involuntarily snapping it shut on anything it touches.

There are not many **mammals** in the huge lakes of North Florida, although quite a few come to the shores for a drink. In the grassy areas within the lakes resides the **Florida Water Rat**, which provides a food source for many predators. **Raccoons** are also common in these large lakes and occasionally engage in mischief throughout local neighborhoods. **Marsh Rabbits** are commonly seen in weeds around lakes, and short grassy areas along the shore can have staggering numbers of **Cotton Rats**.

CLEARLY MARKED

This Yellowbelly Slider is easily seen all over North Florida in lakes, with its yellow ear patch and bars on the side

The commonly seen turtle of lakes is the **Yellowbelly Slider,** which may be joined by cooters, depending on whether the lake has a lotic contribution. Out in the deeper water, huge **Alligator Snapping Turtles** lie on the bottom in wait of unsuspecting fish. Not as large, but of substantial size is the **Florida Softshell Turtle**, much bigger and elongate than the **Spiny Softshells** found in lotic waters. **Eastern Mud Turtles** thrive in lakes as well, feeding on crayfish and tadpoles.

A few snakes are common in large lakes, virtually none larger than the leviathan **Florida Green Water Snake**. These huge olive-gray serpents ease through the shoreline grasses in search of medium-sized fish, amphiuma and siren. Grabbing their prey with long, sharp teeth, they drag the quarry to shore, find the head and swallow them in record time. At any size, this snake delivers an extremely painful bite and makes a poor pet. The western Panhandle has **Mississippi Green Water Snakes**, which are slightly smaller, but every bit as mean spirited.

A modest number of **Banded Water Snakes** exist along the shores, with the red color phase common in places like the north shore of Lake Jackson where red clay soil borders the lake. One of our most handsome snakes, and one that has disappeared at an alarming rate is the **Eastern Kingsnake**. Half aquatic, this great snake hunts water snakes and turtle eggs, taking some of the bounty of rats in the process.

Two interesting "swamp snakes," the **Mud Snake** and the **Black Swamp Snake** reside in large lakes in diminishing numbers. Mud Snakes are the largest aquatic snake in North America, attaining a record length of seven feet. They feed primarily on amphiuma and siren (two large aquatic salamanders) which they grab with their large teeth, wrap themselves around and stick with their barbed tail to hold on to while they find the prey's head with their mouth. Black Swamp Snakes are mostly peninsular creatures that are occasionally under boards and logs along the shoreline.

Poisonous snakes aren't common around large lakes or marshes, although rattlesnakes will look for rats in the grass that grows near the shoreline. Other snakes may be found in this area when water is low as they need to drink about once every week in the warm season.

Alligators have become quite common in recent years, thanks to the protection of the Game Commission. Given their overpopulation in some areas, it seems unfortunate that we still give such close attention and stringent protection to them, while snakes like kingsnakes are vanishing at an alarming rate.

Gators are not the ferocious creatures many make them out to be. They have a natural fear of humans, and we should keep our distance as well. It is very unwise (and illegal) to feed these powerful creatures, as they begin associating people with food. One unwitting and sad method of feeding gators is to let your dog swim in waters occupied by these undiscriminating animals.

Greater Siren

A few **amphibians** are common around large lakes, despite many enemies. The two aquatic, large salamanders, amphiuma and siren, are thick in some lakes, and tremendous, unexplained die-offs of siren sometimes occur in late winter. A great place to witness **Greater Siren** is the spillway on Highway 90 where it crosses under the bridge. This section of Lake Miccosukee also contains the **Slender Dwarf Siren**, as well as **Red-spotted Newts.**

These giant salamanders live their lives all across the South

PRIMITIVE

The grass in these large lakes is often full of **Pig Frogs**, a smaller aquatic cousin of the Bullfrog. Sounding like the grunts of a pig, identification is proof positive when one observes the dark stripes on the back of the thigh and the fully webbed hind toes (for aquatic life). **Bullfrogs** are found along the shore, along with **Leopard Frogs** in the grass and **Southern Cricket Frogs** seemingly everywhere on shore. In the warm season, **Narrow-mouthed Toads** hide under debris near shore waiting to breed at the onset of rain. The beautiful **Green Treefrog** is not uncommon on branches and long weed stems year round.

Two-toed Amphiuma

An albino amphiuma

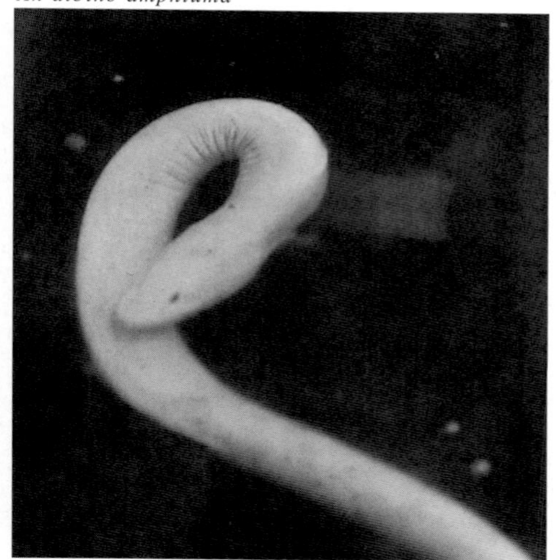

SWAMP CREATURES

Being a progression of eutrophicating lakes, marshes have many animals in common with big lakes. Creatures that were mentioned to be found in the grassy edges of lakes may be even more common in marshes, like **Green Water Snakes**, **Pig Frogs**, **Green Treefrogs**, **Florida Water Rat** and much more. **Red-winged Black-birds** are common breeders, with one male often mated to several females. This type of polygamy is a testament to the amount of food available, and an indication of the primary productivity of marshes.

Coots—these innocuous guys winter in huge numbers across our area on large lakes

One family of **birds**, called rails, are chicken-like aquatic birds that are common, often winter residents, in marshes. **King Rails** are nonmigratory, fresh water rails that stalk crayfish and "minnows" in marshes with some open water. Winter resident **Virginia Rails** prefer very dense vegetation for their Florida stay, while the **Sora**, here from August to June, enjoys more open grassy areas.

The following somewhat off-beat rails are the three (fat) musketeers of open areas and are easily found in marshes. In winter, the **American Coot** hangs out in open waters within marshes, or con-

HELL DIVERS

gregates in large flocks in larger lakes. The **Common Moorhen** is at home in marshy situations with some open water, and is told from coots by their red bill. A huge favorite is the **Purple Gallinule**, which has such gaudy colors it almost seems unreal.

Other marsh-loving birds include two species of bitterns. Impressive **American Bitterns** winter in tall, marshy areas, mimicking reeds and tules with their head and neck. Diminutive **Least Bitterns** arrive in spring, breed and seem to take the American's spot for the summer, before departing for the tropics in fall.

Common Yellowthroats live almost exclusively in marshes, and are joined in winter by **Sedge Wrens**. **Pied-billed Grebes**, frequently found in large lakes, may be in open waters of marshes as well. Even some land birds like cardinals will nest over water in marshes, finding more protection there than in wooded areas.

Pied-billed Grebes have several nicknames, but they've never surfaced with charred tail feathers

Ponds are essentially small lakes, but there are quite a few, and their biology is not always the same as lakes. For instance, there are more nesting **Pied-billed Grebes** (hell divers) on ponds, and there are often only **Banded Water Snakes**, and no **Greens**. Species diversity is less in ponds, but one fish factor does lead to a high species composition. In the absence of many game fish, which may be the condition of a pond, there are sometimes several kinds of "minnows," far beyond mosquitofish that are virtually always present in fresh water.

The **Starhead**, **Lined** and **Golden Topminnows** join **Least Killifish** in ponds and marshes, where cover offers protection against larger, predatory fish. **Golden Shiners** may be caught and used (or sold) for bass bait, but check the game laws on catching them. Some ponds also have **Tiger Salamanders** breeding, and their larvae are also used for bass bait by those who seem to know all the angles. They are joined by **Central Newts**, often in their yellowish adult stage, and the occasional larvae. Clearly, the population of amphibians rises with the decrease of predatory fish. Nowhere is this more true than in the community we discuss next, "perched ponds".

In some parts of North Florida, often in Longleaf Pine forests, special ponds exist that we call "perched ponds." They are shallow indentations in the limestone that are *ephemeral*, meaning they dry up in drought conditions. Because they are such a temporary community, they are not inhabited by fish, or certainly not predatory species.

This plays right into the hands of the **amphibians**. Larval frogs, toads and salamanders are quite defenseless little creatures, and fish have a way of munching on them at a debilitating rate. But in ephemeral waters, fish cannot survive, and larval amphibians become the dominant animals. Tadpoles eat algae and other plant material, but larval salamanders are insectivorous and begin eating their classmates, the larval insects strewn through the waters of these small ponds.

The common salamander of these perched ponds is the **Mole Salamander**, and it is joined in certain areas by the rare **Striped Newt**. This creature may be found in several small ponds just south of Tallahassee's Capital Circle on Highway 61. Seining in the winter will get you these two creatures, as well as a pretty good cold.

The species diversity of frog and toad larvae in ephemeral ponds is amazing. Several species of treefrog tadpoles, including the **Barking**, all breed here. In addition, there are **Cricket Frogs**, **Narrow-mouthed Toads**, **Leopard Frogs** and sometimes **Spadefoots**. It is interesting to note the larval insect diversity, including dragon flies. These ponds should not be overseined, nor the inhabitants overcollected—especially the Striped Newts. This is a fragile biotic and abiotic community that could be damaged by heavy-handed human activities.

Not far from the ponds mentioned above are several sinks, places where acid has eaten through the limestone and reached the aquifer. With sinks, as opposed to a spring and their ensuing river, the water never crests over the surrounding embankment to create a lotic situation. Sinkholes are great fun for swimming and relaxing, although the weekend boom boxes and beer cans strewn everywhere do get a little obnoxious. Leon Sinks, just south of Tallahassee on the Crawfordville HW, are well kept and worth the hike. It has always been sad to me that so many of the locals, especially those from rural areas, have such disrespect for the pristine ecosystem we have been blessed with in North Florida.

Sinkholes are related geophysically to one of the communities that is truly exciting for its unique animals present, geologic history and fantastic formation. I am talking about caves. In some places tannic acid has eaten away much of the limestone from the surface downward, attacking what was once a coral reef. These communities were common from the Miocene to the Eocene and housed quite a number of interesting invertebrate life forms.

DRIVING HER BATTY

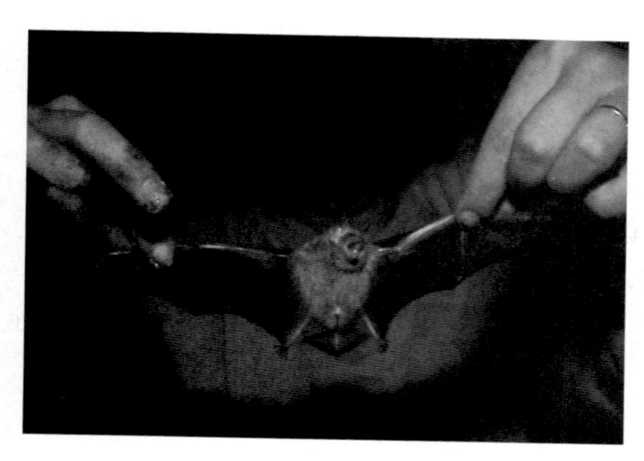

Former student derives excitement from holding a bat deep within a cave on a class field trip

Caves represent a view into the past virtually unmatched on earth today. Nothing could be more exciting than creeping down through dozens of feet of limestone, representing millions of years, and finding on the cave walls the fossils of arthropods, echinoderms, sponges, coelenterates and especially mollusks that dominated the coral scene toward the early part of the Cenozoic Era. Not far from the western edge of North Florida, one can visit Florida Caverns State Park and be astounded at what limestone, time and life can create. It is a place one can have a great family outing in beautiful country at a reasonable price. All over Florida, State Parks have preserved some of the "real" Florida for our children's children.

It is fascinating to observe cave creatures which have become adapted for subterranean life over millions of years. My favorite is the **Georgia Blind Salamander**, which can be found with lots of hard work and good luck. These creatures, like so many cave animals, lack pigment and are pinkish white. There is no light where they live, so maintaining pigment would result in wasted energy. Joining this modest little amphibian is the **Blind Cave Crayfish**, similarly colored and with eyes also greatly reduced and vestigial. There are also fish adapted for caves, with little pigment, sightless and highly adapted for cave life.

This doesn't mean that all creatures you encounter in caves will be as described above. Nature is organized in gradients and some species are just beginning to evolve toward cave life. Some of the species that seem drawn to caves include the Camel Cricket and **Slimy Salamander**. These could one day branch and develop a cave species, but we may blow up the world by that time.

One of the curious mysteries about caves was the question of the food chain in the deep recesses underground. Obviously, any light had been left way behind, so photosynthesis was not possible. Chemosynthesis is an ocean-bottom phenomenon as well. And "energy cannot be created . . ." as Brother Einstein pointed out. So where does the food chain start? The answer seems to be that catfish swim in and out of these caves, and apparently their fecal matter is deposited along the way like NATO supplies. Tiny invertebrates living within the caves munch on these morsels (at least they aren't like rabbits and eat their own . . .) and these invertebrates are, in turn, eaten by the salamanders. The crayfish seem to eat tiny animals as well as catfish droppings.

These are the major fresh water environments of North Florida. I would challenge anyone, in any place, to show me an area five times the size of this with such varied limnology, as well as the animals that live in these lotic and lentic places described in this chapter. When we consider the fantastic terrestrial climax communities discussed in earlier chapters, it really gives us pause to marvel at what we have in our Garden of Eden. Could there really be more?

The Marine Ecosystem

The entire upper Gulf coast of Florida has great fishing, productive ecosystems, lovely beaches, terrific birding, excellent shelling and incomparable grass beds. I can think of no other coastline in the world that has so much diversity, both in terms of ecotypes, as well as animal species.

Starting from the easternmost coastline, it becomes clear that we are blessed with zillions of acres of salt marsh. This community is created in low surge situations, where soft sediments are accumulated and maintained by the roots of plants. In some areas salt marshes seem to span forever, stretching for many miles along the coast.

The importance of salt marshes cannot be overstated—they are nature's nurseries. Well in excess of three-fourths of the fish harvested in our waters are spawned in these muddy ecosystems, and the loss of even a percentage of them would have incalculable results. They are the interface between land and sea and are actually critical to many creatures from land as well.

The dominant plant in salt marshes is needlerush (*Juncas*) and it can be seen at times for miles. It is a simple stalk with no leaves, but with a very sharp point on the tip. It has a brownish color, making the marsh appear rather lifeless from a distance, but salt marshes are anything but that. Running

MILES OF MARSH

all through the marsh are tidal creeks, with cordgrass (*Spartina*) lining the edges. This green blade tolerates deeper water than needlerush and is sometimes found in thick patches along the outer edge of salt marshes standing against the mild waves.

Salt marshes spread all across the North Florida shoreline in areas of low surge

Slight elevation makes a lot of difference to the vegetation of the marsh. Some areas within the salt marsh are mere inches higher than needlerush, but result in bare salt pans where fiddler crabs may be found in abundance. Growing in small patches on these pans are two succulents eaten by Native Americans in 'yestercentury,' *Salicornea* and *Batis*. Where the marsh moves upland and gives way to drier ground, *Distichilis* lines the sand, a simple grass with narrow blades and sharp, pointed tips. Occasionally, in the middle of a salt marsh, higher ground accumulates and islands with Red Cedars, Cabbage Palms and salt tolerant pines dot the landscape. Creatures such as **Raccoons** and **White-tailed Deer** use these islands for shade and shelter while wading birds roost in their tree limbs.

Salt marshes are harsh environments, so a few species have learned to live there in big numbers.

ONE OF MANY

Close look at a tiny Periwinkle lifted out of a salt marsh with tens of thousands

A small gastropod that is incredibly abundant, on virtually every needlerush stalk, is the small Periwinkle Snail. Unlike their larger hunting cousins, these scrape bacteria off stalks, and even the mud, for their sustenance. They climb stalks to escape the predatory Blue Crabs, who delight in seizing periwinkles, crushing them with their strong pincers, and consuming their meat. Some snails actually get away though and, depending on what part of the marsh one gathers snails, one may find tiny scars from Blue Crabs on snail shells.

My students at Leon High School conducted research on this phenomenon and discovered that periwinkles at the mouth of tidal creeks had the highest number of scars (.7 per snail) compared to those in the rear of the marsh (.15 per snail) where crabs seldom venture. Moreover, from color coding studies (nail polish), we concluded that snails were quite sedentary, seldom moving more than 30 to 40 meters in any given season. Lastly, we conducted extensive research on various emergency methods for removing nail polish from my wife's $1500 dining room table after a spillage that resembled the Exxon Valdez in severity.

Another predator on Periwinkles (as well as oysters) is the Crown Conch, a chunky gastropod with one distinguishing feature. Around the top of the shell, there is a circle of protrusions that resemble the crown of royalty. This was enough to provide the name, as well as the scientific species epithet, *coronata*.

Another abundant animal in the marshes is the complex of three fiddler crabs, all in the genus *Uca*. The abundant and widespread species is *pugilator*. A local species,

FIDDLING AROUND

This rare Fiddler Crab, *Uca longisig-nalis*, scurries along the mud at Wakulla Beach

named for a sleepy town, is *panacea*. My personal favorite, with long claws and beautiful blue-green hues on the front, is *longisig-nalis*.

Fiddlers share the diet of bacteria with the snails, but get theirs from scraping sand off the shore and sorting through it, sifting bacteria out. Upon finishing, they leave tiny balls of sand on the shore that are no doubt devoid of a speck of bacteria. Fiddlers are used for bait, such as in the pursuit of **Sheephead.** They could be over harvested, and have virtually disappeared in some areas. They can appear absent, though, as they often return en masse to the moisture in their burrows to escape danger and to wet their gills.

Aside from many species of game **fish** spawning in salt marshes, there are resident, though small species of "minnows." The **Long-nosed Killifish** is an elongate, silver fish an inch or two long with black bars on the side and yup, a long nose. Their hardiness makes them good bait, but hook them through the lips and get ready for a fight. The **Sheepshead Minnow** is a fat little fish with a small head and light bars on the side. They make sorry bait. The **Salt Marsh Killifish** is a fairly hardy creature that grows to several inches in length and attains attractive speckles. But if it's a fight you want, seine up some baby mullet, put them out on your favorite rod, and buckle up! They seem to attract the meanest, nastiest fish in the sea. **Silversides** also come into salt marshes at

Mullet are bottom feeders, abundant all along our coast

MARSH DWELLER

high tide and make good bait, but die easily on the hook or in low oxygen. Certainly, other small fish enter the salt marsh area as well, but these are the most frequently encountered.

Salt Marsh Snakes have the perfect camouflage for their habitat

There are no amphibians regularly found in salt marshes due to the salt, but two **reptiles** rely heavily on this area for survival. The **Gulf Salt Marsh Snake**, a smallish creature that lives on the fish in the preceding chapter, hangs out on the edge of tidal creeks most of the day. When a person walks along the edge of a creek on one bank, this snake darts across the creek along the bottom and often winds up on the opposite shore.

Salt marsh snakes have dark stripes down the body (lengthwise) like ribbon snakes, but the two would never be confused. Their ancestor, the **Banded Water Snake** has bands around it, similar to a **Cottonmouth**. This venomous species is rare in salt (or fresh water) marshes, but I have run across several **Diamond-backed Rattlesnakes** in the needlerush. Apparently, two fresh water, harmless snakes occasionally enter salt marshes after rather odd substitute food. The elegant **Rainbow Snake**, which normally eats siren and amphiuma (eel-like salamanders)[see Chapter 5] searches for the American Eel (genus *Anguilla)* along the coast and particularly salt marshes. Even more commonly, the **Glossy Water Snake** enters salt water, probably after soft-shelled crabs when unable to find soft-shelled crayfish.

Most turtles either live at sea or stay out of salt marshes, but the **Diamondback Terrapin** will spend a great deal of time in and around marshes. Named *Malaclemys* (bad turtle) because they are said to bring bad weather to boaters, the explanation seems to be found in the fact that they leave the water (therefore becoming conspicuous) with a dropping barometer. All superstitions aside, it is therefore understandable that boaters relate these creatures to storms. However, with their excellent taste condemning tens of thousands to soup bowls, it seems they may regard the sight of our species with at least as much dismay.

With all the fish available in the salt marsh, it would seem **birds** would be abundant and perhaps unique. And where there may be good concentrations of waders at low tide, the two unique types of birds in salt marshes have no connection to fish. One is the **Seaside Sparrow** and the other is the **Clapper Rail**. Both are year-round residents in the needlerush and cord grass.

Seaside Sparrows eat fewer seeds than most of their family, preferring insects. Their bill is thin compared to other sparrows, and they are quite dark for camouflage. Joining them are **Sharp-tailed Sparrows** and occasionally other species. Thrown in the fray are resident **Marsh Wrens** and **Sedge Wrens**, who are winter residents like the Sharp-tails. These four make for quite a difficult task of identification, as they're generally seen flying away as we are trudging through muck and getting stuck with needlerush. Add a couple of sparrows that don't belong there, and you are confronted with one impossible ornithological task.

UNOBTRUSIVE BIRDS

Clapper Rails with their compressed bodies slip through marsh grass hardly moving a blade

Clapper Rails are easily the noisiest thing in salt marshes, issuing their loud *eek eek eek* for no apparent reason. As discussed in Chapter 5, rails are slender, chicken-like birds that slip through marsh grass unobtrusively. Clappers only live in salt marshes, but are joined in winter by **Sora**, **Virginia Rails** and **Yellow Rails** on rare occasions. The **King Rails** mentioned in fresh water marshes do not occur in salt marshes, and these and Clappers were probably evolved from a superspecies and are ecologically separated. The extremely rare **Black Rail** ekes out a living in salt marshes, but is virtually never seen (although it is sometimes confused with young Clappers, which are black).

Oyster reefs grow all along our coast in shallow areas of low surge. These reefs provide homes for many species of fishes and invertebrate marine life and help shelter the coastline from wave damage. Areas where calcium flows into the gulf, such as near the mouths of spring-fed and alluvial rivers (see Chapter 5), may have tremendous oyster growth and add to the biodiversity of the coastline.

Oysters, clearly the keystone species of the reef, are bivalves, belonging to the Phylum Mollusca. They have very sharp bill edges for the protection of themselves and those who hide within their ranks. As this is a low-surge community, the substrates around oyster reefs are soft and muddy. **Flounder**, **Red Drum** and mullet congregate around the reefs and create great fishing situations. One of the great birds of our area is the **American Oystercatcher**, which slips its compressed (like a knife) bill through the bills of the oyster and snips the muscle, making the oyster fall open for lunch.

Several interesting animals live with the oyster community, but great care should be exercised in turning over masses of oysters, due to the sharp bills. The Porcelain Crab is almost completely flat, and lives in the slimmest crawl ways between oysters. They are as big around as a dime (and about that flat!) and have virtually no pinch. Snapping Shrimp have huge pincers, although they can hardly hurt people, and snap around in the muddy water as a way of distracting and escaping their enemies. Mud Crabs and the larger Stone Crabs may be found underneath the oyster beds and they can, in fact, deliver quite a nasty pinch. And speaking of nasty, the **Toad Fish** hides in burrows around oyster reefs, and will actually bite fingers that come their way. A hideously ugly fish that seems to be all mouth, it sometimes bites hooks with shrimp and leaves the fisherman wondering how to remove the fish.

There is quite a lot of salt marsh along the eastern portion of the North Florida coast, up to about the mouth of the Ochlockonee River. Spared strong surge, areas east of the river's mouth are peaceful enough to develop the salt marshes, and to some extent, the oyster reefs we discussed. Areas from Bald and Alligator Points west to Pensacola have sandy beaches scoured by relentless pounding with hard-bottom surfs. There are also barrier islands, however (see Chapter 1), so there exist many low-surge places such as salt marshes on the bay side of islands and other protected areas.

Sanderling

Our three most common birds of the beach, Sanderling, Black-bellied Plover and Willet, are familiar to beach walkers at any season

Most of the sediment from the mighty Apalachicola River is deposited from Cape San Blas eastward, so the beaches from nearby Mexico Beach become whiter and whiter as one moves west. Beaches in Panama City and Pensacola reflect this beauty, as do those in Alabama and Mississippi. West of the Mississippi River the same conditions exist (even worse) making Louisiana and Texas beaches dingy and their waters normally brown and unattractive. So truly, the beaches in west Florida are among the most beautiful in the world.

The "beach" is its own community, with certain species in abundance. **Birds** are usually the first creatures seen on the beach, and three types of shorebirds dominate the scene. The **Willet** is a large, loud, gray sandpiper that shows black and white stripes in its wings when it flies. They are very common winter residents, but a few stay in summer to breed in the salt marshes with their brownish coloration.

Willet

Black-bellied Plover, breeding plumage

Black-bellied Plovers and **Sanderlings** are also abundant on beaches, with the lion's share nesting on the Arctic tundra. The latter is a small, whitish sandpiper that scurries around probing its bill in and out of the sand like a sewing machine. Black-bellied Plovers in winter are grayish on the back and white

Lesser Scaup

underneath; in flight the black patch under the wing confirms their identification. In spring, just before they leave for Alaska, most Black-bellies gain their black undersides and most Sanderlings turn brownish. Some stay as nonbreeding residents, but remain in winter plumage. This is because the same gene that controls plumage development also controls seasonal development of gonads, also inhibiting the urge to migrate. The end result is that, although these three bird species are essentially winter residents, they may be seen all year on our beaches.

Several species of drab-colored seabirds dot our coastal habitat in winter before most head north to nest in summer

Many other sandpipers are seen here as well, with some like **Short-billed Dowitcher**, **Western Sandpiper**, **Dunlin** and **Ruddy Turnstone** (all more or less winter residents) being fairly common. As you can see, summer is not a great time for water birds at the coast, but there are some birds around all year. Clearly, summer is for snake hunting, fishing and swimming.

Horned Grebe

Brown and White Pelicans and Double-crested Cormorants

Red-breasted Mergansers

Northern Gannet

Common loon

Several plovers are easily found at various times on our beaches. These have a neck ring (or a hint of one), short bills and chunky bodies. **Semipalmated** and the breeding **Wilson's** have dark backs while the **Piping** (orange legs) and **Snowy** (black legs) have light backs and are small like the Semipalmated. **Killdeer**, with two rings, are uncommon on beaches, preferring pastures, fields and even residential areas. Winter birds to watch for on or over the water include **Common Loon**, **Horned Grebe**, **Northern Gannet** (deep), **Brown Pelican** (resident), **Double-crested Cormorant**, **Lesser Scaup**, **Red-breasted Mergansers** and other diving ducks.

SEABIRDS

GULLS AND TERNS

People often confuse gulls and terns

Very common on and around shores are gulls and terns. Gulls are heavy-bodied scavengers on shorelines (and sometimes inland) with slightly hooked beaks and gregarious habits. In our area the **Laughing Gull** is a resident with a distinctive black head from early spring through fall and a dark back. The larger **Ring-billed** and huge **Herring Gulls** are winter residents, with a few nonbreeding birds becoming pale and possibly dying in late summer.

Laughing Gulls

Forster's Tern

Terns are whitish, sleek gull-like birds with dagger bills that they use for diving into the water for fish. The large **Royal Tern** has a yellow bill and flies out deep for fish. It is joined by the **Sandwich Tern** with a yellow tip on a black bill. Huge **Caspian Terns** are sometimes seen with their red bills, often feeding in shallow water. **Forster's Terns** are everywhere in the cool season, with the very similar **Common Tern** slipping through in late spring and early fall. A few **Gull-bills** may be seen feeding over salt marshes, or nesting on beaches in early summer. They may be joined by the tiny **Least Terns,** whose *klee klee* notes make them quite conspicuous.

Royal Tern surrounded by Sandwich Terns

Often joined by some of the above, **Black Skimmers** nest on the causeway to St. George Island and really put on quite a show. The only bird in the world with the lower mandible longer than the upper, skimmers cut through the water flipping top dwelling "minnows" into their mouth with apparent ease. Colonies of skimmers should be preserved at all costs, as their numbers have been on a slippery slope for years across the Gulf States.

Ring-billed Gull

The only **mammals** to speak of in the surf waters is the **Bottle-nosed Dolphin**. Common and playful, they chase mullet and other fish, and occasionally scare the beejeebers out of surf fishermen with their shark-like dorsal fin. Their tails are horizontal, which propels them to the surface for air more quickly than the vertical tail fin of sharks. All marine mammals are afforded complete protection under Federal law, and it is a serious crime to possess even their parts.

The three plumages of Herring Gulls

Obviously, there are loads of **fishes** in the Gulf waters, but sharks are on the minds of many people. The truth is, shark attacks in Gulf waters are virtually unheard of, with almost all being cases of mistaken identity bites in murky water. Our common sharks are the **Sand**, **Black-tip**, **Nurse** and **Bonnethead**, with several other species possible. People fishing for sharks should use steel leaders, fairly heavy line (the tail can cut line) and try not to kill and keep every shark you catch. Their numbers have really fallen in recent years and the mindless slaughter of creatures such as these and snakes has no place in a civilized society.

Far more scary to most than sharks are some of the rays in our waters. The famous **Sting Ray** maintains a barb well out on its tail, coated with a toxin, that may inflict serious damage to the feet of swimmers in the surf. Meat tenderizer may be the best antidote, and shuffling one's feet through the shallows provides great protection against these shy, retiring creatures. Other rays are found in our waters, but the vast majority are, unfortunately, "stingarees."

Undoubtedly hurting far more people than all the sharks and rays in North Florida combined, the hated **Sea Catfish** (hard head) patrols the Gulf waters in huge numbers as a summer resident in every imaginable location. Taking mostly dead shrimp, they are the phantom menace of fishing, creating all kinds of temporary excitement, followed by disappointment when the reality of the identification of this hard fighter sets in. But don't let the frustration of "just another catfish" become compounded with a wound from the barbs of their dorsal and pectoral fins. There is an easier way to remove them than most people practice, one that minimizes the possibility of painful stabbing and days of tormenting pain.

Carefully slide your fingers down the line and slip your second and third finger under and around the two pectoral fins (the ones that stick out on the side). Instantly, you have control of the fish and this makes removing hooks easier and a lot safer. By the way, some people (it was probably first electricians) remove hooks with needle-nosed pliers, which I recommend. Their barbels (whiskers) are inoffensive.

The **Trout** and **Redfish** of the oyster reefs are certainly catchable in the surf as well, but other species may be added to the list. The **Black Drum** will take shrimp off the bottom and is most common in early spring. Trout love warm weather, but head up into rivers in late fall when it gets cool. Redfish do much the same thing but are shy fish that don't get large by being stupid. One of my favorite fish is fresh **Whiting**. Living on the bottom that gives them their light gray color, these guys leave no doubt about taking a hook and put up a nice fight for a smallish fish. Use fresh shrimp and be sure to peel the bait and thread it onto the hook. Spring Whiting do not have much size, but by late fall, excellent specimens may be caught all along the surf.

Swimmers should keep an eye out for **Jellyfish**. These "cannonballs" or "cabbageheads" are abundant at times, and can deliver a fairly substantial sting. But far worse is the Portuguese Man-of-War which occasionally drifts into our waters. Long tentacles on a purple float signal pain and swelling for anyone unfortunate enough to be caught in the long strings of stinging cells.

There are some interesting and abundant invertebrates within the beach sand we walk on. Mole Crabs are bullet-shaped crustaceans that filter feed in shallow sand each time waves wash over them. Only seen by digging blindly for them, these harmless creatures make good bait and are interesting to share with kids. Far more abundant is the Coquina, with an amazing assortment of colors (thus the name *Donax variabilis*). These creatures make the beach more than just a place to burn the living fire out of yourself, and wish you looked like that person walking past you.

There are many interesting species of "sea shells" along the Florida coastline, most of which belong to the Mollusk phylum. Some places are OK for shelling within this area, but clearly the best place is just beyond the Apalachicola River to the west. Taking a field trip to the Cape San Blas/ St. Joe State Park peninsula joins great fishing and shelling with excellent birding and the absolutely neatest place to study marine invertebrates on the entire Gulf coast.

Cape San Blas is about a half hour from sleepy Apalachicola. A walk along the beach around the tip of the cape is excellent for water birds, and a fishing excursion is recommended. But several miles east of the cape is where the shelling gets super, and dozens of species may be found in abundance. After a storm, this place is unbelievable, with shells by the thousands everywhere. One word of caution: Don't drive out on the beach without a permit, especially on weekends.

Last but not least, and surely the thing I miss most about North Florida (except for Julia Mae's) is St. Joe Bay. Snorkeling through Turtle Grass beds is one of the truly great experiences with life on earth. There is a mind numbing diversity, not only in terms of species, but the sheer disparity of phyla represented makes it look like a watery zoology textbook. Much more information is available on the creatures to follow in Chapter 7.

The bay actually has two layers of grass. The first hundred feet or so is Shoal Grass (or manatee grass), slender stalks without too much found in it. Still, a few passes with a hand net, or one seine full, will reveal grass shrimp, small gastropods, **Pipefish**, and much more. Resist the temptation to dally here, as paradise awaits. And my advice is to wear some kind of footwear as urchins and pen shells are not always kind to bare feet.

DON'T PASS THE BUCK

Sand Dollars are easy to miss as they are often covered with a thin layer of sand

On the way out, there will be curious bare spots where the timid will enjoy resting. Using your fingers, scrape through the sand and discover the bounty of sand dollars buried just below the surface. Exciting to the amateur zoologist is the presence here of Cephalochordata, the Lancelet. These primitive Chordates have a partial spinal chord in the anterior and literally swim through the sand. They may be caught by using a fine net, like a pool net, and scooping up large amounts of sand, letting it sift out. Sometimes, after it all leaves, you will be left with one of the neatest creatures of the sea.

Once you finally reach the Turtle Grass (with a little Manatee Grass), set up your dive flag (please!) and discover what drove Jaques Cousteau! Floating gently over the grass bed in clear water, you will first see a myriad of sea urchins, the only creature out here that eats the grass. Most will be purplish, but some are pink and others almost white. They may be handled without fear, but watch for the rare Purple Sea Urchin. These black creatures have extremely long, sharp spines, and some care is required not to puncture your fingers.

ENTIRE COMMUNITIES

This is not a dangerous place, but several other cautions should be made. You do not wish to step on the Saw-tooth Pen Shell, the fan-shaped shell that is actually a live bi-valve. Equally un-pleasant are skir-mishes with Blue Crabs, but they are uncommon in Turtle Grass. At times, however, you may find two together, which represents the male guarding the female as she sheds her shell. How nice of him to be so chivalrous, especially when this is the only time she can, or will, mate. Males, we're all the same. You may see a **Sting Ray** here and just make sure you don't put your hands in **Toad Fish** burrows. This all may sound risky, but in all my years of taking kids here, I don't recall a single booboo.

Many Pen Shells have various encrusting organisms growing on them, often with several other phyla present

Large **Sponges** are found in this area that contain all kinds of invertebrates living commensally inside, such as Snapping Shrimp, larval worms, polychaetes, and heavens knows what else. These sponges are not unlike their ancestors which lived over a half billion years ago, and have survived on the sea floor ever since.

Jellyfish, except for the benign Comb Jelly (not a true Jellyfish), are absent, but Sloppy Guts Anemones are abundant all over the bottom. Looking like a foot long brown tube lying just under the sand, you will see the flowery anemone's tentacles on the end sticking up. One simple touch (they are harmless) and the tentacles disappear into the "gut" at an amazing speed! Kids love spooking them, and it does the creature no harm whatsoever.

W**orms** are represented by the larval stage of the Polychaete, a segmented worm that is about the most abundant animal in our waters. These little red larvae may be studied under a dissecting scope (or binoculars held backwards) and their segments and "many spines" (thus the name) are easily studied. They are an important food source as larvae to untold numbers of predators, and the adults create the mounds we see so commonly on low tide flats.

E**chinoderms** are well represented in St. Joe Bay. Aside from the Five-keyhole Sand Dollars and urchins, there are Red-footed Starfish terrorizing the bivalve population. But even more abundant, though somewhat secretive, are the tens of thousands of **brittlestars** hiding all over the bay in plant roots and colonies of other invertebrates like sea squirts and clams.

M**ollusks** seem like they are always abundant, no matter where one goes in salt water. The huge class of **Bivalves** is well represented with scallops a frequent find in the grass beds. Check with the local Park Ranger about the season for taking these, but few treats beat fresh scallops (but you are going past Julia Mae's on the way back). There are other clams, too, as bivalves are abundant all through the bay.

These bivalves did not escape the attention of the **Gastropods**. These extremely strong predators pry open bivalves and scrape out the soft meat with their radula.

Then they lie buried in the substrate for weeks digesting their meal. In the bay, there are several gastropods, including the Lightning Whelk, Banded Tulip, Fighting Conch and Crown Conch. They are all neat in their own right, but the story of the Lightning Whelk is fascinating.

All gastropods originally had their opening on the right side, as you hold the creature up on end. But in the time since the last ice age, as Native Americans moved down to our coastline for the bounty of sea life, this creature has undergone quite a change. We know from middens (Indian trash piles) that they ate tons of Lightning Whelks. But they were virtually all *right-handed*, as are other species today. Before that, the fossil record shows the species occasionally mutates a left-handed specimen, not unlike left-handedness in humans, but rarer.

The thing was, these left-handed ones were considered evil (sinistral) by the Native Americans and were not taken. Therefore, populations of Lightning Whelks slowly shifted to left-handed ones until today, they're virtually all left-handed. This is a perfect example of artificial selection as humans have acted as a substitute natural world.

There are octopus in this bay. Common Octopus, with the rather unflattering name of *Octopus vulgaris*, live deep past the Turtle Grass. These gentle creatures have no quarrel with humans, and are content to flee at our approach. Sometimes in winter, one will come near shore to die, and will allow excellent looks at a unique creature. The diminutive Dwarf Octopus is quite another story. Found occasionally in abandoned mollusk shells, this little hellion will bite the fire out of you! Octopus make lousy pets and are not common, so let's let them be.

SIZE DOES MATTER

One other group of mollusk is the Chiton, a segmented encrusting organism that looks like a doodlebug clinging on a shell or stick underwater. They are small in our waters but are eaten in the Caribbean and called "sea beef."

A***rthropods*** are represented by crabs mostly, and the Spider Crab is quite common in the bay. This creature is easily caught and can hardly hurt you with its spindly pincers. They are tan colored and do bear a remarkable resemblance to a spider's shape. Crabs are scavengers on the sea floor and are critical to the life and health of the ocean for that reason.

More of an ancestor of spiders is the ancient **Horseshoe Crab**. These children of the **Trilobites** are common in the Turtle Grass, and huge females are often seen dragging their mate along at a slow pace. These "crabs" are totally harmless, and safe for children to play with. Their blunt "tail" (telson) has no venom and can hardly puncture skin, being so dull.

The Spiny Burr Fish puff up, so their size, and their spiny nature, make them less appealing to predators

There are some neat **fish** in St. Joe Bay. A common and entertaining creature is the **Spiny Burr Fish**, which looks like a swimming pin cushion. This is a fish you can actually swim down, and it will puff up as you hold it. But beware, if your hand gets over its feeble looking mouth, it will absolutely light up your whole day! Ouch! Joining burr fish in less numbers are **Puffer Fish**, who do a pretty fair job of blowing themselves up. And the trifecta comes when the bizarre **Cowfish** sallies forth from the grass, moooooving at the speed of concrete. With a rock hard exterior

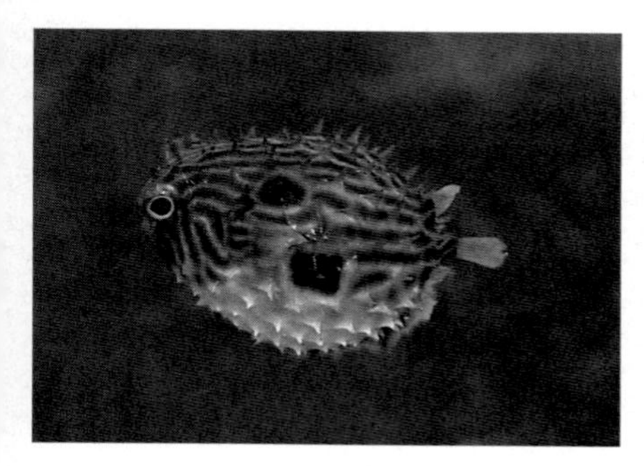

and horns to die for, this is a harmless character kids will fight over. If **Pipefish** aren't neat enough, try locating the closely related **Sea Horse**. These two unique critters suck up tiny organisms with their snouts and are quite harmless to hold. One thing about fish to remember though is that they are covered with a mucous layer that fights disease. For this reason, it is best to lay them in your hand, rather than holding them with your finger tips, so they will survive your curiosity.

Along the bottom there are colonies of two creatures. One is **Sea Squirts**, the soft-bodied thing that goes mush under your feet. This does kill the individuals, so you might wish to tread lightly. Also, pulling up one that was attached to examine it, or to squirt your girlfriend, almost surely kills it as well. Just be careful and try to keep their mortality to a minimum.

There are also huge numbers of Razor Clams. These are mollusks, of course, but are listed here with the sea squirts as the animalian keystone species of the bay community. Within them and the squirts are thousands of tiny creatures all living together in relative harmony. Ocean life has been living in such colonies for hundreds of millions of years and has worked out remarkable mutualistic relationships where the entire colony seems to depend on each other. Now they depend on us to make sure the bay is not polluted further, and that our grandchildren will have the opportunity to float slowly over the Turtle Grass and see the wonders of the living bay.

Do you miss all the marine invertebrates if you visit in winter? Absolutely not! At low tide there are uncountable stranded creatures all over the tide flats. Most of what we described may be found easily by walking through the shallows and poking around. In winter, the Turtle Grass dies and washes out to the deep water. There, it is devoured by untold trillions of bacteria, which multiply like dueling calculators in late winter and early spring. Then, as it warms up and the animals start becoming more active, the bacteria washes into the shallows and forms the base of the grass-bed food chain. It is a wondrous plan for a fantastic ecosystem.

There is actually more to do in St. Joe State Park than snorkel. **Mammals** such as **White-tailed Deer**, **Raccoon** and **River Otter** are easily seen, and occasionally approached quite close. **Skunks** may be seen at night while driving up and down the park road, as well as more familiar species such as **Opossums** and **Nine-banded Armadillos**. Larger predators such as **Gray Foxes** and **Bobcats** still roam the woodlands, so a walk or drive very early in the morning (always the best time for mammals) is recommended.

There are a lot of wintering **birds** in the St. Joe Bay area. Most of the usual suspects may be found here, but also less common species such as **Bufflehead** and **Common Goldeneye**. I have recorded with others some extremely rare northern birds in winter right in Eagle Harbor, including **King Eider**, **Harlequin Duck** and **Eared Grebe**. **Gannets**, **Bald Eagles** and **Peregrines** join the list of frequently seen birds, and show the excellence of this winter haven.

The spring migration is quite good on days trans-Gulf migrants are falling out of the air. There is a great trail for migrants just inside the park on the right. There's a parking area and a boardwalk over to a nice Sand Pine community. Stay on the trail as it curves left and it leads to a beautiful hammock of oaks that grew as a result of the Indian middens in the middle. This is a wonderful little forest for migrants and it also offers

pleasant glimpses of the bay. The smoke billowing out of the plants in Port St. Joe may be diminishing, as these businesses are shutting down.

PINING

Ancient Lighter stumps are relics of a time when waters were lower during ice ages

My favorite time in the park is during the fall migration. Many birds, most of them peninsular

AWAY

(circum-Gulf) migrants, follow the coastline east toward the Florida peninsula. However, they get confused because of the lay of the land, as the peninsula juts out west from the mainland and then curves around to the north. Many birds headed east take a south turn just past Port St. Joe, then take a right turn at the peninsula and eventually head up the northbound arm into the park. They are quite lost, and fly really close right past lucky observers.

Sharp-shinned Hawks cruise over St. Joe Peninsula occasionally snatching small landbirds for a snack

SONGBIRDS BEWARE

Raptors such as **Sharp-shinned Hawk**, **Broad-winged Hawk**, **American Kestrel** and **Turkey Vulture** are common, but many other species are seen. Many songbirds like **Palm Warbler** and **Barn Swallow** are everywhere, with dozens of other species in evidence. The peak is around the beginning of October, but even in November, exciting birds may be seen migrating up the peninsula, such as **Sandhill Crane**, **Snow Geese**, **Common Loon**, late hawks, and you never know what else. The only thing really predictable is the place's unpredictability.

The State Park offers very nice cabins for reasonable rates, and the staff is quite accommodating to their guests. All year round there seems to be interesting things to do, and the park's animal life may be experienced any month of the year. For reservations, call (850) 227-1327.

Marine Life on North Florida's Coast

The animal kingdom is divided into large groups called *phyla,* which are collections of creatures with certain physical features in common. Most authorities claim about 27 of these phyla, with each being subdivided into *classes.* You probably remember from school that classes are in turn broken into *orders*, which are composed of *families*, made up of several *genera*. Finally, each *genus* (singular of genera) represents different *species*. The only real definition in any of the seven is for species, since this level represents a population of organisms that only breeds with their own population (naturally, in the wild, to make a fertile offspring).

In this chapter, phyla are boldfaced italics, and classes are boldfaced and underlined (at first mention). The English name of invertebrate species are not boldfaced, but are capitalized (Banded Tulip), whereas a nonspecific group like "conch" or larger taxa such as "worms" are lower case.

Owing to the fact that insects, which are scarce in the ocean, are about half the species in the world, there are more species of animals on land than in the sea. But there are far more phyla of animals represented in the ocean than on land, as few of the 27 have ventured out of the water. The vast majority of land animals are either ***Chordates*** or ***Arthropods***, but many shells in the sea have several phyla living as encrusting organisms all together.

This chapter deals with about ten of the phyla that occur along the North Florida coastline and the ecology of some local species. They live in several identifiable communities along the coast, and many are closely tied to each other. Natural communities include places like oyster reefs, muddy bottom and sandy bottom communities, estuaries and turtle grass beds.

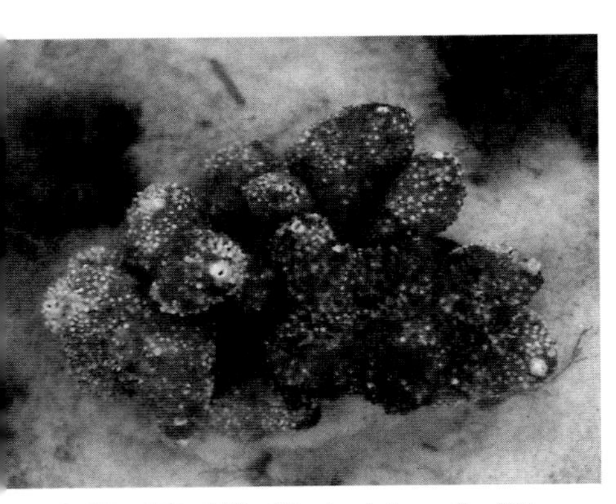

IRREGULAR SYMMETRY

The most primitive phylum of animals is ***Porifera***, the sponges, which had their beginnings over a half billion years ago. Their name means "pore bearing," and indeed, they are replete with thousands of tiny holes for filtering water. Many are even shaped in such a way as to encourage water flow through them, not unlike how the shape of a soaring bird's wings causes lift. They are extremely simple animals, many with irregular symmetry, who were thought to be plants up until a little more than a century ago. Symbiotic green algae growing within them is partly responsible for this.

Lacking bilateral or radial shape, this sponge will grow in no definite pattern

Sponges are little more than a net that sifts the water for tiny particles of food. They have cells which are all quite similar, or undifferentiated, and a skeleton made of either calcium or silicon. Some are vase shaped, and others are simply blobs with no special form. Dead cells, called spicules, have interesting shapes under microscopes, such as the barbs on barbed wire. These wash onto shore and are no more popular with scavengers than live ones are to predators.

RADIAL SYMMETRY

These sponges are round, which seems to improve efficiency as water passes through them

Sponges are important to the marine community, though, as they serve as homes for many species of marine animals. One large sponge, broken apart, will reveal everything from snapping shrimp to gobies, with larval polychaetes abounding. They are a virtual community within themselves. Over the eons these tiny creatures have learned that living inside of a bad tasting creature pays off.

Breaking sponges in half is hardly a mortal blow as they simply grow into two animals. They frequently reproduce through a process called budding, where a piece just breaks off, floats in the ocean, attaches somewhere and grows. In a similar process called fragmentation, pieces of the sponge break off through outside forces, but the results are the same. These two forms of asexual reproduction are not unlike what many plants can do, and may have led early observers to place sponges in the plant kingdom.

Some of the more common sponges in our area are Dead Man's Fingers, the vase-looking Basket Sponges, Loggerhead Sponges, the somewhat stout Yellow Sponges, lovely-smelling Garlic Sponges, the small but attractive Red Beard Sponges and the Hermit Crab Sponges one sees on the backs of the small arthropod. Most species in North Florida are calcarious types, with those made of silicon being much less numerous.

A colonial phylum of lesser known animals is the ***Bryzoa***, or Moss Animals. They may be hard or soft, depending on their composition, and some found washed up on the beach are mistaken for plants. Commonly seen along shorelines is the Brown Moss Animal, a tan clump of soft tissue that few people would be able to identify. There are also Sea Mats, Staghorn and Lettuce Bryzoan and Sheep's Wool. Some bryzoan is distinctively purple, lining rocks and shells with its soft covering.

Far more advanced than sponges, but far less so than the creatures to be discussed later, are ***Coelenterata*** or ***Cnideria***. The first name refers to the hollow gut found in specimens of this phylum, while the alternate name means "nettle." Either is acceptable, and both certainly paint a picture of the sea anemone and jellyfish that are found along the North Florida seashore.

Coelenterates are basically a cup, often with a basal disk and tentacles that are laden with stinging cells called nematocysts (or cnidocytes). They have two alternative body forms, with one class, **Scyphozoa** (jellyfish), floating on top with tentacles hanging down, and another, **Anthozoa**, living on bottom with their tentacles up in the water column. Coral (mostly tropical) and anemones are often referred to as "polyps" whereas jellyfish are frequently dubbed "medusa" after the woman in mythology with snakes for hair (sounds like a babe to me).

The barb of jellyfish is longer than those of anemones and may pierce human skin. Touching an anemone generally results in a feeling of them sticking to us, as their barbs barely penetrate our skin. They are therefore quite harmless and safe for children to play with. Many jellies are quite offensive, and swimming with concentrations of them is unadvisable.

'UST A BIG GLOB

Cannonball Jellyfish sometimes wash ashore in huge numbers

Coelenterates grab their food with their tentacles and paralyze it with their stinging cells. Food is then stuffed into the enteron (hollow gut) and digested extracellularly. Jellyfish float along with the currents searching for food, while the stationary anemones find a real gumbo at the bottom. Jellyfish came from anemone-like ancestors eons ago, as depicted by their larval stage. An early larvae looks like a paramecium (possibly on their line of evolution) but it becomes a polyp-like creature, such as an anemone. Then, through a process called transverse fission, one of these larval polyps reproduces several young jellyfish that float off and begin new lives. This process, where the evolutionary stages are seen in the larvae of an organism, is called "ontogeny recapitulates phylogeny," meaning the ancestral stages are summed up in larval development.

The Man-of-War can inflict fierce pain with its wicked stinging cells on its long tentacles

HURTFUL CREATURE

The most common jellyfish in our waters is the cannonball or cabbagehead. There doesn't seem to be any pattern to their appearance, but at times they fill the waters and beaches with their fat bodies. They will sting, but less so than some other jellies. Comb jellies are seen occasionally as well, but are neither harmful nor true Coelenterates.

Another jellyfish mimic is the Man-of-War. They are fortunately more common on the western gulf and not usually a threat

in our waters. South winds bring them up from the tropics, and Texas beaches are sometimes covered with tens of thousands of them. Still, swimmers in Florida may find their fiery tentacles once in a while and experience undeserved pain and suffering.

These marvelous creatures may be the most unique organism on earth, as they are true examples of polymorphy. Each animal is made up of several individuals (the bell, tentacles, gonads, etc.), with each reproducing its own part. These bluish creatures from the South Atlantic are exceptional but best admired from a distance.

Sloppy Guts Anemones really look like mammal entrails, though most often buried under the sand or mud

Two fairly common anemones are found within our waters, but they are shy and retire immediately upon contact. On rocks, wood and other solid objects, the Cloak Anemones sit with their searching tentacles waving in the brine. At times, orange strings full of nematocysts seem to protrude from their closed bodies while they sit helplessly attached to their favorite substrate.

CAN THAT BE AN ANIMAL?

The Sloppy Guts Anemone is a real crowd pleaser found on sandy and muddy bottoms. Its tube, usually under the sand, looks like an old brownish intestine with the flowery tentacles waving in a circular pattern above the sand. One touch and poof! the creature disappears down the tube like lightning. Actually, the animal is about two inches long without the tube, and in the classroom we removed several and raised them in test tubes. It was

great fun to watch them shoot down to the bottom of the tube, or to take small food morsels from my students. They may be found in places like St. Joe Bay or Alligator Harbor readily and dug up to be raised in captivity.

Coelenterates are amazingly simple animals with few systems as we know them. They have a primitive nerve net they sense with and little else except three skin layers, tentacles and the ability to make gametes for reproduction. They and the primitive hydra made a huge leap for the animal kingdom when they gave rise to worms.

The Sea Pansy, looking like a purplish flower, inhabits slightly deeper waters than shorelines but is seen occasionally washed up or in trawls. Sea Whips have long, thin "limbs" coming off them, loaded with their food gathering devices. Other less common polyps inhabit the sea floor and filter out tiny bits of food streaming through the water column.

Jellyfish and anemones are examples of radial symmetry, which means that their bodies are essentially round. This is a shape that works well when organisms feed by contacting the environment. It is a poor shape, however, for anything that moves. For this reason, when the descendants of these radial creatures began going from one place to another, their bodies became elongate. This was the beginning of worms, and there arose several phyla of these mobile creatures.

With the advent of elongation came bilateral symmetry. Creatures now had more or less equal left and right sides. Moreover, they had a front (anterior) and a rear (posterior). With these exciting new inventions came sensing organs in the anterior, so they would know what they were running into. And the posterior, for obvious reasons, became a smart place for such functions as waste elimination. So a body plan that would transcend the ages was conceived for worms.

By far, the most abundant worm group in the sea is the class **Polychaeta**, from the phylum of segmented worms, ***Annelida***. Polychaetes are named for their "many hairs" which they use in locomotion, primarily. Many are ravenous predators, hiding in burrows on tide flats, and waiting for tiny invertebrates to sally past. Roaring up to the surface and seizing their quarry with a pair of fangs much like centipedes, they are the terror of the beach. Down into the hole the prey is dragged until it is killed and consumed. Fortunately for us, they don't come in size XXXL.

Some species of polychaetes called fire worms have an interesting reproduction. On the third full moon of each month (there really are three in a row) the fire worms emerge about an hour after sunset and find a mate. Clasping and exchanging sperm (they are hermaphrodites) they roll around in the surf all night, practicing reciprocal fertilization. At dawn, they drag themselves back into their burrows and my guess is they take a looooong nap.

The product of this scandalous behavior is tens of millions of larvae, creeping into every place you can imagine on the gulf floor. They are simply everywhere! The hordes of the older little pink worms were not missed by the fish, whose worm eating habits are not confined to freshwater. So the smaller kin of the ferocious predators serve as lunch for the multitudes.

The other two common classes of segmented worms are earthworms and leeches, and these will be covered later in Chapter 8. But there are many more worms in the sea, with varied shapes and morphological characteristics.

The phylum ***Platyhelmenthes*** includes many types of flatworms, and some are in our waters. The **Tapeworms** are internal parasites that may be found in aquatic or terrestrial creatures. They have marvelous adaptations for internal existence such as a low osmotic pressure, natural resistance to low pH, and much more. They are neither popular nor often seen, so we'll leave them now and discuss other worms.

There is another class of flatworms, the **Turbellarians**, which is free-living in the sea, and believed to be on the direct line of ancestry to vertebrates and, of course, humans. Some of these are incredibly gaudy and almost surreal, as they inch their way along the bottom or ocean surface. One of my favorites is *Glaucous,* named for the silvery appearance. These pondersome creatures eat various species of tiny Coelenterates, heavily-laden with stinging cells. But the digestive tract within the worm is soft enough to avoid firing the barb, so these stinging cells migrate out to the skin line of Glaucous and become defenses for the new host! This is just one of many, many examples of amazing relationships among the marine animals, who have had twice as long as land species to work out these complex symbiotic interchanges.

There are other worm phyla found both in the sea as well as terrestrially. ***Ribbon Worms*** may be found in murky water throughout the North Florida coastline, as well as certain freshwater ponds and streams. ***Roundworms*** may be internal parasites found in fish and other aquatic creatures as well as land animals, or may be free living. Worms are clearly everywhere in our environment and offer great life histories and fascinating secrets.

MIRROR IMAGES

Mollusks are about as abundant and diverse as worms, and a darn sight more interesting! These are soft bodied creatures (the Greek word mollis=soft), usually have hard shells, and the lion's share are in either the **Gastropoda** or **Bivalvia** **(Pelecypoda)**. The former has a single, spiraled shell while the latter has two equal shells facing each other.

Gastropods, like polychaetes, have both male and female sex cells, and are therefore monoecious like "perfect" flowers. This enables both partners to come away from mating with fertilized eggs and increase the number of their species. Though they lack the romance of Fire Worms, these conchs and whelks leave a fascinating coiled string of egg cases, each with a dozen or so tiny gastropods that will hatch and develop in well aerated aquaria.

These "marine snails" are ferocious hunters, and seem to be especially fond of their bivalve cousins. These are eaten by merely grabbing the bivalve with their muscular foot and, by sheer strength alone, prying them open and scraping the soft animal out of the soon-to-be discarded shell. This is usually followed by a protracted dormancy under the substrate until hunger calls.

We have several gastropods in our area which are easily found and identified. Probably the easiest to recognize is the

Lightning Whelks (left) are left-handed, unlike other gastropods such as the Banded Tulip (right)

Lightning Whelk, because their opening is on the *left* side of their shell, when held upright. Other gastropods have theirs on the right side, as did this species many years ago. What happened to these particular whelks is a truly classic example of artificial selection, and lays the groundwork for an understanding of the same natural selection that was first described during the time of Darwin and his contemporaries (see page 154).

UNDERWATER ROYALTY?

Another fairly common species of whelk is the Crown Conch, found on sandy and (especially) muddy bottoms along the gulf coast. Their name is derived from the circle of protrusions around the top of the shell, reminiscent of a crown. They are quite abundant around oyster reefs where they periodically pry open helpless oysters. In the Wakulla Beach area, there are quite a few in the shallow lagoons which are tagged—left over from the research done on them by Florida State University.

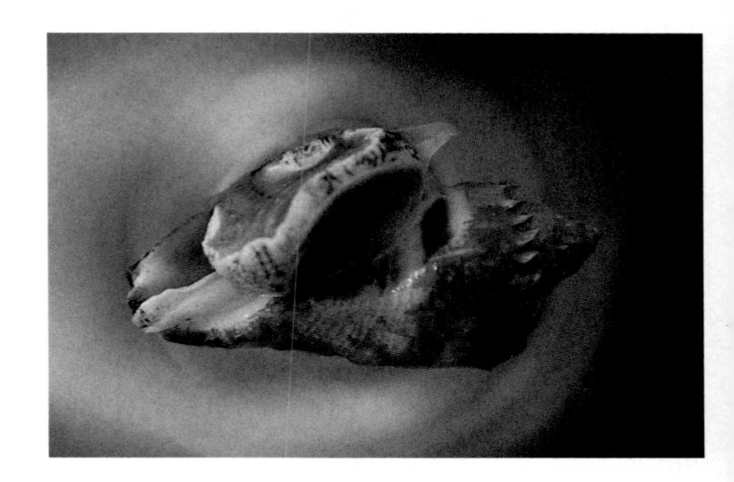

Crowned Conches have beautiful tops for no known purpose

Banded Tulips are colorful gastropods whose bands easily identify them. More common in our estuaries such as St. Joe Bay, they also ravage clams, scallops and other assorted bivalves. Tulips are smaller than some species but make up for it with their hues of reds, purples and browns. A quick glance will detect the bands going around the shell, while the thin-shelled Pear Whelk has vertical lines on their rather dainty shell.

Another really interesting gastropod is the Fighting Conch. Their shells actually bear the scars of past conflicts, with pieces missing or severely distorted. They are found along beaches with high surge as well as many other locations. They have extremely thick shells that protect their soft bodies during their aggressive forays.

The Moon Snail is a rounded gastropod often found on the beach that resembles the closely related Shark's Eye. Quite abundant is the elongate Lettered Olive with its "hieroglyphics " all over the shell. A blur of smaller species inhabit our waters and beaches, requiring a detailed field guide for identification.

For their sizes, bivalves are incredibly numerous creatures, which is why we see their shells piled all along our beaches. Because of their scrumptious taste, quite a few predators took notice of their abundance and developed ways to feast on the tender, tasty meat. We mentioned gastropods earlier but, as bivalve eaters, starfish are just as dedicated.

The most famous of the bivalves would have to be the oyster. These delicious creatures are the keystone species of the oyster reef, a unique community along the North Florida coastline. These reefs not only provide homes for specialized animals such as Porcelain Crabs, they cut water surge and encourage plant growth along shorelines. These areas are, in turn, loaded with fish, such as mullet, redfish and trout, as well as the bulldog-like Toad Fish. Oyster shells are quite sharp along the bills, which provides protection not only for themselves but all that inhabit their reefs. The Crown Conchs don't seem to mind, though, and may be amazingly abundant for a carnivore. The clown prince of shorebirds, the oystercatcher, is fairly common around reefs as well. Its feet are endowed with extremely thick, rough skin for walking on oysters and its compressed bill is perfect for slipping in the oyster and snipping the muscle that holds them shut.

Between the conchs, oystercatchers and starfish that feed on oysters, it seems hard to imagine that they don't disappear. But female oysters lay hundreds of thousands of eggs in a single season, and though each larva (affectionately known as a "spat") has only a minuscule chance of seeing adulthood, enough mature to repopulate the reefs. In fact, after natural disasters such as tropical storms and hurricanes, when oyster populations are decimated, their comebacks amaze even marine biologists.

Look for oyster reef communities in shallow lagoons and estuaries where surge is low. Along our coastline, many such communities exist in the protected areas between the mainland and barrier islands. These oysters have huge impacts on the local economy, as well as waist lines.

Scallops are filter feeders much like oysters and other bivalves, but they seem to prefer clearer water. They are especially common in grass beds, and some areas off the St. Mark's Lighthouse, St. Joe Bay and Panama City abound with scallops. Like the oysters, they are an important component of the economy of coastal counties and all the more reason to maintain healthy marine areas.

Scallops are fascinating little creatures. They are one of the first creatures on earth to develop eyes and you can see their blue peepers by holding one up and looking between the shells. They are also capable of serious movement when they spew water out their syphon and undulate through the water to escape enemies. Just for fun, try rubbing a gastropod all over your hands, and then pick up a scallop. With nary a brain, they totally freak out!

These syphons suck water in for filtering and spit used water out. Gastropods have but one valve and shell, and are thus referred to as "univalves" by some authorities. I choose the term "gastropod" as the translation "stomach/foot" really fits them perfectly.

Quahogs are bivalves with extremely thick shells, commonly unearthed in muddy substrates. In Alligator Harbor they are abundant but their shells are strewn all along many beaches such as Cape San Blas. The thick shells offer greater protection against wave action and various animalian drills that would otherwise have them for lunch.

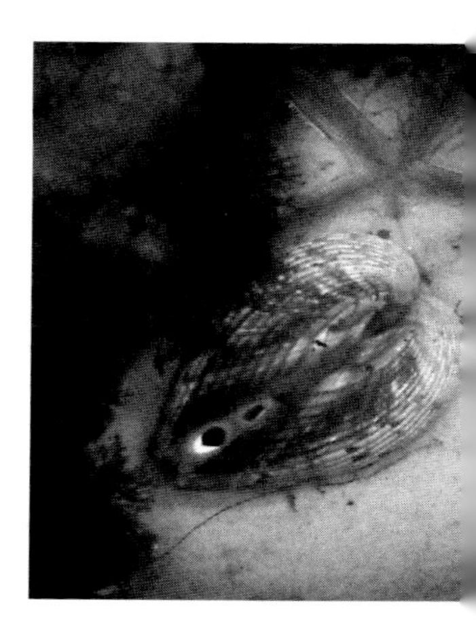

Normally seen as a multitude of shells on the beach, this living cockle siphons water for its nutrition

The most abundant seashell, however, must be the cockles. They vary from grayish to reddish with moderately thick shells, and doubtlessly serve as a food source for numerous predators. They decorate peoples' beach houses and seem especially adapted for catching the ashes of cigarettes. This shell does break fairly easily, sometimes exposing jagged edges that may cut the bare feet of playful children.

The delicate and beautiful Angel Wing is common on our beaches and whole specimens are prized by shell collectors. Also attractive is the Sunray Clam with its vivid colors and beauty. Like the gastropods, there are many small species of bivalves of many sizes and shapes which are beyond the scope of this book. Learning them, though, is a fun and rewarding hobby that many shell collectors enjoy.

Lastly, tiny coquinas inhabit beach sand by the thousands. Named *Donax variabilis,* they may be any of several colors and patterns. They normally remain buried and thus hidden from beachcombers until one digs for them.

Space does not allow the discussion of even a portion of the coastal Panhandle's bivalves, but any shell book will serve as an excellent guide.

Possibly the neatest of all mollusks are the **Cephalopoda**, including our octopus and squid. These are extremely advanced and bright marine animals, possibly the highest of the invertebrates on the evolutionary ladder.

Octopus are imposing creatures, with great strength, suction cups of steel, a menacing beak, the ability to move quickly and even jet through the water with their syphon, and eyesight as keen as many humans. They are spirited fighters indeed, but are generally shy and retiring.

The favorite food of the Common Octopus is crabs, which they grab with the suckers on their eight tentacles and kill instantly with their sharp beak. They are usually hiding in crevices on the bottom, except when foraging, but their higher metabolism disallows them from staying dormant as long as other mollusks like whelks and conchs. While hiding, they possess the ability not only to change color with the surroundings but also to adjust the texture of their skin to mimic that of the material they are in contact with. I know of no creatures other than cephalopods that possess this unique ability.

Octopus are also quite bright, which is a different matter from the above adaptations. They are so intelligent that they have, when presented with a crab in a jar, unscrewed the lid and dined on the hapless crustacean. One word of caution to those who house them in aquaria: octopus are escape artists, and can slip through the tiniest of cracks. Once out of water, their death is quick and sad.

Students examine an octopus in St. Joe Bay

PUT THAT ON A BUN

A second word of caution. Our Common Octopus (*O. vulgaris)* is normally a benign creature that can be handled safely under normal conditions for short periods of time. One fine day, however, I was being filmed with one at Gulf Specimen Marine Laboratories in Panacea, and had to start my little spiel over a couple of times. My guess is that the creature began to suffocate out of water, but just as I got to the part about their being inoffensive, this struggling beast ripped into my hand like me with a Julia Mae's seafood platter, and all in attendance were hysterical with me calmly finishing my speech (camera fortunately on my face) as blood spurted on the ground.

There is a second species of octopus in our waters, the diminutive Dwarf Octopus. This replica of the larger variety hides in abandoned shells and artificial objects while not prowling for tiny crabs. But (in a last word of caution) don't be fooled by their size: This fellow has a personality like a Pigmy Rattler and will bite savagely when restrained. Yes, it's happened to me and no, I won't tell you about it . . . .

Squid are essentially elongate octopus with ten tentacles that chase fish in the water column. What they lack in strength they make up for in speed. Their tentacles are sure, and their beak is deadly to small piscine prey. There are places where squid may be abundant, but this is not a commonly encountered creature in our waters. They are often used in medical research and their nervous system and eye development examined. Our species is the Dwarf Squid.

Obviously, cephalopods lack the outer shell that mollusks and most gastropods have, but possess other methods of defense. They do have an internal mantle that gives them stability and serves as an attachment for internal muscles. In their close cousin the cuttlefish, this mantle is sold to pet owners for parakeets to sharpen their bills and are called cuttlebones.

There are other mollusks in our area. One is the chiton, a small creature with a shell like a roly-poly that attaches itself to hard surfaces and hangs on for dear life. They are actually abundant in some areas, where they seem to be stuck to every shell, rock or piece of wood in the sea.

Lastly, there are gastropods without shells called "sea slugs" or "sea hares." They normally stay out deep but will enter shallow water annually to lay their eggs in quiet bodies of water. These inoffensive, soft-bodied blobs have but one defense: Nothing would dare eat them with all the hideous enzymes in their skin! They also have the ability to emit a purplish dye not unlike the "ink" an octopus squirts, but this has never seemed terribly effective.

E***chinodermata*** is many people's favorite group of marine animals. It includes creatures such as starfish and sand dollars and the phylum as a whole has many interesting characteristics. Their name refers to the spiny skin that covers them and protects them from predators. They are also masters of regeneration, as for example, the starfish who are famous for growing back lost arms. Their water vascular system efficiently powers movement in their bodies and controls their unique tubed feet. But oddest of all, their curious patterns of five on their bodies make them bizarre in the animal kingdom. Five arms, five radial canals, five imprints (on sand dollars) and so forth. Echinoderms are truly an interesting, unique group of organisms.

The **starfish** is the crown jewel of this phylum. Normally with five arms, they move slowly along on the ocean floor looking for their favorite food, bivalves. Upon finding one, the starfish grabs it with all arms and articulates its mouth (on the undersurface) to the bill opening of the bivalve. Gentle but constant pulling pressure from the arms causes the clam's muscles to cramp and eventually relax a bit. The ensuing gap between the bills is sufficient for the starfish's stomach to evert (come out on a gut) and slip into the slightly open shell of the bivalve. The stomach surrounds the soft body inside and begins the digestion process. Eventually the starfish yanks the soft body out of the shell and pulls it back inside its own self. The bivalve shell then washes up harmlessly on shore and beachcombers are none the wiser.

'he brittlestar middle ottom) has 'snake tail" rms, unlike he four pecies f starfish hown vith it

WHO DOESN'T FIT?

In our area, many species of sea stars are out in open waters and frequently wash in after storms or very high tides. Some of these species are the Pointed, Gray and Mottled Sand Starfish. Inshore, in grass beds, are the smallish Red-footed Starfish. With round arms (unlike those in deeper water with flat arms) and beautiful hues of red and garnet, they are as attractive as they are interesting.

UNDERWATER PINCUSHIONS

Superficially resembling starfish but somewhat unrelated are the brittlestars, or **Ophiuroidea.** The name means "one with a snake's tail" and this describes the spindly arms perfectly. In the middle of these five snake tail arms is a pentagonal basal disk with all the organs housed in it.

Brittlestars are far more mobile than starfish and can actually swim. Occasionally this leads to trouble, though, as attacks from fish may occur. This results in the brittlestar popping off its basal disk and releasing its organs into the water. While the fish gleefully fills up on innards of the attackee, our hero drops to the bottom and soon regenerates all that was lost, thus having the guts to do it again.

This creature is often overlooked but may be among the most abundant animals in an area. They tend to hide under objects or congregate in roots or shells in huge numbers. They seem to prefer grass beds and may be found shallow or deep. On the bottom they forage for decaying matter and serve as one of the all important scavengers of the sea.

Sea Urchins (**Echinoidea**) are the pin cushions of the sea. Our Short-spined Sea Urchin is abundant in grass beds and may vary in color from pink to almost white. Their spines are not especially sharp and may be handled without incident. Somewhat more delicate (and dangerous) is the Purple Sea Urchin, which is a dark purplish-

Sea Urchins leave little secret about their defense, with dozens of spines for armor

black with very long, pointed spines. They tend to live in open water more and hence they likely need the greater protection.

The short-spined Sea Urchins are about the only animal in the grass beds that actually eat the grass. The vegetation is important for cover and as a physical substrate for encrusting organisms. Spineys are more scavengers and cling to rocks or move along the sandy bottom.

Urchins are used in medical research a great deal because their eggs are extremely large and can be studied as fertilized ones differentiate. In the orient, urchin gonads are eaten as a delicacy, but all protein sources are valued in some parts of Asia.

Upon close examination, long tubed feet wave among the steady spines and hold to substrates and food items. They literally sit on their mouth as it is on the bottom (oral surface) and their anus is at the top (aboral surface) where they excrete waste. The famous mouth has five (of course!) teeth-like structures that aid in eating and the entire mouth parts are called "Aristotle's Lantern" (who discovered it), because, when removed from a dead individual, they resemble the old Greek lanterns.

Not known for their grace and beauty are the Sea Cucumbers, or **Holothuroidea**. Those of shallow water, often in grass beds, are only 2 to 3 inches long and have very pronounced ridges heavily laden with large tubed feet. These Red-footed Sea Cucumbers are uncommon but terribly cute and interesting. Several larger species are found out deep and are the size of a large dill pickle.

ANIMAL OR VEGETABLE?

Sea Cucumbers burrow their short, fat bodies into the substrate for protection, while eating detritus on the bottom

Sea cucumbers have quite a series of defenses. First, upon being attacked, they writhe their bodies around like they are sick. This discourages some aggressors. If not, small rips open up in their bodies and fluids begin leaking out. If more discouragement is needed, actual organs will ooze out of the body with the water becoming foul. If the predator persists, larger cracks open and white, viscous tubes shoot out like children's string from a can. Up to this point, the sea cucumber can recover, regenerating the lost parts. But the final stage is quite suicidal when the hapless creature, to avoid being eaten (and its kind then being included among predators as a food source), virtually disintegrates into a shapeless blob of protoplasm on the sea floor. No self-respecting sea creature could dine on this mess for long, although upon witnessing this event in our touch tank at Leon High, one very hungry Blue Crab did take a couple of bites.

Some large cucumbers become proverbial communities. Tiny creatures such as minuscule crabs make their way into the rear digestive tract for food (arrgh!) and protection. More often than not these cucumbers burrow into the muddy substrate and add to the protection described above. I certainly wouldn't relish the thought of being the attacker of one of these cucumbers when they get into a pickle.

As we might have almost suspected, there are five classes of echinoderms, but the **sea lily** isn't a creature likely to be encountered in our shallows. Where they exist, they are among the most beautiful animals in the sea, and their regeneration rate is the fastest of the entire kingdom.

The phylum ***Arthropoda*** is well represented in the sea and our waters by the class **Crustacea**. A huge group of creatures, the flagship is the crabs, but many other diverse forms exist. Crustacean refers to the hard shell and is the defense of most species. Being in the "jointed-footed" phylum speaks volumes about their locomotion (far and away better than most marine taxa), but much else is accomplished with the use of these appendages. Different pairs of "legs" are used for such chores as mating, egg carriage, defense, sensing and digging, as well as, of course, walking. Being arthropods, they also have compound eyes and many species have excellent vision. Their thorax and abdomen are fused into one huge armored piece with their head fairly well protected, too. Indeed, crustaceans are quite successful in the world's seas, and common and easily seen along North Florida's coast.

Blue Crabs have fantasies about pinching our toes and fingers (and we have fantasies about eating their pincers)

CRABBY PERSONALITY

Crabs are hard, squarish devils with five pairs of legs (thus the name decapods) with the front being nasty pincers. They are basically scavengers, though some species like Blue Crabs will kill less fortunate neighbors. Their eyes are on stalks and their eggs are carried under their abdomen, which is essentially an ancestral tail folded underneath.

Speaking of the toe-eating Blue Crabs, they may be our most common and widespread crab of the North Florida coastline. As despised as they are to swimmers, they are more highly prized to seafood lovers and the commercial fishing industry. Crabbers set out square traps made of chicken wire, suspended in the water column under a Styrofoam ball. Traps are baited with dead fish and checked periodically. Hundreds are gathered in a day and taken fresh to local seafood houses and restaurants. Soft-shelled crabs are eaten in their entirety but most commonly crabs are represented by a stuffed likeness. When this is not available, the claws will do in a pinch. I was a slender man when I discovered seafood and to this day I have found no cuisine that tops the fresh seafood of places like Spring Creek or Julia Mae's.

In the grass beds the ominous looking but quite harmless Spider Crab lurks. The size of a Blue Crab, but a dingy brown, these benign crustaceans are shy and retiring. They make excellent pets and mix well in salt water tanks with other marine animals. Blue Crabs don't.

Somewhat related to Spider Crabs are two other critters which are as inoffensive and interesting as any marine animals. The Arrow Crab is a strongly pointed creature of deeper waters, but is sometimes found on beaches. They are delicate and slender with an amazingly narrow anterior. Sponge Crabs are small creatures which pick off pieces of sponges and grow them on their backs for camouflage. This is a fairly common inshore and offshore crustacean.

Slightly deeper and moving freely through the water column is the Swimming Crab. A beautiful, iridescent, slimmed-down version of the Blue Crab, these are sometimes seen in tidal creeks and other waterways. They will defend themselves and have sharp pincers. See also the beautiful Calico Crab and rectangular Box Crab of deeper waters.

ARMY OF CRABS

Stone Crabs and Mud Crabs live under objects such as clumps of oysters and retreat to the bottom of muddy pools when uncovered. They are slick brown with very strong, though not sharp, pincers. Stone Crabs get much larger than Mud Crabs and are taken for food by humans.

Hundreds of fiddler crabs scurry along the shore, hoping for safety in numbers

Fiddler crabs represent several species of bacteria eaters along protected beaches, including the Common, Green, White-faced and Panacea Fiddlers. They are easily recognized by their burrows and small size. Males have one long claw they use to signal the females to come down their burrow to mate. The rhythm they use in this signal keeps species from hybridizing with others. The square-shelled Black Marsh Crab inhabits the Juncas and Spartina in abundance and is most often seen hiding underneath boards and other debris washed in from the gulf.

Fiddler crabs are used for bait by many, especially when fishing for redfish or sheephead. They are difficult to hook, but some fish attack them aggressively. Reds have huge, grinding molars that easily reduce the hapless crab to pulp, while sheephead tear them apart with their incisors. Though abundant in some places, fiddlers probably shouldn't be over collected.

Hermit crabs are a favorite with kids, being abundant and harmless. The tiny Dwarf Hermit lives in small gastropod shells such as abandoned periwinkles. They and their tracks may be seen in shallow water and along beaches all across the North Florida coastline. Larger is the Flat-clawed Hermit Crab whose pincer acts almost as the operculum of gastropods, covering the hole of the shell for protection. The largest of the inshore hermits is the Striped, with long appendages bearing the telltale brown stripes. In deeper water the huge Red Hermit may be dredged up or found by divers.

Hermit Crabs are scavengers, working the bottom in the all important recycling role. Outside of their borrowed shell they don't look much like a crab, having a long, soft abdomen for curling into the snail's old home. It holds them tight, though, and attempting to remove them will normally kill the creature inside. Allowing your children to take them home from the beach will not only ensure their death but will add a new chapter to your book on odor.

On the drier parts of the shorelines up to the sand dunes are the Ghost Crabs. These nocturnal scavengers burrow in the dry sand and forage for dead animals washed in with the tides. They will, however, kill defenseless animals such as nesting birds when the occasion permits.

Lobsters are not the common dweller in our waters that they are farther south, like the Florida Keys. However, there are quite a few lesser known crustaceans along our coastline that should be mentioned. Bulldozers, sometimes called Slipper Lobsters, are dredged up in moderately deep water, where they feed on clams.

Shrimp are an abundant food commodity for predators and humans alike. Commercial fishing industries throughout the world harvest untold trillions of shrimp each year while the number taken by marine carnivores would exceed our imagination. All along the gulf coast shrimpers make great money and seafood lovers eagerly await fresh "prawns," which expands both the job market and waist lines all along the coastline.

Our most common shrimp are the White, Pink and Brown Shrimp, all breeding at different times from spring well into summer. Rock shrimp are hard-shelled creatures of the bottom but still a favorite on the platter. Red Cleaning Shrimp are fascinating creatures that actually eat bacteria off wounds on marine animals and will clean cuts and under fingernails on human hands in aquaria. They make good pets and are a big favorite in the classroom.

Very different from other shrimp are the two Mantis Shrimp species. They have forelegs which are quite similar to Preying Mantids of the insect world and are armed with spines for impaling fish and other small marine life with the speed of a bullet. They are caught fairly frequently in trawls and should be handled with care. The edges of the carapace are sharp and could inflict cuts.

Barnacles of many species exist and they are a fascinating study. Essentially, they are a small, upside down shrimp lying in a round cup the inhabitant created. Two doors open and shut which allows the resident to filter the water with feather-like appendages called cirri, but also protects them against intruders.

Being stationary but not being a broadcast spawner like so many immobile marine invertebrates has its complexities when it is time to reproduce. Barnacles have solved this problem by the males having a packet of sperm called a spermatophore which they cleverly and suddenly pop into the female's oviduct with slight of hand (or a smartly designed appendage). The fertilized eggs take off as tiny larvae called cypress and upon landing on a suitable substrate, they begin developing their shell. As interesting and unique as barnacles are, be careful of their sharp edges and never let small kids play on or around these unforgiving crustaceans.

Tiny crustaceans go almost unnoticed along our coastline as well. Amphipods, commonly called beach hoppers, hide under seaweed and debris, and overturning hiding places like boards causes explosions of tiny "bugs" jumping everywhere. These are an important food source not just for shorebirds, but less conspicuous hunters such as wolf spiders. Closely related to amphipods are copepods, possibly the most abundant creature in the ocean. Copepods, or "whale food," are not easily seen in our area due to their size and habitat but exist by the billions out to sea.

Before there was life on land these primitive beasts laid their eggs on shore and plodded along the Paleozoic sea floor

A "crab" that is not really a crab is the unique horseshoe crab. This non-crustacean is from the class **Merostoma**, which amazingly has only four species worldwide. Our species is still quite common in our area and is as harmless as it is interesting. Its "tail" (telson) is blunt and is for the purpose of pointing at possible attackers to ward them off, as well as serving to flip overturned individuals right side up. It also makes a great handle, and hoisting them out of the water for children's inspection is a great education.

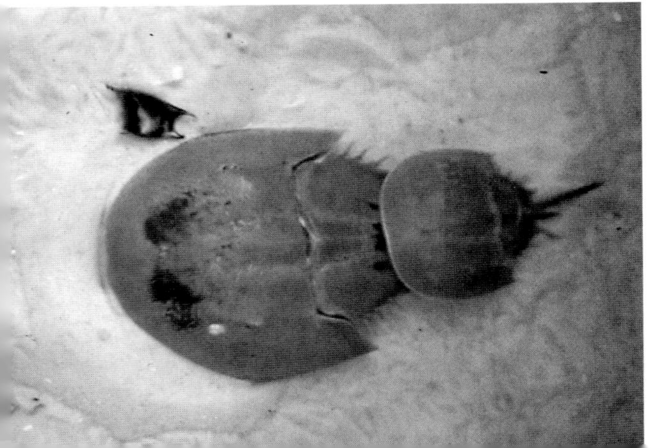

It seems that horseshoe crabs may actually be related to spiders, despite the common name of "crab." These and other vernacular names are often of little use in determining the relationships of organisms. Catfish, jellyfish, starfish and crayfish all have "fish" in their names but represent four different phyla of animals (frankly, I've had my doubts about catfish being fish, as well). But horseshoe crabs apparently descended from trilobites over 400,000,000 years ago, and the lineage is clearly seen in our hero's larvae which look impressively like a tiny trilobite.

Horseshoe crabs come to our shores to mate in late summer with the large females making a beeline for shore. The males, which are cruising parallel to the beach, intercept the gals and clasp with them to fertilize the eggs. Tens of thousands of eggs are laid all along the shoreline in the sand, and will eventually hatch when the next series of high tides return. Up on Delaware's shores these eggs are extremely important for migrating shorebirds like Red Knots, who gobble them up with great enthusiasm before their arduous flight down the Atlantic Ocean.

Our final phylum in this marine invertebrate chapter are actually chordates, which may be a surprise to some readers. There are actually some members of the phylum ***Chordata*** that have no backbone and frankly bear little similarity to more traditional chordates such as fish or birds. These "invertebrate chordates" are immobile, marine, filter feeders and are easily overlooked.

An extremely abundant animal in many areas is the Sea Squirt, placed in the subphylum (with other species) called Urochordata. As their translated name implies, they have a spinal chord in their tail, though only for a portion of their lifetime. So as you can see, the plot of their life history thickens.

Sea Squirts look like big raisins with tan skin attached to docks, ropes, rocks and other hard surfaces. In grass beds, other squirts actually grow in big colonies on the bottom with a plethora of other creatures living within them such as brittle stars, tiny gastropods and bivalves, small fish and Lord knows what else. Washing in to shore in places like Alligator Harbor are species such as White Sea Pork.

Sea squirts have one of the truly amazing stage developments in all of biology. Adults release gametes into the water in a process called broadcast spawning, which is employed by the majority of sessile (immobile) marine animals. The ensuing fertilized eggs develop into a tadpole-like larva that swims around and finds a place to attach with its mouth. It has a portion of a spinal chord in its tail to aid it in locomotion.

At this point, it lives off the fat in its tail (again, like the amphibian tadpole), and, as the tail is absorbed, the mouth articulates 180 degrees to the place the tail used to be. The creature then becomes a filter-feeder and lives out its adult life in that spot. But the fact that it had at least a portion of a spinal chord in at least a portion of its life qualifies it as a chordate.

Sea squirts have a tough, leathery outer cover made of cellulose, which they gain from the microscopic algae they ingest, and have few natural enemies. Although it seems like great fun to pluck them and squirt the closest girl around with water from their bodies, it is less fun and perhaps fatal for the creature itself. Similar results are gleaned from stepping on their colonies in grass beds. They do have an alternate designation, Tunicata, named for the (monk's) tunic it wears. The species in the grass beds is actually the Leather Tunicate.

The other invertebrate chordate subphylum is the Cephalochordata or lancelets. These are two-inch colorless elongate animals that live in, and actually swim through, sand. They are fusiform and have a mouth and gill slits on the anterior with a slender, tapering body. Their portion of a spinal chord is actually in their head, thus the name of their subphylum. Where they live, such as in bare areas of grass beds, they may be caught by scooping up large amounts of sand with a pool net and letting the sand empty out. When studied in biology labs, they are often referred to by their genus name, *Amphioxus*.

The Hemichordata (Acorn Worms) are considered part of the phylum Chordata as there does seem to be a portion of a spinal chord in their midsection. The Parchment Worms, Annelid polychaetes, live in papery tubes sticking up out of sand like horseshoes (always in pairs) with the creature itself in the submerged portion of the tube. Neat animals, they are capable of bioluminescence and will occasionally have symbionts living with them in the tube.

The last subphyla of ***Chordata*** is the Vertebrata, or creatures with a backbone. Marine and freshwater fish will be dealt with in Chapter 9.

One of the truly great experiences for kids and their parents alike is to dip out the incoming Sargasso Weed along the coast when south winds are bringing it ashore. By using a pool net or other fine mesh and removing the weed carefully, one can find an abundance of fascinating marine life remaining in the bottom of the net. Most look astonishingly like the weed itself, such as shrimp, crabs, and slugs. There are even fish that mimic this vegetation! This weed floats all the way from the middle of the Atlantic Ocean (Sargasso Sea) by use of gas bladders and winds up on the northern gulf shores as food for innumerable beach animals.

These are the major phyla of marine invertebrates along the North Florida coast, though by no means the entire cast. Soft and hard ***Bryzoa*** (moss animal) in beautiful colors like purple are often seen on beaches and shallows, ***Ctenephora***, the comb jellies, float harmlessly through our waters, ***Brachiopoda*** (Lamp Shell) congregate on bars by the thousands, and several other minor phyla coexist with the ones previously discussed. Several good guidebooks are out there, and sorting through these creatures is great fun and knocks the rust off the brain. And who knows—you may find something really exciting and new amidst all the cool creatures with their marvelous life histories and incredible adaptations.

Freshwater and Terrestrial Invertebrates of North Florida's Coast

There is no doubt but that the ocean abounds with invertebrates as seen in the last chapter. On land, the diversity among creatures without backbones is found in the insects, although there are several other phyla represented. This chapter is devoted to those phyla and a brief overview of the insects that crawl and fly their way to being half the species of animals in the world. Once again, the phyla are boldfaced italics and both they and classes are underlined.

Included are portions about several worm phyla, some land-living gastropods, several groups of noninsect arthropods and of course, the ubiquitous insects (Plate 3). Omitted in the interest of space are quite a few insects, including bristletails, springtails, mayflies, stoneflies, earwigs, lice, zillions of bugs, planthoppers, aphids, lacewings, untold numbers of beetles, caddisflies, crane flies, midges, and quite a few others.

Worms of several phyla are found alll across North Florida with segmented worms (***Annelida***) being the most conspicuous. These **earthworms** (wiggleworms) are important in the commercial market as fish bait but have many interesting secrets as well. At the top of that list is the fact that they eat dirt! They actually eat their way through the ground ingesting soil and digesting organic material for their food. What is left over is deposited on the surface as castings, the little dirt mounds that represent the bane of a greenskeeper's existence. Darwin himself conducted a great deal of foundational research on the effect of earthworms on soil and plant growth as they aerate the earth and allow carbon dioxide to flow through the softened dirt. No doubt watching Charles meticulously weighing all this worm poop prepared his neighbors for the shock of his assertions about us "springing from monkeys" (which is not quite what he said . . .).

In fact, all kinds of creatures eat earthworms, from moles to robins

MORE THAN FISH BAIT

As with the fire worms of the preceding chapter, earthworms are monoecious, that is each individual produces both sperms and eggs. These hermaphrodites undergo reciprocal fertilization by lying together essentially anterior to posterior, recognized by the "little ring" on the front end that gives the phylum its name. After mating, both parties deposit a cocoon-like sack of eggs and no doubt have a rejuvenated appetite for a plate of dirt.

In freshwater, the third class of Annelida swims and makes life pretty miserable for neighbors. **Leeches** are ectoparasites, sucking blood from hosts with vigor. They are black with red bellies and are two to three inches in length. They'll become engorged with blood after a good feeding, and as the meal becomes dehydrated, it is more manageable. They are certainly not above the blood of our species, although any damage is far outweighed by the grossness of finding a leech.

Leeches were used medicinally in "yester-century" by ignorant doctors. When people were sick, a good "blood letting" was administered where the little devils supposedly sucked out all of the bad blood. Amazingly, today, they have reentered the scene in operations to reattach limbs lost in accidents. It seems their anticoagulant (causes blood to flow freely) increases the chance of the severed limb being accepted by the body. Nowadays, it seems the roles have been reversed as the science of reattachment, without leeches, wouldn't have a limb to stand on.

Flatworms are poorly represented in freshwater or on land, but one species does seem to turn up occasionally under boards and other objects resting in damp areas. These are tan with dark lines running down their bodies and an interesting pointed nose. They are slender and gooey, but quite inoffensive to humans. As with some salamanders, though, be wary of sticking your fingers into your body's orifices. Their protection is in their skin, and this can mean some nasty enzymes.

There are many **flatworms** found within larger host animals as endoparasites. Tapeworms are flat, clear worms with fake segments and an anterior scolex for hanging onto the gut or other organ within. At the very least, tapeworms will sap animals of nutrition and energy but may cause more serious problems, depending on the level of infestation. Domestic animals like our pets seem especially vulnerable as healthy wild mammals have natural defenses.

F**lukes** are a diverse group of small endoparasitic flatworms. They attack various of the internal organs, such as the liver (Liver Fluke). Many also have complicated life cycles where eggs are deposited, lie dormant, hatch, and larvae actually infest intermediate hosts such as snails before being picked up by the eventual host by being ingested with grass or other plant material.

One genus of flatworm that has been through its share of research by our species is the *Planaria*. It has remarkable regeneration abilities and, even at its considerable level of primitivity, can be conditioned easily. One of the foundational experiments in science dealt with memory retention in planaria and found that memory is stored in every cell in the body.

Roundworms are represented by a single class, **Nematoda.** For this reason, many people now refer to roundworms as nematodes, such as with advertisements on TV about pesticides that kill root nematodes, etc. They are small critters which may be abundant in some poor animals, and some can even pierce and enter woody plants. Nematodes may be identified as being round but not having segments like Annelida. They are a tremendously diverse group, with most members actually being free-living in soil and aquatic habitats.

There are a few examples of **Gastropoda**, a ***Mollusk***, on land in North Florida, and, of course, in freshwater. Several aquatic snails roam the lakes and rivers of North Florida with the most famous being the Apple Snail (*Pomacea*). This is the preferred food of the rare and local Limpkin, as well as the Snail (Everglade) Kite (a peninsular bird). In spring-fed rivers where *Pomacea* are abundant, they constitute over three-quarters of a baby alligator's diet.

Many people recognize *Pomacea* by their eggs, which are pink and clustered on stalks and tree trunks. I can find nothing to confirm the myth that they only lay eggs on a full moon, but many reproductive cycles are tied to the four week revolution of earth's satellite. Apple Snails have diminished in many areas and seem to be clean water indicators.

Some snails inhabit land as well, with certain species being introduced and harmful to crops and gardens. As gastropods, both members of a mated "pair" produce fertilized eggs, and they can become abundant in residential areas almost overnight. These snails have few natural enemies and their long-term effect on the environment remains to be seen.

Slugs are gastropods without shells that plod slowly across a slime tract they lay down. They are quite innocuous to humans, but hands that touch these should be washed thoroughly. They are vegetarians and detritus feeders and pose no threat to crops in our area. This is the ponderous creature some delight in putting salt on for fun, but one hopes this type of animal treatment is short-lived in adolescence and disappears altogether as society matures.

Mama crayfish carries her young under her abdomen, flailing her pincers in the air to all attackers

READY FOR WAR

Arthropoda is a mammoth phylum of "jointed-footed" invertebrates. Their bodies are divided into various arrangements of two or three distinct sections, and their eyes are compound, though some are nearsighted. Part of the disparity of arthropods is owing to their polyphyleticness, as they seem to have descended from more than one ancestor. Unlike most organisms with variation, the greatest part of their radiation, except for crustaceans, seems to have taken place on land.

The waters of North Florida are replete with a member of the class **Crustacea** called Crayfish or, locally, crawfish or crawdads. They build dirt chimneys around their burrows and are critically important to certain fish like Pirate Perch or Pygmy Sunfish in the dry season. Here you see a mother Crawfish with dozens of young on her abdomen.

With as little as many people care for insects, the **Arachnida** stand alone as folk's least favorite. If ticks and mites aren't bad enough, try an informal opinion poll on spiders and scorpions. They all have eight legs to come after you with, a fused head and thorax called cephalothorax to bite you with, most feed on other animals and none seem to be our friend.

Scorpions are primitive, fearsome beasts with a deserving reputation for danger and pain. Their sting can be fatal —or make you wish you were dead. Our native species, lowly in size, has a sting as bad or worse than many of the larger ones found in the tropics. They are found in dry, sandy soil usually, often hiding under boards and other debris. Their stinger is a barb at the end of their tail that flies over their back with great speed and accuracy, killing the prey they have seized with their front pincers.

Most interesting is the mating ritual of the scorpion. The smaller, quicker males approach more powerful females with great caution. The males have on their minds what all males do, but the females probably view them as little more than lunch. Upon close approach, they lock pincers, and it immediately looks bad for the guy's side. The female whips her tail over the top, but the swift male sidesteps the attack and pops his sperm right into the genital aperture under the tail and immediately hauls a---bdomen for cover.

There are 8000 species of spiders in the world, and sometimes it seems every one has built webs across trails in North Florida woodlands. Most webs go up during the latter part of the summer when various flying insects are peaking. Spiders hatch in spring and have to grow to a size capable of building a web. Most webs find a large female and one or more diminutive males. The horror of walking into a large web may be an overreaction as few spiders that live out in the open have a serious bite.

UNUSUALLY EXPOSED

Of course, not all spiders build webs. We have a huge family of wolf spiders patrolling the dirt for small insects that look ominous but are quite benign. They are ecologically the tarantulas of the East, but most are small and retiring. Night is a great time to see the real population of wolf spiders, by looking down a strong flashlight beam at the ground. The little blue eyes you see are the retinas of these ground gleaners, all probably wondering why the moon just got so bright.

Jumping spiders are neat to watch with their active, big eyes and motions as quick as Michael Jordan's. When they creep up a certain distance from an unsuspecting fly, they almost seem to break the time warp as they are suddenly standing atop a hapless insect with fangs flailing. They will frequently enter homes and are admittedly a little pugnacious but won't actually bite unless grabbed. I certainly wouldn't trade them for all the nuisance bugs they eat!

Black Widows are normally seen under boards and other trash instead of out in the open

We do have two spiders in North Florida that pose serious health threats. The Black Widow, named for her color and habit of eating her mate, is shiny black with a red hourglass under her abdomen. Their habitat is generally sandy soil, and most often they build their webs under various forms of debris. Work gloves go a long way to preventing bites when doing yard work and small children should be closely monitored when playing in this type of habitat.

The Brown Recluse is similar to the preceding in habitat and habits and has received much attention over the past few years as serious bites have been identified. It has a unique design on the back which has earned it the vernacular "violin spider" but any small black or brown spider should be given both a healthy respect and a wide berth. Thought uncommon in North Florida, they have been recently found abundantly near Panama City.

Orb Weavers are large, colorful spiders with huge, strong webs. The Golden Orb Weaver, or "banana spider," is a gorgeous animal with a large, golden web and a nonaggressive personality. In North Florida they are very common in hardwood forests and can even catch small birds in their webs. The Garden Orb Weaver, with strong markings of black, white and yellow, builds its more whitish web nearer the ground and more in the open, such as grassy areas. Both have declined due to pesticides and habitat loss.

The common "house spider" is a shy, retiring creature whose only goal is to eat your bugs. They are especially abundant in carports and garages and eat untold numbers of pests. They probably should not be handled carelessly but are quite nonaggressive toward humans.

One really neat spider that escapes attention due to habitat is the Diving Spider. They are a half inch long with a bold black-and-white stripe down the side. They feed by scooting underwater and nailing small fish, tadpoles and insect larvae. They do not seem to be aggressive to humans but make for an interesting study at night with a flashlight in shallow pools and ditches.

Seeming a bit out of place, this crab spider appears to have been transported from the sea

There is a huge family of arachnids called crab spiders which are found all over virtually every habitat in North Florida. One favorite is a species that is amazingly convergent with actual crabs, with a shell and everything! Another type I have grown to appreciate is a small, yellowish beast that sits atop pitcher plants with legs folded back like wings and pounces on unsuspecting flies that mistake their identity. There are good spider books available to sort out the dizzying array.

Less dangerous but more obnoxious arachnids are ticks and mites. Both are ectoparasites found in the woods in increasing numbers usually throughout the summer. Ticks are quite a bit larger than mites and hang out on the ends of bush limbs to hitch onto unsuspecting mammalian passersby. They become engorged with blood and then reproduce, much like other blood suckers of the animal world. One tick is the "winter tick," very abundant in the cool months.

Some mites are commonly called "chiggers" and cannot be seen when they mount a human for a meal of blood, as they are tiny larvae. The adults actually eat smaller arthropods and their eggs. Various remedies exist for treatment of chigger bites, but the best, for them as well as ticks, is the following: Powder your lower pant legs with sulfur (I tie a string around each one). As your life can be made miserable by these nasties, taking this precaution will be well worth the effort.

Centipedes (**Chilopoda**) and millipedes (**Diplopoda**) are superficially alike but vastly different in key areas. Both are long, slender arthropods with exoskeletons and many legs that scurry along through leaf litter searching for food. But that is where the similarities stop.

Centipedes are voracious predators with poison fangs and an appetite for anything small. They have thin exoskeletons for faster movement and have one pair of legs per segment (somite) that sticks out. Their name "hundred legger" is probably an exaggeration, but not on the scale of millipedes who have far fewer than a thousand legs.

Throughout most of North Florida, there seem to be two types. The Red Centipede inhabits our moist hardwood forests and is a slight animal of two to three inches. But don't be fooled, they'll bite hard if handled, as I found out at Alum Bluff in front of six students. The Gray Centipede is larger and seems to prefer sandy soil and pine woods. Do not even think of giving one the chance to nail you! Both are largely nocturnal and generally unearthed when logs and boards are moved.

Millipedes are brightly colored, clownish-looking inhabitants of moist forests. Their heavy shell and horrible musk (emitted from the *repugnatorial* gland) protect them as they move at a speed similar to wet concrete. They have two pairs of legs underneath each somite that move in waves as they slip across the forest floor. They can barely outrun their rotting vegetation quarry and are quite inoffensive when handled.

Many people do not realize that a common species of **Crustacea** exists in just about everyone's yard. The Pill Bug, known by thousands as a roly-poly, is an isopod somewhat related to the beach hoppers of our coastal shorelines. These Pill Bugs roll up into a ball for protection and are completely harmless to little children playing with them. These dark gray midgets eat plants and rotting detrital material.

I**nsects** are by far the most diverse group of organisms in history. Spurred on by the development of flowering plants, they have radiated into about every terrestrial niche imaginable. It is a shock to first grasp that half the animal species in the entire kingdom belongs to just one class. They burrow underground, crawl along the topsoil and fly through the forests and glades. You can't get away from insects and, though spending billions of dollars, can't make any disappear either.

Insects have three body parts, a head, thorax and abdomen. Most have wings and fly very well, aided by

compound eyes that provide excellent short-range vision. Many produce multiple generations each year allowing natural selection to overcome everything from pesticides to natural enemies such as spiders and various vertebrates.

Much smaller than their Paleozoic cousins, this dragonfly lies in wait for the next winged meal

Our most primitive insect occurs along our coastline and is commonly seen on docks. Silverfish look like a quick, slender roach with a silvery hue. Sometimes called firebrats, they make good bait as inshore fish are used to them as a food item (always the best bait!). They are of interest to entomologists as they demonstrate many of the features of our planet's earliest insects.

A favorite of many are the dragonflies and their allies. Most common types include Darners and Damselflies (solid wings that fold back), but related individuals are clubtails, amberwings, skimmers, bluets, forktails and dancers (the latter three with clear wings). These chase smaller flying insects with amazing aerial ability and visual acuity. Their most conspicuous time is late summer and fall when insects in general are quite abundant. Look for the Green and Blue Darners.

Two grasshoppers mate in late summer to produce next year's crop

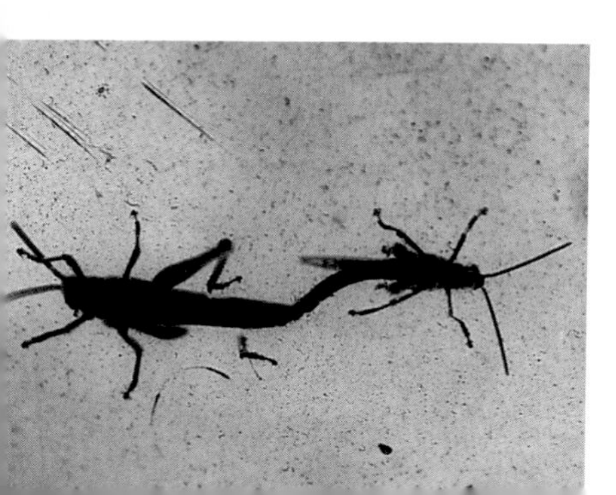

Grasshoppers are abundant in fields and pastures and consume vast amounts of vegetation. They can jump several feet and spring to flight when pushed. Most species are green with many brown as well, making cryptic coloration an important part of their survival. Katydids are grasshoppers with hunched backs and very long antennae looping over their back. Many Southerners quickly recognize the sound produced when Katydids rub their wings together.

Crickets are flightless, ground-dwelling insects which are compressed for their life under debris on the ground. They do "sing" and some species vary their pitch with the air temperature, allowing some to know the temperature outside by their songs. Crickets eat rotting vegetation and are important commercially as excellent bait for "bream" (sunfish).

This cricket creeps along the ground searching for organic snacks

Two crickets to watch out for are the harmless camel crickets which seem to be moving into cave life, as they are almost always seen by spelunkers underground. These and Slimy Salamanders may be radiating to fill this cave niche in the next few millennia. Also, beware of the primitive mole cricket which will pinch hard if handled.

These Walking Sticks fertilize eggs while they visit the countryside

Walking Sticks and Praying Mantises are related, though in different families, and resemble each other superficially, although their biology is radically different. Mantids are rapacious predators with very long forelimbs that have spines on all three elongated joints. It is said that the seizing strike of a mantis is the fastest movement in the animal kingdom, and our eyes cannot even pick up a blur from the grasp. Walking sticks are herbivores who literally wouldn't hurt a fly.

The mating process of mantids is certainly unique in the animal kingdom. When the pair couple together the male lacks the ability to release his spermatophore. In a few moments the female bites clean through his neck and the ensuing nerve spasm completes the copulatory experience by releasing the packet of sperm. The female mops up by devouring her mate with his body serving as nutrition for his progeny.

Praying Mantises camouflage perfectly with leaves while waiting for small insects to amble past

HIDDEN KILLER

This and the antics of spiders is in direct contradiction to the mating of scorpions, where the male escapes harm to mate another day. Scientists believe that the uncommon scorpions need to conserve their numbers of individuals whereas the other two groups favor the genetic variation that results from each male only mating one time.

Walking Sticks are vegetarians that get larger as one approaches the equator. We have one kind that reaches six inches and camouflages perfectly with twigs. Generally seen in the open only during mating, watch for the diminutive male riding along and almost invisible. Also beware, as females can squirt a noxious chemical with amazing accuracy, normally at your eyes, when mad.

Cockroaches are flattened scavengers that have made a home for themselves in the crevices of our houses, cleaning up after us as negatively phototrophic (runs from light) garbage insects. They are native creatures but the German Roach, in every way an alien, seems harder to control and far

A nest of Red Wasps represents a painful reminder that we must watch where we're going in the woods

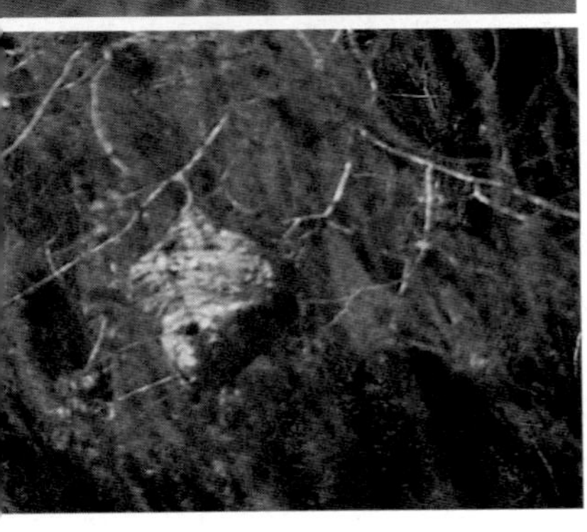

The telltale nest of the White-faced Hornet houses the greatest aggression and worst sting of any of their group

more adaptable. In both instances, controlling an animal's food source goes a long way to manipulating their numbers. Clean the kitchen!

Social insects are amazing animals as they have developed casts where various jobs are available for each sex and level. We have two major groups of social insects with termites, plus ants, bees, wasps and hornets. Our termites are wood eaters, as so many unfortunate households have discovered. Many are also nondomestic, living in forests on rotting wood and other vegetation. These are benign creatures which provide a bounty of food for many animals.

There are several freshwater insects to go along with the diving spider mentioned earlier. The Water Boatmen are propelled along the water's surface by their long hind legs, spending large amounts of time clinging to vegetation, but consume microscopic algae. Backswimmers are less erratic and swim with their heads down, looking for tiny insects—another chief difference, the latter will bite the ever loving beegeebers out of you. Also common are the huge Giant Water Bugs, the slender and elongate Waterscorpions and the Water Striders (not spider) that seem to sail across the water's surface with the greatest of ease.

STAY AWAY

Diving Beetles are a terror on smaller animals with their large sickle-like jaws and will even attack larger animals including small vertebrates in their ponds. Considerably more civilized is the Whirligig Beetle that seems to be on a caffeine/sugar high on the surface. When captured, these harmless insects emit an odor that smells for all the world like pineapples.

READY T

Stink Bugs are wide, short insects, rounded in back and triangularly pointed in front. They give off a stringent musk for protection that many animals find extremely sharp and disagreeable. In entomology, there are many groups that use olfactory cues for much of their biology and these range from musks to pheromones.

Cicadas are insects that frequently have life cycles that last over many years. Eggs may remain dormant for up to seventeen years before an outbreak of these benign creatures occurs. Their exoskeletons stick to the bark, and many a child has wondered what creature must have left such a thing.

Antlions are seldom recognised as adults and seldom seen as larvae, but their conical pits in sand are well known to many outdoors people. The larva lies buried in the sand and waits for ants and other tiny insects to fall in the pit. It is hard to crawl out, and the antlion makes the task worse by throwing sand up on the escapee, causing the struggling victim to slide back down to the jaws of certain death. Adults are elongate with long wings, modest antennae and resemble damselflies.

Dung Beetles, having other less polite vernacular names, are generally seen pushing mammalian dung across roadways and trails. They are stout and strong, pushing large "objects" by turning around and shoving with their hind legs. Dung is used for food, as much nutrition is never digested the first go-round. Frequently seen in administrative offices.

CHANGE CLOTHES

A lone cicada prepares to shed its exoskeleton and leave it on the bark of this tree

Click Beetles are shiny black, two-inch creatures with the amazing ability to snap the joint between their thorax and abdomen which flips them up into the air. This helps them escape predators, and also gives them a 50-50 chance of landing right side up. Huge fake eyes are on the head which startle enemies, a stratagem found in other creatures such as cutworms, etc.

Fireflies are bioluminescent animals with the twist of being able to turn it off and on repeatedly. The several species give off signals of different duration to ensure mating with the correct kind. Humans can attract these "lightning bugs" with a flashlight if they watch carefully at the signals being given off. I cannot imagine what must go through a bug's mind when they land on us . . . .

Perhaps peoples' favorite insects are butterflies and moths. The best known of these seems to be the Monarch. This brick-red traveler from the North arrives in Florida in October in huge flocks as they seek to cross the gulf. They pile up along the coastline with sulfurs, skippers, frittilaries, various moths and other species before their mass exodus when the winds shift out of the north.

Monarchs have foul-tasting wings that birds like Blue Jays learn about quickly, though this is not an inherited knowledge. Eating them causes the ignorant predator to regurgitate it, a little late for the individual butterfly but not the species. This characteristic was employed by yours truly when conducting stomach content studies of migrant songbirds on St. George Island under Skip Livingston at Florida State. I ground up Monarch wings off my truck grill and fed them to mist netted birds with an eye dropper, causing them to regurgitate their last few meals. Unpleasant for the birds, it did, however, beat the heck out of being killed and having your stomachs cut out.

The advantages of these unpalatable wings were not lost on another species of butterfly, either. The Viceroy, also a migrant through our parts, looks a great deal like Monarchs, and seems to be afforded much of the protection

Monarchs receive from their nasty wings (a classic example of mimicry). The two are distinguished by the white spots in the forewing of the Viceroy in contrast to the same spots being yellow in Monarchs. Butterfly enthusiasts may hope birds don't get wise to that. The Gulf Frittilary, incidentally, resembles the Monarch vaguely and may attain some protection that way.

Swallowtails are a large, popular group of butterflies that may be seen throughout the warm season. Our species are the Black, Tiger, Zebra and Spicebush Swallowtails. They may be quite common in cities and remain in peoples' yards and gardens for days at a time.

Moths are basically nocturnal creatures with excellent camouflage like owls and goatsuckers for sleeping during the day without being detected by intruders. Many moths have bright flash colors in their wings to startle predators when moths take flight, and some are very large and beautiful.

The lovely Luna Moth appears on full moons in North Florida with its soft green coloration and long flowing tail. Individuals called "hawk moths" may be the Regal, Polyphemus or Cecropia Moths and are very large, brown creatures. Sphinx Moths are extraordinary hummingbird mimics as no predator in its right mind would chase a hummingbird. Their caterpillars are sometimes called "hornworms," familiar to farmers and gardeners alike.

The Lappet Moth is hardly known, but their larvae, tent caterpillars, are certainly recognised throughout North Florida. Their presence is obvious, if not by their silken "tent," then by damage they do to the foliage. Their presence is frequently noted by the Yellow-billed Cuckoo, which nests right by the tent caterpillars and takes them for their young day by day. One might wonder who would want to eat caterpillars but Mexicans actually deep fry certain species such as skippers and even can them for sale as "Gusanos de Maguey." Whatever.

Mosquitoes are ectoparasites (females) with a larval stage that feeds on algae and rotting vegetation in the water with a few being predaceous. Many eggs are laid in the water and some on shore, where rains and high tides (salt marsh mosquito) emerge and hatch them. Mosquito populations may be controlled, to a point, by eliminating stagnant water sources in yards and neighborhoods. Ponds may be turned into mosquito traps by transplanting the Mosquitofish (Gambusia) from nearby lakes. They will ravenously consume larvae and multiply to match the food source.

The Asian Tiger Mosquito is introduced and causes misery with its itching and tendency to carry diseases, such as dengue. This *Aedes* has a white stripe down the center of the thorax, earning it the species name *A. albipictis.* They are common wherever there are waterholding containers and do not survive well in more pristine areas. The genus *Aedes* also contains members which may carry diseases such as yellow fever, dengue, encephalitis, like the *A. egypti.*

There are many species of gnats in North Florida and most are only observed incidentally by humans. Some tend to fly into our eyes seeking moisture and may become an irritation, but the real irritant in North Florida, especially coastal areas, is the Sand Gnat or "no-see-um." Sand Gnats are blood-sucking ectoparasites as common in cool weather as hot. Being hard to detect, it seems they always bite before being noticed. Bug sprays offer limited protection, but many native

Panhandlers (?) swear by the product "Skin So Soft" as a repellant. In some places along the coast in late winter, such as the St. Mark's Refuge, enormous flocks of Tree Swallows by the thousands amass to feed on the tens of millions of Sand Gnats in late afternoon.

The tabanid flies are the scourge of North Florida woodlands. The females open up a wound and lap up blood on our skin that is not only extremely painful, but itches for quite some time. Deer, Horse and Yellow Flies are three of the more common "biting" fly species but many others exist. Males feed on flowers and are seen far less but may be told from females by their eyes meeting together on the top of their head. They meet the females at the water where they reproduce, and the larvae hatch out in warm months. Gallery forests (along rivers) and other moist woodlands may become nightmares in early and late summer when various Tabanids are out in force.

There are several dozen *families* of flies in North Florida, and a description of these would take a second volume. Some, like the nasty Stiletto Fly or the insectivorous Robber Fly, are really neat creatures and worthy of further study by young naturalists.

Fleas are ectoparasites of warm-blooded animals that are wingless but jump to escape enemies. They lay their eggs on dirt, and most flea hatching and subsequent problems take place in the warm season. Fleas that bite into human skin are real problems, especially those that carry the bubonic plague and typhus. Veterinary medicine continues to upgrade products for our pets that kill and/or repel fleas. There are monthly pills out now that repel fleas handsomely, so consult your vet to see the latest advances for your pets.

House Flies are domestic insects essentially that do not sting, but feed on organic material. They are famous for laying their eggs in dead meat, and the hideous maggots hatch out. The entire larval life cycle is really quick, and the fly population is suddenly raised. Don't underestimate the value of reducers like flies. They keep our countrysides clean and recycle valuable nutrients.

Termites are social insects that eat rotting wood, and occasionally smash a family's dreams by destroying their homes. Rotting wood should be kept away from houses and routine inspections by pest control companies go a long way toward preventing disaster. Many wild species of termites are quite benign and may be found by rolling logs in forests. They offer an abundant food source for many creatures and are a favorite food of certain skinks (Eumaces).

Ants are also social insects but mostly prefer food other than wood. Some carnivorous species bite painfully while others are nonaggressive. Large, ominous looking ants are often quite harmless while some of our worst species are rather small. Ants are subject to population surge at certain times where they suddenly appear and later disappear.

The famous Fire Ant, an introduced species from southern South America, has taken over in some places, displacing native species and endangering certain vertebrates such as Bachman's Sparrows, Northern Bobwhites and Horned Lizards (farther west). The fact that they cannot tolerate colder climates does us in North Florida little good, and natural controls on this species have not been attempted. The total environmental destruction ranks this as perhaps our worst accidental introduction.

Native ants may bite if given the chance, a few sting painfully and some give off a foul-smelling odor. Some build mounds and some do not, but most live in large colonies. The new queen has wings and flies straight up for her nuptial flight. This is her last mating but she continues to lay the fertilized eggs from this encounter for up to seven years. Perhaps of some solace is that she is able to give the entire ant bed instructions, which she does chemically.

A large number of bees, wasps and hornets inhabit North Florida and a complete summary of these is not possible in this work. A few of the more common species/groups are as follows:

Parasitic Wasps have laid their eggs in this poor caterpillar, ensuring food for the larvae

Spider Wasps are insects that turn the tables on spiders. The common variety in sandy soil is black with some red banding on the abdomen. Spider Killers are large, dark wasps with some yellow on the abdomen that intentionally fly into spider webs and sting the large female. She collapses when punctured and is taken to a burrow where an egg is laid on her. The larva hatches out and feeds on the helpless spider. But the worst surely must be the Parasitic Wasp that lays its eggs directly on a caterpillar (see picture) and the larvae hatch out and consume the caterpillars.

WHAT A WAY TO GO

DIRTY HOME

Several Dirt Daubers have laid eggs with paralyzed spiders for food in this house of dirt

Similar is the Dirt Dauber which paralyzes spiders and buries them in dirt/mud cases under bridges, eaves and other artificial structures. Many eggs are laid and feed on the spiders, having been put in a state of suspended animation. Dirt Daubers are nonaggressive and Spider Killers will only sting when provoked, but this sting is exceptionally painful.

Bumble Bees and Honey Bees are highly social Hymenopterids that make honey from nectar. The former are large and black with yellow rings while the smaller honey bees are yellowish and quite migratory. Carpenter Bees look like Bumble Bees but will be observed flying around wooden structures, trying to decide where to burrow a nest hole. They are not ill-tempered and may carry on their activities with people milling around.

Honey Bees have a cast system of sterile (female) workers, male drones who tend the hive and the queen, who is responsible for eggs and hive instruction. Many migrating hives are escapees as humans maintain hives for more reasons than just honey. Having these pollinators will greatly increase the quantity of crops such as fruits and clover, sometimes by a factor of twenty.

Honey Bees also were made famous by the "waggle dance" observed by scientists where one bee will dance on the hive wall to alert the hive of a food source. The bee becomes a clock, and by orienting to the sun, she tells the hive which direction to fly ("twelve o'clock" means to fly toward the sun, "six o'clock" indicates away, and so forth). Her level of excitement indicates the proximity of the food and also the abundance of it. Plus, she brings the odor of the flower to the hive so the workers can know to what species the food source belongs.

Hornets and wasps are territorial, carnivorous species with ill tempers and nasty stings. The robust White-faced Hornet makes huge paper nests shaped like big footballs that hang from trees, especially along Panhandle rivers. Friends, look into my eyes: These are extremely dangerous creatures and have killed people with susceptible body chemistries. Close approach will trigger a sudden protective mechanism where they'll chase you down and brutally sting you en masse repeatedly.

The Red Wasp is a common species sometimes called "paper wasp" that nests around old sheds and under house eves. In nature, they may be found abundantly along water courses and on limbs of trees such as cypress. Their sting is very painful and long lasting. They also have a territorial instinct, and, though not as aggressive as hornets, you are certain not to enjoy their "waspitality."

More dangerous, by sheer numbers and being common in North Florida, are Yellow Jackets. A nest of paper is also constructed, or they may use burrows with hidden nests. Like the above species, these are carnivorous and extremely aggressive. Human deaths from Yellow Jackets are not rare, and those surviving attacks are seldom the same. Upon finding Hymenopterids nesting in your yard, do not attempt to get rid of them yourself. Honestly, one sting can kill! Choose to live in harmony with them, or hire an exterminator who will know how to handle the situation while you watch in safety.

1. Lizards

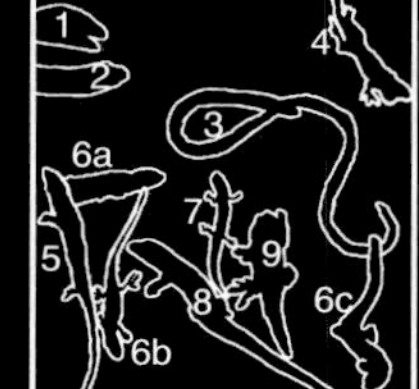

1. Broad-headed Skink (male)
2. Eastern Glass Lizard
3. Slender Glass Lizard
4. Green Anole (green)
5. Green Anole (brown)
6. Five-lined Skinks *
   (a) female (b) young (c) male
7. Ground Skink
8. Six-lined Racerunner
9. Fence Lizard

*Southeastern Five-lined skinks appear identical to Five-lined

2. Snakes

3. Arthropods

1. Tiger Swallowtails (five)
2. Golden Orb Weaver
3. Robber Fly
4. Monarch
5. Katydid
6. Gray-mantled Grasshopper
7. Garden Orb Weaver
8. Canopy Millipede
9. Lubber Grasshopper
10. Skipper Butterfly
11. Cutworm
12. Spider Wasp
13. Pill Bug
14. Bartel's Wolf Spider

4. Amphibians

5. Mammals

1. Eastern Fox Squirrel
2. White-tailed Deer fawns
3. Red Fox
4. Coyote
5. Raccoon
6. White-tailed Deer doe
7. Bobcat
8. Red Wolf
9. Eastern Cottontail
10. Gray Squirrel
11. Gray Fox
12. Nine-banded Armadillo
13. Gray Squirrel albino
14. Opossum

1. Cattle Egret
2. Snowy Egret
(a) flying
(b) standing
3. Great Egret
4. Wood Stork
5. White Ibis

8. Male Ducks

9. Large Shorebirds

10. Small Shorebirds

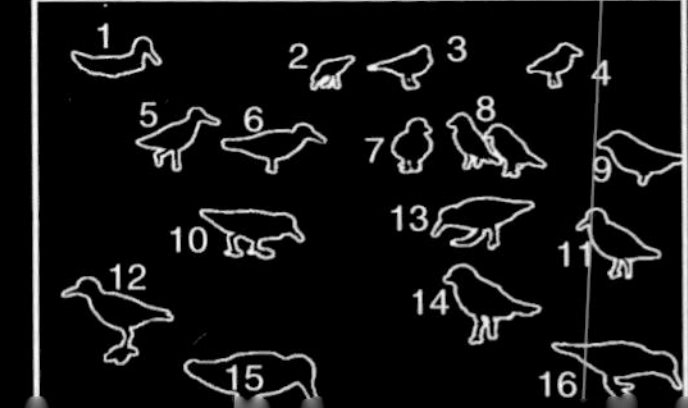

11. Birds of Prey

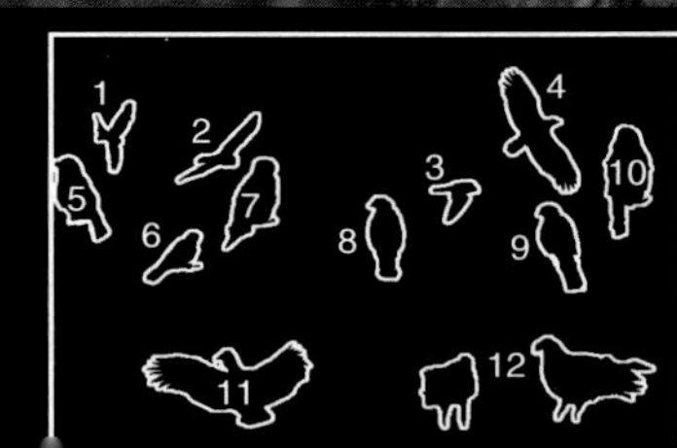

1. Swallow-tailed Kite
2. Northern Harrier
3. Merlin
4. Bald Eagle
5. Red-shouldered Hawk
6. American Kestrel (female)
7. Peregrine
8. Broad-winged Hawk
9. Mississippi Kite
10. Red-tailed Hawk
11. Black Vulture
12. Turkey Vulture

12. Woodpeckers & Flycatchers

13. Miscellaneous Landbirds

1. Red-breasted Nuthatch
2. Blue-headed Vireo
3. Brown Creeper
4. Golden-crowned Kinglet
5. Cedar Waxwing
6. Blue-gray Gnatcatcher
7. Eastern Meadowlark
10. Common Nighthawk
11. Chuck-will's-widow
12. Sedge Wren
13. Savannah Sparrow
14. House Wren
15. Chipping Sparrow
16. White-throated Sparrow

14. Colorful Songbirds

15. Warblers I

1. Kentucky Warbler
2. Connecticut Warbler
3. Yellow Warbler
4. Canada Warbler
5. Nashville Warbler
6. Swainson's Warbler
7. Yellow-rumped Warbler (winter)
8. Cerulean Warbler
9. Blackburnian Warbler

11. Common Yellowthroat
12. Blue-winged Warbler
13. Prairie Warbler
14. Golden-winged Warbler
15. Hooded Warbler
16. Magnolia Warbler
17. Chestnut-sided Warbler
18. Prothonotary Warbler
19. Black-throated Green Warbler

16. Warblers II

1. Ovenbird
2. Yellow-throated Warbler
3. Black-throated Blue Warbler
4. Mourning Warbler
5. Pine Warbler
6. Black-and-white Warbler
7. Blackpoll Warbler
8. Wilson's Warbler
9. Northern Waterthrush
10. Yellow-breasted Chat
11. Worm-eating Warbler
12. Bay-breasted Warbler
13. Tennessee Warbler
14. American Redstart
15. Louisiana Waterthrush
16. Palm Warbler
17. Orange-crowned Warbler
18. Cape May Warbler

17. Thrushes & Mimic Thrushes

1. Gray-cheeked Thrush
2. Eastern Bluebird
3. Brown Thrasher
4. American Robin
5. Northern Mockingbird
6. Gray Catbird
7. Hermit Thrush
8. Swainson's Thrush
9. Veery
10. Wood Thrush

Fishes of North Florida

Three common sharks: Blacktip, Bull and Sand, respectively

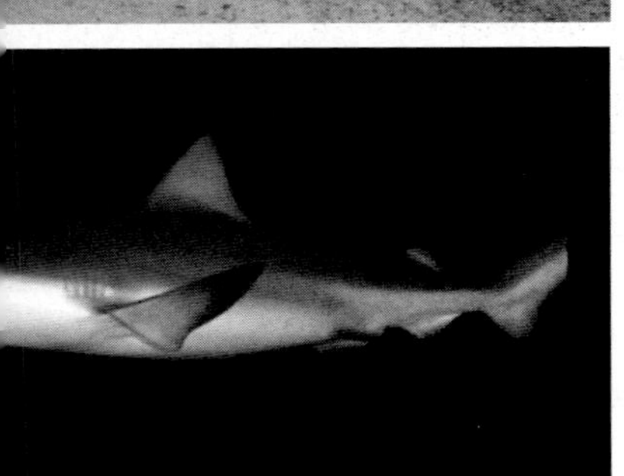

Fishes are one of the most successful groups ever to live on this rock. Today, there are more species of fish on earth than all other vertebrates combined. They include over twenty thousand varieties of bony fish alone, and they have filled about every conceivable niche from the coldest Antarctic waters with their antifreeze blood to the pupfish in near boiling potholes in American deserts. North Florida boasts the normal gulf and Atlantic fish species, plus a nice assortment of freshwater members in the varied North Florida wetlands.

Like virtually all coasts, North Florida has a small collection of cartilaginous fishes, or sharks and rays. Our shark list is lacking species which are likely to commit attacks on humans, and, in fact, the number of shark attacks on humans in the twentieth century on the entire gulf coast is less than a dozen. Our most common species include the **Black-tip**, **Bull**, **Nurse**, **Hammerhead** and **Bonnethead** (shovel-nosed) **Sharks**, with some pelagic varieties being found in deeper waters, where we are far less likely to swim, or on the Atlantic coast. Sharks have been overfished and are a resource we could lose without wise use and a better mind toward conservation.

SWIMMERS BEWARE

Unfortunately our common ray is the **Atlantic Sting Ray**, the phantom menace of the shallows. Joining it in lower numbers are the **Clear-nosed Skate**, **Guitarfish** and **Electric Ray**. The first has the famous egg cases called the mermaid's purse while the last shocks substrates to kill small animals for food such as polychaete worms. Sting Rays, with their jagged dagger half way out the tail, can be avoided in the warm season by shuffling one's feet in shallow water. When there is an accident, use meat tenderizer or take a traumatized victim to the hospital.

The tail of the Sting Ray is armed with the nastiest of barbs

It's hard to discuss fish without mentioning the terrific fishing our location has to offer. Marine fishes, which we shall look at first, are well represented and give anglers opportunities for great sport and delicious meals. Fishing may be done inshore or offshore, but our emphasis will be those gamefish in our shallow bays and estuaries. Omitted are such notorious beasts as grouper, snapper, cobia (ling cod), mackerel, jewfish, bluefish, tuna, triggerfish, marlin, and many more.

Speckled Trout are the most popular inshore gamefish. Their bold markings and beautiful hues make them an attractive fish, while their meat, properly prepared, is among the best of the area. Trout are warm water fish, being scattered all over the marine environment from spring to fall. They may be caught on fresh shrimp (suspended on corks), fish lures and jigs most successfully.

Often caught the same day and taking much of the same bait, is mighty **Red Drums**, or redfish. These "reds," as they are often called, may exceed twenty-five pounds and fight like virtually no other area fish. Check the local game laws on size restrictions and limits on reds. They will also take spoons in places such as grass beds but smart individuals (big ones) are best caught with live bait. **Black Drum** are caught in early spring on shrimp in the surf or in shallow bays.

Trout and redfish move up into rivers at the onset of winter and may be caught easily on some days with lures and even dead shrimp. Try deep holes and places where vegetation is available.

Whiting is an abundant and often under-appreciated fish of the beach waters where white sand is found. Their cryptic coloration makes them disappear on the bottom, where they forage for many small invertebrates. When fresh shrimp are presented on the bottom while surf fishing, be ready for a great fight from an albeit smallish fish! They take the bait with the same gusto that you will enjoy their fresh, light, tasty meat.

Striped Mullet are a staple along our coast where their fresh meat is exquisite. They are not especially predatory (they will accept worms) so catching them with cast nets works best. Folks catch them off bridges in rivers using worms or dough balls and cane poles. Their meat is best fried. Young mullet are absolutely—bar none—the best bait anywhere for people wanting to have their rod ripped out of their hand. This really includes the smaller **White Mullet** which is also common in our waters but seems to prefer saltier areas than the Striped.

MONSTER OF THE DEEP

Flounder are common, highly predaceous fish of several species in our waters. Their depressed shape adapts them for life on the bottom where they spring up from the substrate with cavernous jaws full of monster teeth and seize unsuspecting prey that eases past these specialized animals. There are many species of flounder and their light, flaky meat is "flat" good.

Flounder resemble two very common small fish called **Tonguefish** and **Sole**. Together, the three are unique in the vertebrate world in not having bilateral symmetry. Their body and head is turned sideways rather than being truly flattened like a ray, so there are major body parts on one side that do not exist on the other. All other vertebrates could be split down the middle and would appear essentially the same on both sides. There is one more fish of this scheme in the far North that could be mentioned, just for the **Halibut**.

Lying on the bottom, waiting for passing food, flounder are the kings of camouflage

Some lesser gamefish occur in our waters including various croaker, with light, tasty meat but not great size. **White Trout** and **Sand Trout** also remain smallish but have the same wonderful flavor as their larger cousin. And for winter fishing when nothing else is biting, try sheephead. A small hook and fresh shrimp will nab these aggressive feeders and fill your table with light, delicate meat as good as any "bream."

T**arpon** surely must be the king of the gamefish, though uncommon our way. A huge, top-level predator, they patrol our bays and shorelines for smaller fish and often are the unidentified fish in stories about the huge one that got away. Shy fish, they're best caught by bouncing pinfish along the bottom on full moons between the islands or in clear bays. Tarpon fishing can be hours of waiting and ten minutes of incredible excitement that justifies all the wait and worry.

Gar are creatures from "yestereon" that watched the dinosaurs come and go. Their long, toothed snouts are unmistakable. They seem to be forever rolling on the surface, especially in warm weather. This is because they have primitive lungs and they have the ability, along with Mudfish (bowfin), to "gulp" air from the surface when the water is low on oxygen. During the days of Pangea when the fresh waters were very warm, this gave gar and mudfish a competitive advantage over many species that were exterminated. Even today, in the baking North Florida summers, this pair survives many mudholes where bass and "bream" give up the ghost.

There are many **Long-nosed Gar** in salt water, as well as **Alligator Gar** in West Florida bays and estuaries. A more freshwater species, abundant in South Florida as the **Florida Gar**, but less so in North Florida, is the **Spotted Gar**.

All are primarily picivorous but not appreciated as a food fish since their roe tend to be poisonous and their meat less desirable than other species. They also have a tendency to break fishing lines with their sharp teeth.

Slender and graceful, the sleek needlefish whips through the water in search of minnows

Looking like a very slender gar with a slick greenish-silver hue is the **Atlantic Needlefish**. These patrol the surface grabbing minnows and terrorizing little kids fishing in canals. Upon catching one and removing it from the hook, be sure the line is not frayed after the fight. A very interesting fish looks like a small needlefish with no top "needle." This is the Halfbeak, a plankton feeder that scoots around estuaries and bays skimming the surface with an open mouth.

Pinfish are irritating for their habit of taking shrimp off hooks

There are some species of marine fishes which are quasi-gamefish, which some eat and others consider trash fish or bait fish. The **Pinfish** is a voracious but small bream-shaped fish with colorful bars and a small mouth. They make great bait and have light, flaky meat, but the return for the investment of cleaning one is about that of a bream (sunfish). **Pigfish** (grunt) are about the same ilk as Pinfish and become somewhat of a nuisance when fishing with dead shrimp.

MARSH BUDDIES

Several really unique marine fish are found in our waters, such as those which puff up when threatened. The **Spiny Burr Fish** is common in grass beds and is easily caught by hand (though they will bite!). **Smooth Puffers** are less common but will also make a real balloon out of themselves (and minced meat out of your hand). Even more bizarre is the **Cowfish** which looks like a match box turned sideways, led by a pair of horns. **File Fish** are common in our waters and resemble small triggerfish of the deep. And be wary of any fish you catch that is truly red. Though there are benign species, two varieties have poisonous spines and may inflict serious injury. As a general rule, unknown animals with reds or yellows may be exhibiting aposematic (warning) color and should be approached with caution. Nature is trying to tell us something.

Several small fishes are abundant in our shallow marine waters that are interesting and also used for bait a great deal by anglers. The **Long-nosed Killifish** is an elongate fish with vertical bars that is very common, especially in clear water situations. They survive on hooks well and make excellent mackerel bait. The shorter, fatter **Sheepshead Minnow** with a big belly, small head and pale, vertical bars prefers more turgid wa-

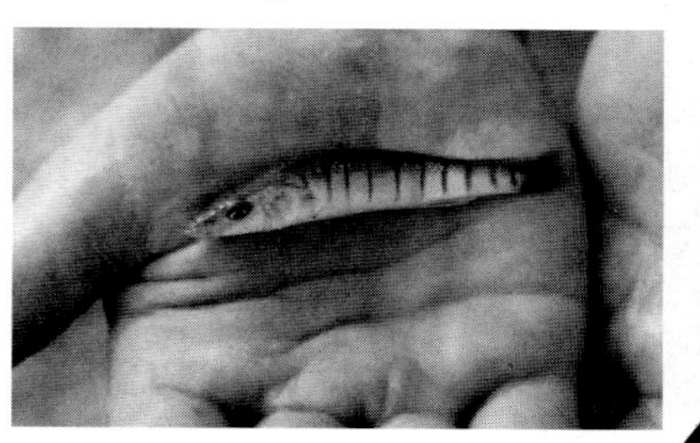

Our salt marshes are replete with Long-nosed Killifish and Sheepshead Minnows

ters such as salt marshes and makes poor bait. Curious how poorly it survives low oxygen, given its affinity to pupfish. Several other small fishes in the genus *Fundulus* join the above pair as inshore inhabitants.

HUGE SCHOOLS

TRASH

One of these, the **Salt Marsh Killifish**, provided me with an amazing discovery one morning. On the St. Mark's Refuge, near Gander Springs, I rolled a log near a creek that empties into a salt marsh, and there was this species, high and dry, waiting for the tide to return. On a subsequent trip, with fish enthusiast Richard Perry, another was discovered doing the same thing. Some fish are known for becoming dormant during certain tidal phases, but this behavior resembled a tem- ... estivation and a unique incident for a Panhandle fish.

Tens of thousands of Silversides roam the shallows along our ...tline

Silversides are abundant in salt water and make excellent bait, although they need plenty of air to survive. Their silver dorsolateral stripe is diagnostic and trout find them irresistible. In fresh water there are other species, loved by bass and gar alike.

FISH

Catfish are abundant in fresh and salt water and are unique in themselves. The barbels are used to detect food items on the bottom, and their skin appears devoid of scales. The meat of most is a delicacy, although they must be skinned before preparation. Catfish have extremely sharp spines on the top and sides that may inflict serious injury. Taking them off a hook is perilous and no method is foolproof. (See page 148-149.) People have died from catfish barbs so extreme caution must be taken.

In the marine realm **Sea Cats** are extremely abundant in the warm season, often causing some to give up fishing for Whiting because the worthless catfish hog the bait. Unfortunately, these cats have a poor taste, but the practice of tossing them up on shore to die is unwise (if not cruel) as beach combers have stepped on their dorsal spines and been seriously hurt. The larger **Gaff-Topsail Catfish** has an excellent flavor.

Inedible Sea Cats are abundant in our waters during the warm season

In freshwater, there are several species of catfish. The group of bullheads constitutes the fish normally sought by anglers, and the flavor is outstanding. The Trio of madtoms are tiny creatures, but are interesting and successful in aquaria for home and classroom. They will, however, eat about anything of equal or smaller size. The **Channel Catfishes** are also caught in North Florida waters and are excellent table fare. All catfish should be skinned before preparing.

LUNG BREATHER

Mudfish or Bowfin are voracious predators who gulp air like their cousins, the gar

Looking like a catfish but more related to gar is the **Bowfin**, or mudfish. They live in large lentic and lotic waterways and often take artificial lures or shiners with a mighty fight. Like gar, they have primitive lungs and gulp air in the summer.

Some fish have the ability to survive in either salt or freshwater, such as the mullet and gar we previously discussed, as well as certain gamefish. The **American Eel** is such a fish, actually beginning its life far out in the Atlantic Ocean in the Sargasso Sea. These are frequently caught, even in winter, on shrimp in shallow water. They also will enter rivers, and some females that become landlocked reach enormous size. This creature should not be confused with several amphibian "eels" such as siren and amphiuma that rarely enter salt water.

Shad, or "spot," can be an abundant fish in marine waters and parallel freshwater species exist in many big lakes throughout North Florida. These algae eaters are preyed on by larger predaceous species as well as birds and dolphins.

The **Toadfish** is the lord of oyster reefs, burrowing into soft areas and eating fish, shrimp and crabs that mistakenly ease past their hollow. A profoundly ugly fish, the Toadfish bites those attempting to handle them, and having a larger mouth than body, offer no cuisine for humans. Found in the same habitat is the **Lizardfish**, with a head like the reptile and an appetite like a horse.

Giving the Toadfish a run for its money in the Mr. Ugly contest is the **Batfish**, which bounces along the bottom on modified pectoral fins that look for all the world like legs. Found in close proximity an amazingly high percentage of the time is the **Sea Robin**, with bright flash colors in its wide pectoral fins and a fusiform shape like a submarine. Batfish and Sea Robin. Hmmmm.

Going together like the preceding are the **Sea Horses** and **Pipefish** of the grass beds. Both suck up tiny invertebrates with long snouts and hide masterfully in the blades. Pipefish are pencil-thin with virtually no fins and Sea Horses, with their mystical shape, actually allow the males to brood the eggs in a specialized pouch.

Two somewhat sensational fish which may swim up rivers from the gulf are the sturgeon and the lamprey. **Sea Lamprey** are in the delta of the Apalachicola River, and one species of **Brook Lamprey** may be found in streams of West Florida. **Atlantic Sturgeon**, from the family that gives us caviar, are throughout North Florida in very low numbers.

Some fish like mullet have no trouble swimming from salt water to fresh water while others can not survive the changes in salt concentration. A third group, sharks and rays, may make their way up rivers certain distances by staying near the river bottom. Salt water is pushed up rivers at the bottom in aquatic structures called salt wedges, and in larger rivers sharks, rays and many other species have traveled hundreds of miles inland.

However, it is time to discuss strictly freshwater fishes and their habitats. Let's remember that this great ecosystem is divided into two halves—moving water (lotic) and nonmoving (lentic). What we shall see is that many fish prefer one or the other while some are equally comfortable in either situation.

There is quite a number of inconspicuous or rare fishes that only occur in extreme West Florida and are not covered by these species accounts. A list of these species includes Southern Brook Lamprey, Dixie, Clear and Speckled Chubs, Bandfin, Bluenose, Flagfin, Blacktip, Bluestripe, Blacktail, Longnose and Blackmouth Shiners, Silverjaw Minnow, Quillback, Black Madtom, Highfin Carpsucker, Sharpfin Chubsucker, River, Blackfin and Grayfin Redhorses, Blackspotted and Western Starhead Topminnows, Shadow and Spotted Bass, Green Sunfish, Saddleback, Logperch, Florida Sand, Choctawhatchee, Crystal, Coastal Plain, Okaloosa, Gulf, Goldstripe, Cypress and Blueside Darters. These fishes easily make the Pensacola area the most unique and diverse ichthyological area in Florida.

The pike are represented by **Chain Pickerel** in large lakes and the **Redfin Pickerel** in rivers and streams. A race of the latter, the **Grass Pickerel**, appears to prefer lentic habitat, but this is not always an allopatric arrangement. Chain Pickerel get quite large and dash the hopes of many bass fishermen at the end of a long fight.

The vegetarian **Grass Carp** and **Golden**

Shiner are common in many weedy lakes throughout North Florida, but most true shiners are actually small lotic fish with bronzy backs, a black stripe down their side and a light underside. This is an extremely diverse and confusing group where series need to be collected and carefully identified with more than one source.

The unique **Pirate Perch** is a pugnacious predator living in swampy areas and occasionally surviving in holes created by crayfish. They are strange fish with their anus in their throat. Pirate Perch survive well in aquaria and their uniqueness and lack of close affinity to other fish makes them interesting specimens for the lab.

The huge genus of killifish (*Fundulus*) is well represented in North Florida and specimens are easily caught with dip nets or small seines. My personal favorite is the common and widespread **Golden Topminnow**. Bluish with golden flecks, their radiance may be seen from shore, and they bring that same beauty to aquaria. Also found in both lentic as well as lotic situations is the **Lined Topminnow**, with its characteristic thin black stripes down the female's body and bold black vertical bars on the male.

Others in this group include the **Banded Topminnow** (near the Apalachicola River), **Seminole Killifish** in quiet lakes, **Pygmy Killifish** with their beautiful tail spots, found in small ponds, and live bearers such as **Mosquitofish**, **Sailfin Molly** and **Least Killifish**.

Mosquitofish are man's best friend, for they eat insect larvae like it's going out of style. Every stagnant tiny pond breeding mosquitos becomes a bug trap by placing some of these *Gambusia* on patrol. Our species is *G. holbrooki* (no longer *G. affinis*) but others occur throughout the United States. They are plain "minnows" whose sex can be told by their anal fin. If its broad it's a female as males have a longer, narrow fin. Getting a male and female for an aquarium means kids getting the chance to watch live birth in fish and having a healthy, active, native fish to learn from. It certainly is not necessary to spend money on tropical fish when the best fish of all are found in the local ponds. From topminnows to the beautiful **Pygmy Sunfish**, your aquarium will be alive with color and activity with free, legal fish, and you and your kids can have a great time doing it!

The **Sailfin Molly**, also a live bearer, and the **Flagfish** both are essentially peninsular fish that enter our region in Wakulla County and hug the coastal ponds. Sailfins can be beautiful in breeding garb and Flagfish are an attractive reddish color.

But the real story of live bearers is the **Least Killifish**, probably the smallest vertebrate in the world. These attractive little fish with red dots on their fins and black railroad stripes on their sides are easily caught in shallow, grassy ponds and feed on very small invertebrates near the surface. Amazingly, the developing baby fish actually grows in the female, becoming nearly a third of the weight. This fish "bears" striking similarities to mammals in their reproduction. They are found abundantly from Cape Fear to Florida and over to Louisiana, but few people seem to know of the amazing secrets of this diminutive creature, our smallest vertebrate.

The **Warmouth Bass** is a small bulldog of lotic and lentic situations. They may be extremely abundant but seldom large enough to provide a meal. They are adorned with beautiful purplish coloration frequently and a mouth fitting the name "bass." Normally found in muddy water they take smaller fishes and other unfortunate vertebrates.

Also in the genus *Lepomis* with Warmouth is the abundant **Bluegill** of both rivers and lakes, the **Dollar Sunfish** of ditches and swamps, **Redear Sunfish** (shellcracker) of lakes, **Spotted Sunfish** (stumpknockers) of rivers (watch for the blue patch in the lower eye), **Redbreast**, occupying the same niche as **Bluegill** but in rivers, and the reddish **Longear Sunfish** of lentic environs. Fishermen refer to these sunfish as "bream" but true bream are European. Like the Warmouth, they prefer muddy bottoms where they "bed" each year and spawn for the coming generation.

Speaking of mud, two unique and rare fishes are the **Mud Minnow** and the **Mud Sunfish**, both found at the extreme Eastern edge of our area. The Mud Minnow, with primitive cycloid scales, a round front and a compressed rear, inhabits swamps and other dark bodies of water. They are able to breath atmospheric oxygen, allowing them to live in almost anoxic conditions. The Mud Sunfish is a monotypic genus (the only member) and looks rather bizarre with its yellowish hue and three brown stripes down the sides.

One genus of mostly common sunfish (which many people call "bream"), are the *Enneacanthus*. The **Bluespotted** and **Banded Sunfishes** are quite common in lentic bodies and are beautiful with their flecks of blue. The **Blackbanded Sunfish**, however, is endangered and little known even within its range.

The term "bass" normally refers to the **Largemouth Bass**, a tremendous gamefish and equally important creature commercially. They grow to enormous size in some of our Karrst lakes and many consider Lake Jackson the bass capital of America. They are caught with lures such as plastic worms and fish mimics like mirror and rebel, and even "bugs" like the jitterbug. But as with redfish, the really big, smart ones are best fooled with live bait like shiners. There are other species of bass in the Panhandle such as **White**, **Sunshine**, **Shadow**, **Suwannee** and **Spotted Bass**, but most are rare, local, or only in a limited part of North Florida.

Striped Bass are essentially salt water and have naturally inhabited the Apalachicola drainage system. The Florida Fish and Game Commission has introduced them into new areas to make more opportunities for anglers, although they themselves have laws against the introduction of species into areas where they do not naturally occur.

Black Crappie are abundant in lotic and lentic ecosystems and make for great fishing at certain seasons. They may be caught with small artificials or taken with minnows and crickets. Related are the **Fliers**, a light green fish with a black bar running down from the eye. They will actually leave the shallow water when pursued in their habitat of swamps and ditches.

Lastly, we have two species of fairly common darters in North Florida. The **Swamp Darter** is a denizen of dark lotic waters with trees and lies on the bottom in typical darter fashion. The **Blackbanded Darter** lives in more typical darter habitat in streams and small rivers. You may recall it was the threatened **Snail Darter** in the early 70's that stopped the

Gamefish kings, Large-mouthed Bass inhabit freshwater systems, acting as top-level carnivores

building of a dam across the Little Tennessee River and stirred up one of our first big environmental conflicts. Very hard to distinguish from other darters, it was later discovered to be elsewhere, but the backbone of those who stood up and were willing to sacrifice for a "minnow" did not go unnoticed.

The Herpetology of North Florida

Reptiles and amphibians are fascinating animals, and their abundance and diversity in North Florida is astounding. The varied wetlands aid in this array of amphibians and aquatic reptile groups, and many dry areas contribute interesting dry land reptiles such as snakes and lizards. But this song could be sung about some other taxa in North Florida as well, since it simply is an Eden for most groups of creatures.

As amphibians arose before reptiles and gave rise to them, we will discuss this marvelous group of cold-blooded insectivores first. As the first true terrestrial vertebrates, amphibians have always seemed to live in the gray twilight between water and land ever since they crawled out of the early seas over 300,000,000 years ago; and all across North Florida they still peep in the night, slither under fallen debris on the forest floor and dive headlong into our aquatic systems.

Our amphibians (a class) (Plate 4) may be easily divided into two orders, with one being the salamanders and the other the frogs and toads. Salamanders (Caudata) contributed to the development of reptiles, just as they were children of early Devonian fish that headed to land. Frogs and toads (Anura) almost jumped out of the fossil record and have only radiated within their order. The Latin name of the order for salamanders means "no tail" while the frog's means "tail."

Our most primitive salamanders are huge, gothic-looking "eels" known as giant salamanders. They are very dark brown or black, nocturnal, and seldom seen. One group, the amphiuma, has two pairs of tiny legs and breathes air, while the other, siren, has one pair and breathes with gills like the fish they share lakes with. Amphiuma are carnivores (and as is so often the case, bite hard) and siren are vegetarians, lacking teeth. Giant Salamanders apparently breed in spring but their entire life history is mysterious and little is honestly known about their breeding.

The **Two-toed Amphiuma** is a large beast, at times over a yard long, that spans the entire North Florida area and then some. They are at home in swamps, large lakes and quite common in rivers where they dodge the Mud and Rainbow Snakes. Amphiuma are occasionally caught on fishing lines and some believe they have discovered a species new to science.

Their smaller cousin, the **One-toed**, was only recently discovered, turning up in alluvium along various rivers and acting as the top-level carnivore in these muddy havens. As one of three new amphibians discovered in recent years, and one whose population may be small, collecting of this species should be held to a minimum.

This diminutive amphiuma rules the roost in muddy bogs in parts of North Florida

SMALL BUT BIG

Siren are truly strange looking creatures with their bizarre mouths, feather-like gills waving in the water and complete absence of hind legs. The **Greater Siren**, which may approach the size of a man's arm, is common in large Karrst lakes and uncommon in some other lentic bodies. Its small cousin the **Lesser** is secretive in acid wetland bogs like Bradwell Bay and uncommon.

Essentially, small siren in North Florida include the **Slender Dwarf Siren** west to about the Apalachicola River and the **Alabama Waterdog** from about that point westward. The former is common in backwaters of Karrst, grassy lakes, and the latter is a blackwater stream inhabitant.

All the above salamanders have essentially one life stage where they hatch and stay about as they are—except growth—until they die. In the pages to come, we will see other salamanders that have two life stages and one that actually has three different life stages, which may be newts to you.

Woodland salamanders are an enormous family (Plethodontidae)—the vast majority of their order in the world. In North Florida they occur in moist forests, especially along rivers, with a small handful venturing into other habitats. Farther north in the Appalachians, woodland salamanders are absolutely everywhere and totally abundant in virtually each little rocky stream. It is in these high-oxygen streams that they got their most outstanding characteristic, that of being lungless. Lungs would act like life preservers and buoy the poor creatures down the fast moving waters and to certain death. Therefore, woodland salamanders are lungless.

Herein lies the reason for the two life stages. After spawning in the brook, larvae emerge with gills and most are an inch or two. Then, upon sexual maturity, they lose their gills and replace them with . . . nothing. They simply absorb the bounteous oxygen through their skin and have no trouble breathing. Many live out their lives under the flat rocks of the stream bed while a few venture into the hills, but stay primarily hidden under logs and rocks.

The most abundant genus of woodland salamanders by far is the Duskies (*Desmognathus*). They are pretty much your basic dark gray and perhaps the toughest vertebrate complex to sort out. Fortunately, in North Florida, we have three species, all of which are allopatric (they don't live in the same places). The males are coal black and the females brown. They breed in the warm months and apparently transform in winter.

This Apalachicola Dusky Salamander, the new species to science, is especially unique due to its albinism

RARE AND BIZARRE

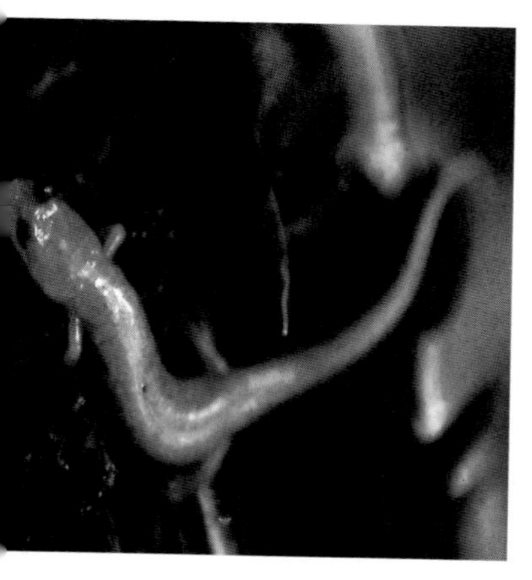

The common but secretive **Southern Dusky** inhabits the wet lowlands throughout North Florida, where it is sometimes associated with the Lesser Siren. In the steephead ravines of the central Panhandle (see Chapter 1 and 3), the **Apalachicola Dusky** was discovered relatively recently among the leaf litter in the clear streams as a descendant of some ice age dusky. In a few minutes one can walk from their habitat, replete with this species, down to the floodplain where the Southern Dusky is easily found. In extreme West Florida, **Northern Duskies** may be found in ravines with gully erosion and may be equally abundant in these pristine woodland streams.

The beautifully handsome genus *Pseudotriton* is represented by two splendid species also not occupying the same habitat. Many closely related creatures are allopatric, as it is an easy way for two species to be ecologically separated. The hefty **Red Salamander** prefers streams and uplands while the **Mud Salamander** is a lowland species, sometimes seen on roads during evening rains in early May. Though they have dark backs, both species have red bellies and are unmistakable. They apparently breed in fall but little is known about their transformation.

The unique **Slimy Salamander**, with the nominate genus name *Plethodon,* has recently been divided into about a dozen species, but the only one in North Florida is the **Southeastern Slimy**. Their gooey skin is full of noxious chemicals to ward off predators and maintain moisture so they can venture far from water. They are black with white flecks like dandruff, very beautiful.

Slimies are examples of direct transformation, much like **Greenhouse Frogs**, and eggs are laid on the ground under logs, etc. Young pass through the larval stage in the egg, and babies are born ready to head out on their own. Amazingly, though, their eggs have never been found in the State of Florida, and obviously more information is needed on many of our amphibian species.

Three lovely members of the genus *Eurycea* occupy three varied habitats in North Florida. The handsome **Three-lined Salamander** thunders through the floodplains after small invertebrates on the forest floor. Up in the ravines and along streams the more dainty **Two-lined** darts for cover when found under logs. A much more slight animal than

COMMANDER SALAMANDER

the preceding, it is easily told by the lack of the black stripe sp ting the back, so obvious in the Three-lined. Finally, looking lik tiny brown version of the Two-lined (with four toes!), the Dw Salamander scurries along the damp woodlands of many are including near the coast and has disappeared in some places c to construction and water pollution.

The family of **Mole Salamande** Ambystomatidae, is represented by one common and five le abundant species throughout North Florida. They have lungs a spend an awful lot of time in their burrows. In winter th emerge on rainy nights and retrace the steps of their ancesto to tiny ponds to find mates and reproduce. Gill-breathing larv transform in a few months and leave the water for subterranean li

The species Mole Salamander, *talpoideum,* is coal black but has vividly marked larvae that a tan with dark, bold stripes running down the anterior. Late wi ter nights with wet warm fronts rolling over produce hordes these, along with spadefoots, various treefrogs and other ar phibians finding their favorite breeding ponds. This family bree from late fall to midwinter and transforms in spring. Notice th this species receives the same name as the family, being th nominate of the family.

The Tiger will eat other species of amphib- ians, and a lot of other animals as well

Huge **Tig Salamanders** are still unearthed occasionall though rarely. Their larvae are sold as bass bait an some records may be the result of escapees. The neotenic variety (axolotl) comes from the west an is sold in pet shops. They are unique in that the never transform and become sexually mature Tige Salamanders looking like large larvae.

BREATHING IN WATER

According to maps, **Flatwoods Salamanders** are found throughout North Florida and then some. But their breeding ponds and habitat have fallen victim to the timber industry and they have now been listed as an endangered species—thanks to the work of people like Bruce Means lobbying the government to do the right thing. I still see them occasionally on rainy January nights on the road past the headquarters at the St. Mark's Refuge.

The splendid **Marbled Salamander** is found occasionally along river bluffs and floodplains in the Panhandle. Their white saddles are striking, but their numbers have dropped significantly in the past twenty years. Also boldly patterned, the handsome **Spotted Salamander** edges into Florida in the extreme northwestern corner around Century and may be found in moist forest wetlands.

Obviously woodland and mole salamander families have two life stages, generally where larvae live in water breathing through gills and adults move to land breathing either through lungs or their skin. However, the family of newts, Salamandridae, are the nominate of the order as they have the famous three life cycles during their maturation.

The larval (first) stage of the newt floats its gills in water absorbing dissolved oxygen

Newts hatch in the water into gill-breathing larvae rather yellowish, with a darker top like most animals have. In time they transform into a lung-breathing, bright red land form called an eft. The Red Eft has skin heavily laden with noxious chemicals and has little to worry about, being a classic example of aposematic coloration.

The efts are not sexually mature, though, and in time return to the water, take on a color more like their larvae, continue to breathe through lungs and finally become sexually mature. Here they live out their lives.

BEAT YA

Finally, two rare species for those keen for adventure: **Four-toed Salamanders** love sphagnum in North Florida but can be the dickens to find. Try ponds with the primitive moss and logs on the edge, associated with a moist woodland. This species looks not unlike a female dusky or a dwarf salamander but is frosted underneath.

In some of the caves of the central Panhandle near the State Line there exists the **Georgia Blind Salamander**. Like many cave creatures, they lack pigment and are therefore whitish. This species feeds off tiny invertebrates while the closely associated Cave Crayfish (also white) forages for detrital material in the black darkness.

Frogs, toads and their allies are built radically different from salamanders. They have huge hind legs for jumping to catch food and escape enemies. Their front legs are

short and stout to land properly and walk around on. The back is hinged so that they can squat and spring, thus giving them an even longer jump. Their mouths are cavernous with a tongue that extends to snare the bugs and other creatures they consume.

Unlike larval salamanders, tadpoles are herbivores, not crossing over into their parent's niche. They absorb their tails as they begin to transform, not unlike their sea squirt ancestors. Larvae have small mouths and grow hind legs first, just as the tail begins to shrink. The two commonest tadpoles are Southern Toads, which are multitudes of solid black ones, and Bullfrogs, a greenish monster with a yellowish underside.

TO THE TOP

The order Anura includes true frogs, treefrogs, toads, and some off-beat groups and species that have no close affinities. Some groups are families and others genera, and attempting to learn classification of this order is difficult and confusing.

A Squirrel Treefrog (smaller) and Green Treefrog seem to be racing up this window pane, held by their suction cup toes

Treefrogs (family Hylidae) have suction cups on the toes and everyone has seen them on their window panes. On most occasions it will be Squirrel Treefrogs, sometimes the Green. These frogs call indefatigably for mates and in fact, the muscles of their chests have the highest concentration of myoglobin of any vertebrate. Treefrogs have large, bulbous eyes with elliptical pupils for excellent night vision and super camouflage for hiding during the day. Breeding in North Florida is mostly a summer phenomenon, from late spring to early fall.

Our most abundant species is the **Squirrel Treefrog**, scarcely more than a half-inch and variable in color from green or brown to grayish with spots. They are generalists who accept about any habitat, including coastal areas such as barrier islands. They are named for their grating calls, a bit reminiscent of a squirrel's barking.

Green Treefrogs are larger and often have a stripe down the side that really makes them a beautiful animal. They have a honking call, often heard out over permanent lakes with small bushes, where they breed. Greens and Squirrels are sometimes all over the road during warm, summer rains, where they may be easily caught and examined.

Several other species are certainly found frequently or heard on nights conducive for calling. The list includes **Barking Treefrogs**, a large, spotted, noisy herp that breeds in the small, fishless Karrst ponds just South of Tallahassee, and other ephemeral bodies in North Florida. **Bird-voiced Treefrogs**, only found in the central and western Panhandle, are residents of great swamps and their calls resemble the chirps of birds.

Pine Woods Treefrogs are abundant all through the coniferous forests, issuing their Morse Code-like rattle much of the year. **Gray Treefrogs** are more generalists, though not especially common. Identification is easy with their bright yellow flash colors on the back of the thigh. However, the species has been split into two, told apart only by their calls.

One of the remarkable discoveries of this period, along with the three new species in the Panhandle is that of **Pine Barrens Treefrogs** in extreme West Florida. Sounding not unlike a Green Treefrog, this rare and exceptionally beautiful jewel issues a slow *quonk* about every other second. They are quite secretive and best caught by following the call to the source. They prefer swamps and especially bogs in their limited Florida habitat.

Two species of the genus *Acris* occur in North Florida and are noisy and abundant around lake shores. The **Northern Cricketfrog** (*A. Crepitans*) is found in the western part of the Panhandle while *Acris gryllus* (two races) occurs throughout North Florida. In the extreme northwestern part of Florida the **Southern Cricket Frog** replaces **Florida Cricket Frogs** which virtually covers the rest of the state. Northerns may be told by the ragged black stripe on the back of the thigh while the Southern has a clean-cut stripe. The Florida Cricket Frog has two such stripes.

Chorus Frogs (genus *Pseudacris*) are tiny members of the Treefrog family, usually less than an inch in length. They have minuscule suction cups, a light colored upper lip, and breed in midwinter. They sing like crazy in the cool months but are not easy to locate, even while singing.

The **Spring Peeper** may be the commonest of the group and may be recognized easily in hand by the "X" on the back (thus the species epithet, *P. crucifer*). They love deep swamps and river bottoms but are not averse to moist woodlands, even in cities. When singing, they sound like someone whistling for his dog, though somewhat slower. Two races occupy North Florida.

The tiny **Little Grass Frog** is a brown, practically invisible critter commonly heard right along roadsides and in marshes. Their call is a piercing, ascending whistle that is almost deafening in large congregations. They may be the smallest terrestrial vertebrate in the New World. This is a species of the Eastern North Florida area, not found west of about Panama City.

More typical species include **Ornate**, **Southern** and **Upland Chorus Frogs**. The beautiful Ornate and the Southern inhabit flatwoods, roadside ditches and various swales, being uncommon but widely scattered. The rare Upland is found north of Tallahassee to about the Apalachicola River in swamps, occuring on Meridian Road at the twin bridges. There is also a small population around Blackwater River State Park.

The family Ranidae includes large frogs that unfortunately are famous for their delicious legs. They lack the suction cups of the treefrogs (and the apparent interest in climbing) and do not have any warts in contrast with many of the toads. Some are medium-sized while certain kinds become huge. Males have a large eardrum called a tympanum, and both sexes have muscular legs that enable them to make almost unbelievably long jumps to escape predators. Most will breed during the warm months, but Leopard Frogs reproduce more commonly in spring in our area. Gopher Frogs prefer late spring and early summer fairly exclusively.

The **Bullfrog** is the largest and most famous of the true frogs. Males sing their *chug o rum* in the warm season and congregate in large ponds and lakes to breed. Tadpoles are very large and green, taking a matter of years to transform under certain conditions. Male frogs have green around the mouths while females are uniform brown with mottling. Their niche seems to be to occupy the most favored spots of shorelines, calmly eating smaller species that challenge their authority.

Leopard Frogs, with their protective spots, prefer hiding in grassy areas making riveting sounds

CAN YOU SPOT HIM?

Pig **Frogs** attain a size nearly that of a Bullfrog and are eaten by humans in considerable numbers as well. The large, grassy lakes of North Florida house most of the Pig Frogs. They are extremely aquatic, stay well away from shore and grunt most of the night. They may be told from Bullfrogs by this habitat, a more pointed nose, more webbing on the toes and stripes on the back of the thighs.

River Frogs are fairly large and abundant in places where people are not. Great swamps, river bottoms and huge shrub bogs such as Bradwell Bay and Tate's Hell are their favorite locations, as their status might be considered "locally abundant." They are very dark frogs with white spots on their chin, and from the mouth comes a serious, rolling snore.

Bronze Frogs are smaller and take refuge in swampy places such as riverbottoms and floodplains throughout North Florida. They are rich brown and easily recognized by their voice, which sounds like a guitar string being plucked to sound like *gunk*. They and their brown tadpoles with pigment in the tail are frequently seen , though not abundant.

Southern Leopard Frogs are the least aquatic of the familiar true frogs. Most frequently found in grassy areas not far from water, they are seldom abundant but fairly widespread. Recognized by their pointed nose and spotted backs (thus the name), they terrorize the arthropod population and even eat smaller frogs when they are housed in aquaria. Spots in the tail of their brown tadpoles are larger than those of the Bronze.

New to science is the **Florida Bog Frog**, a small, brownish creature similar to a Bronze Frog with a yellow upper lip. They have been recently discovered in extreme western Florida and live in seepage bogs, appearing to be quite fond of sphagnum.

The **Florida Gopher Frog** has adapted completely to life away from water, except to breed. They seem to prefer the dens of tortoises and may not see water for months. Their color most nearly mimics asphalt, though the camouflage of such a color seems unlikely. They also have a snore, issued in breeding ponds, or as the season draws nigh, which serves as one of the few effective ways of locating them. The darker **Dusky Gopher Frog** replaces the Florida in extreme western Florida, where the two do not interbreed.

Toads are adapted for life on land as well and are most commonly seen hopping across roads at night. Their hop is short and ploddy, while true frogs cover long distances each jump. Treefrogs do not jump far, but much higher than toads. Toads of the genus *Bufo* have many warts and a paratoid gland behind the neck filled with noxious chemicals to ward off enemies.

The **Southern Toad** is the abundant, widespread species of this bunch. They occur from dry, sandy soil, where they maintain light gray color, to floodplains where they change color to brown and nearly black. They have lateral pupils, like the Fowler's, and large specimens range between two and three inches, tops. The **Fowler's Toad**, confined to extreme west Florida, is light gray with dark spots in the middle of their back. Each of these spots has three warts. The tiny **Oak**

Toad is actually found most commonly in the pine community and is best identified by a yellow line running down its back. They have a distinctive, clear whistle during the warm season.

E**astern Spadefoot Toads** are hardly toads at all. They have smooth skin, the paratoid glands are virtually absent, and the pupil is elliptical, rather than lateral. They have a "spade" on their hind feet for digging straight down into the sand they love, and stay fairly well hidden most of the time. When rain comes, they may suddenly appear in droves, and often breed in staggering numbers after heavy rains in the warm season. They may, however, even be seen after rain in the winter associated with a warm front. Beware of handling these slippery creatures, as some folks have allergic reactions from their secretions.

The **Eastern Narrow-mouthed Toad** is another that hardly reminds us of toads. They have smooth skin, no warts, and are very small. Amazingly, they have a fold of skin over their head that they use to wipe off foreign matter in their eyes. Most often seen near water where shelter exists, you also can find them roaming at night. Rather than hopping, they scramble along on all fours and are much harder to catch than you might think. They make an obnoxious nasal call with their tiny mouth that sounds like a Norelco razor, heard all through the warm season during breeding.

The huge family of Tropical Frogs is represented in our area by the **Greenhouse Frog**, a small critter that is quite variable. This is the sound heard chirping in your yard's border grass much of the year, and good luck finding their breeding ponds. They actually lay their eggs on their backs, with eggs hatching through direct transformation. Like the Slimy Salamander, the larval form exists only within the egg, so tiny frogs emerge and go on their way.

Amphibians are creatures that have been on earth for well over 300,000,000 years. They have survived ice ages, floods, intense solar radiation, poisonous atmospheric gases, a collision with a comet, the entire rein of the dinosaurs, and Lord knows what else. Now, they are disappearing at a rate far faster than anything in history, and though we do not know all the factors, there is little doubt man is connected to their plight.

North Florida is as rich in amphibian life as any place on earth. We can go a long ways toward protecting them by saving wetlands, not polluting bodies of water, or even watching out for toads at night. They are so old and have so many cool secrets. Let's show how civilized we are and let these ancient creatures live on our rock for a few more centuries.

MONSTERS FROM THE PAST

Of course, probably no animals have killed and eaten amphibians more than their progeny, the reptiles. In order to move onto dry land, certain salamanders grew scales, claws, watertight skin and eggs, and became reptiles. Many still live in and around the water and some like sea turtles and sea snakes have even returned to the ocean. And best of all, many live in North Florida!

These overfed alligators date back before their dinosaur cousins stomped over our planet

This male gator has staked out his haunt and watches for enemies along the water course

Our most ancient reptiles are the crocodillians, and alligators are among the most primitive of those. Alligators watched the dinosaurs wax and wane and rode out the catastrophism of the early Cenozoic just fine. With all that, we nearly wiped them from earth with unrestricted hunting in the earlier part of the 1900's, but disaster was averted, as usual, just in time.

Curious how several extremely primitive organisms occur in Florida and the Orient. The other alligator is the Chinese Alligator, there are other giant salamanders in Asia, and even the age-old cypress has an extremely close relative in eastern Asia. I have heard of no explanation for this phenomenon but "the earth does not give up her secrets easily."

The **American Alliga-tor** differs from the **American Crocodile**, which gets no closer than South Florida, by being mostly black (instead of tan brown), having a wider snout, having no lower teeth protruding and by preferring fresh water. Caiman from South America have also been unwisely introduced, though rare, and may be identified by the high ridges inside their eye.

Alligators now inhabit most freshwater bodies in North Florida and are fully recovered, although *it is still illegal to take alligators without a permit from the game commission.* The larger the body of water the larger the gators get. And, although alligators are basically benign creatures fearful of humans, individuals over six feet especially which live around people, should not be trusted. It is illegal to feed alligators, because they learn to associate us with food.

These powerful creatures become interested in mating and being very territorial in early spring, so this is not a great time to push the reptilian envelope. Never before, in our collective lifetime, has such a brawny animal had such a tiny brain—a bad combination (the author claims no college bias when he reports that 'gators have the smallest brain for their size of any vertebrate). One cannot reason what a beast like this is "thinking," because they don't think. They react to a mysterious set of conditions laid down untold eons ago, and our only defense is wariness. Eggs are laid in summer and mothers are very protective (see above warning one more time). Young make a high-pitch grunting noise, which herpetologists at the University of Florida have translated using modern technology to mean, "My mama can eat yo mama." And they can.

Turtles are unique creatures, to say the least. They have a shell, almost like a mollusk, and the vertebrae are fused into the plastron (top) of it. Like frogs, there is a poor fossil record of the evolution of turtles, but we know they are ancient. Freshwater turtles are not to be trusted, although land varieties are docile and most sea turtles are relatively innocuous. There are some turtles from pretty far back as well, such as some of the water turtles. Snapping Turtles of two species occur in North Florida with the **Common Snapping Turtle** being seen fairly regularly. The **Alligator Snapping Turtle** is scarce, lying on the bottom of large bodies of water, dangling its pink tongue like a worm for bait. One cannot imagine the foot-pounds of pressure that come to bear when a hapless fish enters the jaws, chasing wonder worm. Both this and the Common are dangerous creatures and should be handled with extreme care. They can be picked up safely by the tail with the head pointing outward. But please don't kill and eat these—especially gator turtles—as their numbers really are spiraling down. The latter may be identified by a more brown coloration and three rows of very rough scutes down the back.

Mud Turtles are nasty biters as well, though some seem content to close up like a box turtle. The plastron will completely close, unlike the Musk Turtles, whose odor and disposition makes up for the slight lack of physical protection. Four species occur in our area, two Mud and two Musk.

The **Common Musk Turtle** is found in lentic or lotic waters, and their musk earned them the nickname "stinkpot." The larger species, which may be either **Loggerhead** or **Stripeneck Musk** (different races), prefers rivers, especially clear ones. Musk Turtles are famous for climbing up limbs on the sides of rivers (a la watersnakes) and occasionally dropping unceremoniously into boats cruising the rivers.

Eastern Mud Turtles are pretty much everywhere and easily viewed at night in aquatic bodies with clear water. Another race, the **Mississippi Mud Turtle**, overlaps its range in West Florida. Baby Mud Turtles have red plastrons, thus the species epithet "*subrubrum*." Their carapaces are smoother than Musk Turtles' shells and have a hinged plastron.

This flipped Mud Turtle shows the hinged plastron which enables it to close up completely

TURN ME BACK OVER!

Map Turtles are common in certain places in the Panhandle and are chiefly riverine. **Barbour's Map Turtles** are found in the Apalachicola River system with females growing quite large. They have huge jaws for crunching the mollusks so common in the river. In West Florida the Alabama Map Turtle inhabits the Escambia River system all the way to the gulf.

Cooters and sliders are easily our most common and conspicuous turtles. They are forever seen sitting on logs and splashing into the water upon our approach. **Florida Cooters** are found in both lentic and lotic systems, whereas **River Cooters** are essentially lotic. **Yellowbelly Sliders** are more common in lakes and ponds where they can be abundant. Looking somewhat like one of the above is the **Chicken Turtle**, but their long necks belie their identity. They are also a good bit meaner than the others of this paragraph. All four of these are in most of North Florida.

Our last freshwater turtles are the softshells, with two species ecologically separated. **Spiny Softshells** are lotic and **Florida Softshells** are lentic—and grow quite large. This pair must be handled with one hand on the rear and the other just over the top of the shell and above the head. These guys will bite savagely and do not think of handling them like cooters and sliders.

The **Ornate Diamond-back Terrapin** is a salt marsh turtle found occasionally along our coastline. They are quite unmistakable and there is little else to confuse with them, anyway. They crush clams and crustaceans with their massive jaws and make lousy pets. Leave them to breed.

Sea turtles are sadly rare on our beaches today. The **Atlantic Ridley** occasionally winters in quiet bays and lagoons along our coastlines and is making a heroic comeback on their breeding grounds in Mexico. Loggerheads still come ashore in darker shores to nest in summer, though dead ones seem as common as live females. **Green Turtles** are scarce but occasionally found in grass beds, while **Leatherbacks** and **Hawksbills** are virtually unheard of in our waters.

These dead sea turtles, like this Loggerhead, are common sights along Florida's beaches

On land, we have two species of turtles. The **Gopher Tortoise** is a keystone species of the pine community and has disappeared frightfully in recent years. They are now fully protected, an act some say was long overdue. This species is flattened and digs lateral holes into the sandy ground with their huge front feet. Other creatures such as rattlers, gopher frogs, indigo snakes and many invertebrates cohabit with gophers, making their survival of the utmost importance. Gophers are vegetarians, taking many fruits and succulents, including Prickly Pear.

There are several races of one species of Box Turtle in the Panhandle, most notably the giant **Gulf Coast Box Turtle**. They all can close up completely for protection but quickly lose this tendency. These turtles are omnivores and accept dog food and worms as readily as veggies in captivity. The sexes are easily told apart by the concave plastrons on the males for mounting females. A good many Box Turtles cannot be identified to race with all the mixing in the Panhandle.

After crocodilians and turtles, the third and final order of reptiles in North Florida (and the entire world, outside of New Zealand) is Squamata, the lizards and snakes (Plates 1 and 2). Together they make up over five thousand species of reptiles globally. The only reason we have as many turtles in Florida as lizards is that the Appalachians are the turtle capital of the world and North Florida has enough wetlands to keep down lizard diversity. Fortunately, there are plenty of snakes .

The most conspicuous lizard is the **Green Anole**. Its ability to change color allows it to change to green or brown and gives it the incorrect nickname "chameleon." They are widespread throughout North Florida and welcomed in peoples' yards. The male's throat fan is a territorial display. Other species of introduced anoles are in Florida but seldom seen, thankfully, in North Florida.

The ubiquitous but secretive **Ground Skink** rivals the anole in abundance but scurries through the yard poorly seen. This leads to identifications of "salamander" with its smooth, brown skin and slick look. These are often seen under boards and other objects.

In the dry pine woods two species of lizards are common. The amazing **Fence Lizard** clings to trees with its spiny backs looking like bark in color and texture. Nothing is cooler with kids than holding the swift upside down and petting its tummy, making it "go to sleep" (admittedly, the close second must be letting an anole bite your ear lobe and hang on like decoration). **Six-lined Racerunners** are slender, striped lizards with blazing speed and the ability to run on their hind legs when pressed. Both species have bluish underneath (especially males).

Glass Lizards (or legless lizards) are unique creatures found in various forms all over the world. In our area we have four species with the **Eastern** being the common type in moist forests and **Slenders** somewhat more abundant in pine woods. The recently discovered **Mimic Glass Lizard** resembles the Slender closely and appears to be found through much of North Florida.

My personal favorite is the rare and local **Island Glass Lizard**. Though virtually unheard of from the mainland (what's in a name?). They are thick as thieves on the extreme east end of St. George Island. Unfortunately, they are also fast as greased lightning, and my class and I saw a whopping twenty-three before we could catch one!

Skinks are a larger group of native lizards with shiny, smooth skin and occasional bright colors. Aside from Ground Skinks mentioned earlier, three species of the genus *Eumeces* are common and widespread in North Florida. The huge **Broad-headed** is common (especially in spring) in hardwoods, ascending the canopy in summer and becoming scarce (unless you are a Mississippi Kite or Broad-winged Hawk). **Five-lined Skinks** inhabit river bottoms and other aquatic shores. The **Southeastern Five-lined Skink** is a pine woods species, especially taking to logs in the Longleaf community. Males of these three species are brown with reddish heads and little dorsal striping. Females are all brown with stripes and the young have blue tails. This flash color has a nerve poison in the tail which is lethal to some animals, including, regrettably, house cats.

Two rare skinks of the Panhandle include the **Coal Skink** in western Florida, east to the Ochlockonee

River, where I found some black young in my childhood. Somewhat aquatic, they often dive into the water to escape enemies and have probably worked their way down from the North via rivers. Also, in the pine woods lives the **Mole (Red-tailed) Skink**, which I also caught in my youth on Tower Road (off the Springhill Highway) southwest of Tallahassee.

We have stayed somewhat free of introduced lizards in North Florida, but the **Mediterranean Gecko** thrives in some cities. An unconfirmed report has it that a student at Leon High in the early 70's released several at school, and they have since radiated out across the old neighborhood in downtown Tallahassee. I'm sure he didn't know any better.

NOCTURNAL NEWCOMER

Snakes are closely related to lizards without the limbs and tails for breaking off. However, they do not have external ear openings, strongly hinged jaws or eyelids that close. Whereas lizards usually are insectivores, most snakes eat vertebrates, including a few of their close cousins. With much wet and dry habitat, Florida is loaded with species richness of serpents.

The family Colubridae includes all of our nonpoisonous snakes in Florida. The largest genus is the Nerodia, or Water Snakes. They have rough backs, a rougher bite, dull colors and disappear quickly into the closest water when we approach. They are frequently seen basking from about midmorning to noon on limbs over water, then moving to shade during our hellish afternoons. Reptiles can easily die from

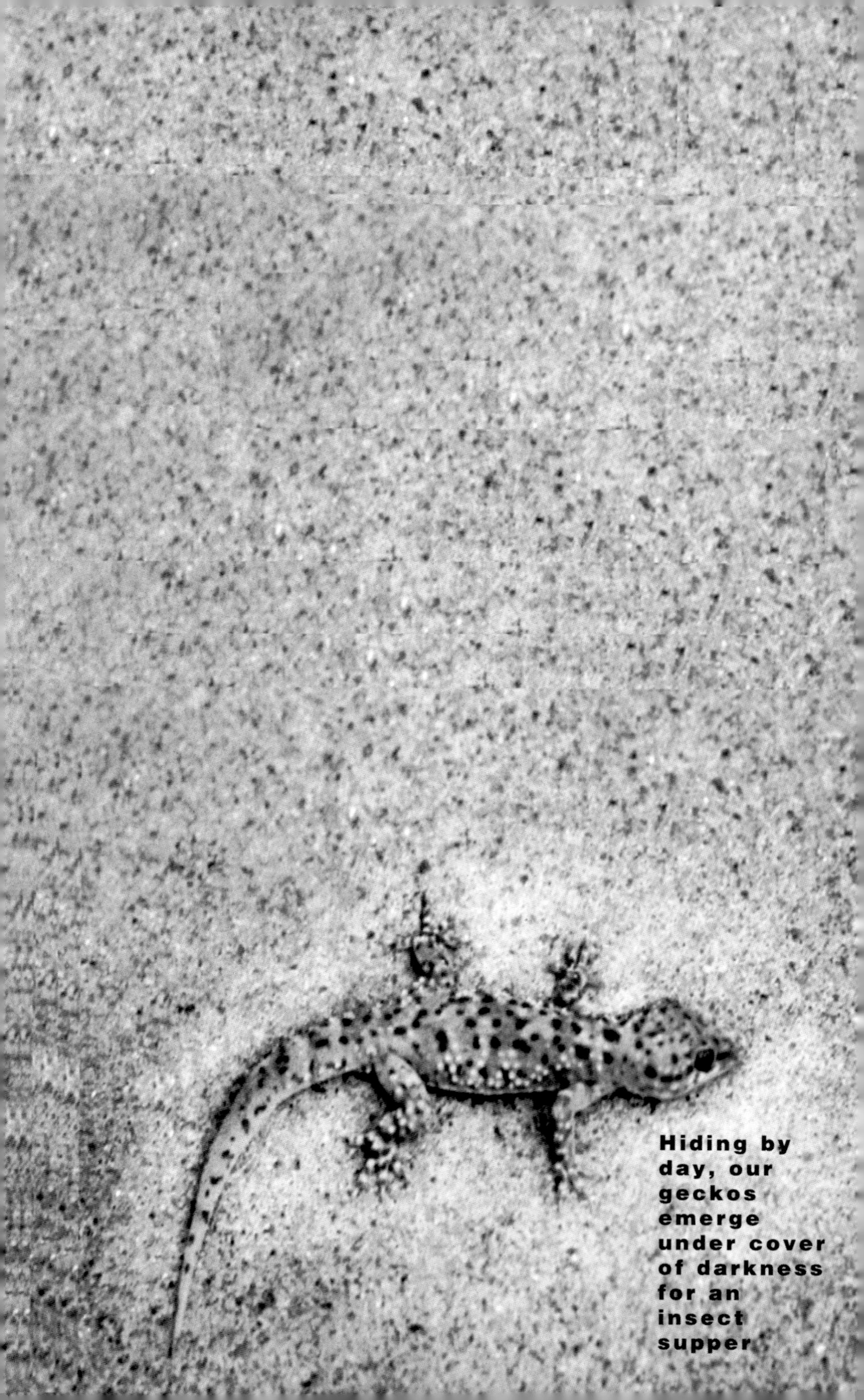

Hiding by day, our geckos emerge under cover of darkness for an insect supper

too much sun and/or heat, but most have to dry off regularly to maintain healthy skin.

The ubiquitous **Banded Water Snake** is found all over North Florida in lentic systems, including just about every ditch and pond available. A generalist, it eats amphibians and fish readily. A sympatric species in large grassy lakes is the vicious **Florida Green Water Snake**. Reaching monstrous proportions to match their temper, they slip surprisingly quietly through water lilies and other emergent vegetation and grab fish and siren with their huge teeth. The **Mississippi Green**, a smaller species, is found in extreme western Florida.

More lotic are **Brown Water Snakes**, the abundant "water pilots" of southern rivers. With dark squares dorsally, they can be told from other snakes, including Cottonmouths. They are also spirited fighters and make poor pets. Living with them on rivers are **Redbelly Water Snakes** that are actually more yellow in the extreme western part of the Panhandle. Like Bandeds, they bite initially, but soon tame to become gentle pets.

Midland Water Snakes are found in extreme West Florida in lotic or lentic situations and are usually reddish with banding. They are quite similar to the abundant Banded, but certain facial markings separate them. Consult a field guide for specific information.

A really neat snake is the **Gulf Salt Marsh Snake**, a Nerodian of the tidal creeks. Eating several species of killifish, they lie on the banks and zip across on the bottom at the first sign of humans. As all salt marsh species are as endangered as salt marshes themselves, these shouldn't be taken and make pretty sorry pets anyway.

Swamp Snakes are very different from Water Snakes, being colorful, shiny, very secretive, rather nonaggressive and not preferring fish and amphibians. This is a loose group with surprising similarities in habits and habitat.

The most famous swamp snakes are the **Mud** and **Rainbow Snakes**. Muds are our largest aquatic serpents, reaching EIGHT feet. They are shiny black above and red checkerboard underneath. The Rainbow has beautiful stripes and a hefty body as well. Both prefer clear rivers and actually incubate their eggs. Their diet consists of amphiuma and siren, held in place by the spine on their tail. Oddly, they have both been seen burrowing in fields (!), and Rainbows have frequently been seen along gulf shorelines, presumably chasing fish eels (Anguila).

Crayfish Snakes eat soft-shelled crayfish, and are typically found in areas with little calcium, so crayfish shells take longer to harden. They are colorful underneath and quite inoffensive. **Queen Snakes** inhabit blackwater streams in the western Panhandle where their brown backs may be spotted on evergreens over sandy-bottomed streams. **Glossy Crayfish Snakes** (once Water Snakes) are chunkier (that is nearly always true of lotic/lentic snakes) with a shiny green back and half moons underneath. A pair of races, split by the Apalachicola River, stretch across North Florida.

Black Swamp Snakes inhabit most of North Florida in grassy lakes and weed-choked ditches. Their glossy black back and red belly are unmistakable. **Striped Crayfish Snakes** sneak along the Panhandle coast from the rest of Florida in small perched ponds, extending west to Carrabelle. They are bizarre snakes, with keeled scales only in the anal region.

The **Eastern Garter Snake** is widespread throughout North Florida as is a type of Ribbon Snake. The latter is divided into the **Eastern Ribbon** (in the western Panhandle) and **Peninsula Ribbon** (in eastern North Florida). Both have bluestripe forms in Wakulla, Taylor and Jefferson Counties as a textbook example of convergence. Ribbons eat small frogs and minnows while garters expand to include (are you ready for this?) slugs, newts and toads. Cast iron stomachs?

There are several species of small, subterranean snakes in North Florida. Their diet is chiefly invertebrates (unusual for snakes), and they are mostly seen on roads on warm summer evenings, under trash piles and after heavy rains. They are inoffensive but make poor pets. Some are apparently related to Water Snakes (Natricine snakes), but all relationships are not clear.

The **Southern Ringneck Snake** is common and beautiful, with an orange belly and ring around the neck. A pungent musker, they actually constrict and eat anoles. Two species of Earth Snakes occur, with the Rough throughout North Florida in hardwoods and the Smooth in the pine woods of the eastern and extreme western portion. The same range finds **Midland Brown Snakes**, with their tiny light mark on the neck. Watch for the pointed head in **Rough Earth Snakes** and the tiny black dots on the **Smooth**. The **Florida Redbelly Snake**, which loves floodplains with Midland Browns, is common but secretive. **Southeastern Crowned Snakes** are found in the western Panhandle and are sandy-soil creatures with a light neck ring separated by black. Rear-fanged and mildly poisonous, they pose no threat to humans. Lastly, the **Pine Woods Snake** is a cruel joke in many field guides, causing snake hunters to lose their sanity over one species that simply cannot be found. Believe me, I know.

SLIGHTLY UPTURNED

VERY UPTURNED

The Eastern Hognose Snake's snout is only a tiny bit upturned . . .

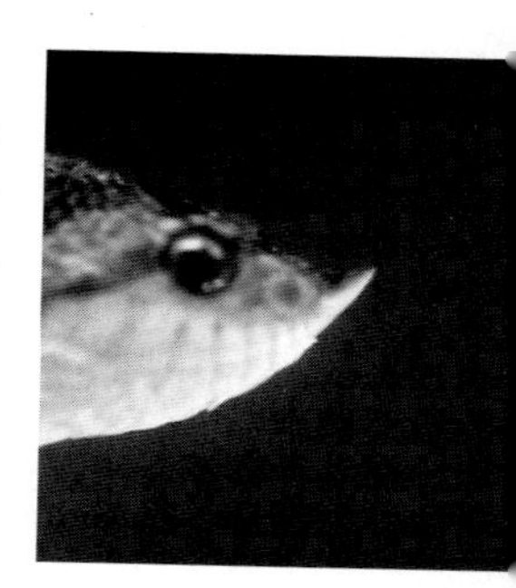

. . . while the Southern's is strongly curved

Hognose Snakes are wonderful creatures that should be experienced by every American once in their lives. Upon a chance encounter, the creature will hiss loudly, puff up with air, spread its hood like a cobra, and strike with its mouth shut. If this hasn't deterred the intruder they roll over to play dead, open their mouth with their tongue hanging out and defecate all over their coils. Astonishingly, if they are turned back right side up, they roll over again!

These "spreadin adders" have rear fangs to puncture the toads they capture (which annoyingly puff up) to give the wartmonster a deflating experience. They even have a mild venom, but still will not bite a human no matter what. They soon stop the act but still make great pets, although being pooped on repeatedly in front of your friends isn't too woopie.

The **Eastern Hognose**, still found in many parts of North Florida, may be black, black and yellow, or black, yellow and red. The smaller **Southern Hognosed,** which is gray, black and white, seems to be disappearing at an alarming rate and is only found on rare occasions in the pine woods with sandy soil. Some believe Southerns are adapted for feeding on Spadefoot Toads.

There are four solid-colored, slender, fast, diurnal snakes of North Florida. The **Southern Black Racer** still zips its way through open woodlands, though it is not the ubiquitous creature we used to see all over our area. A subspecies called the **Brownchin Racer** occupies the Apalachicola River valley, chiefly replacing the white throat with tan mottling. The enormous **Eastern Indigo Snake** is still found on rare occasions in wild areas of North Florida, but their protection was not legislated soon enough. It is illegal to possess one, so admire them from a distance. The **Rough Green Snake** lies across roads in late morning warming itself and giving nature lovers a chance to handle a gentle, beautiful snake. Resist the temptation to keep it as a pet, as they are more trouble than they are worth. That goes for all the snakes in this entire paragraph!

The mighty **Florida Pine Snake** still lumbers through Longleaf communities in search of a small mammal, the pocket gopher. The gray body and reddish tail is distinctive, and the massive coil, loud hiss and vehement strike will snag your attention every time. Finally protected by our slow-to-act government, they have disappeared from most of the former range. Thankfully, these, kingsnakes and rat snakes are all being bred by snake fanciers. Regrettably, there is little stock being released into former haunts, as the pet trade makes more money than environmentalists. *Pituophis,* or lover of pits (holes), spends much time underground.

Rat Snakes are long, slender tree climbers with bodies shaped like a loaf of bread. The **Gray Rat Snake** (white oak snake) is most common in hardwoods while **Corn Snakes** are surprisingly catholic in their habitat preference. The **Yellow** is found in the Eastern part of North Florida in many habitats. All thrive in captivity, although the Grays can be a little temperamental. Buying snakes from pet shops has many advantages, the biggest one being that wild snakes are left to reproduce in nature. Captive-bred snakes are tame and feed well, plus are usually mite and disease-free.

Kingsnakes are beautiful snakes (*Lampropeltis*=shiny skin) that will eat about anything including poisonous snakes, which they are immune to. The handsome **Eastern Kingsnake** spans North Florida except for the area near the Apalachicola River where the pet trade eliminated the **Speckled Kingsnake**, because the government acted so slowly. Even the Eastern has vanished in most areas and desperately needs for the Game Commission to stop worrying about the snake-hunting lobby and do the right thing!

Mole Kingsnakes are rare and local in savannahs of North Florida, but have all but disappeared. Same reason; same problem. Closely resembling Corn Snakes, they have an odd head, a stouter body, smooth scales and a single anal plate often with checkerboarding underneath. These guys burrow a great deal and come out mostly after heavy rains or warm nights.

Scarlet Kingsnakes are small, extraordinary mimics of Coral Snakes. They have red noses where Coral Snakes have black, and the red ring never touches the yellow one (red touch yellow, kill a fellow). Scarlet Kingsnakes are very secretive and most easily caught by stripping bark off large, fallen pine trees. They are most often active the same times as Mole Kingsnakes.

Scarlet Snakes are distantly related to Kingsnakes but eat lizards and small eggs. They have the same

DANGEROUS

ring colors and patterns as the Scarlet Kingsnake but have white bellies and very pointed noses for burrowing. They are found on warm, dry nights by driving through pine woods well after dark, watching the paved road carefully.

It may surprise some but the vast majority of snakes in nature are harmless, nonpoisonous kinds (unless you live in Australia). North Florida is certainly no different. Venomous snakes have been reduced in number along with other serpents and many animal groups. But the "hot" ones are out there and are capable of delivering excruciating bites, if not fatal.

The vast majority of our venomous snakes belong to the family Viperidae, a large world-wide family with long, hypodermic fangs. Their venom is usually hemotoxic (attacking the blood and the heart), but our species are seldom fatal. Our vipers are in the subfamily Crotalinae, or the Pit Vipers. They have a thermosensitive depression between the eye and nostril for detecting prey at night or underground. Vipers have elliptical pupils, large heads, stocky bodies and bad tempers. Pit Vipers join Garter, Ribbon, Water and certain "ground" Snakes as live-bearers of young. By far, our most common poisonous snake is the semiaquatic **Cottonmouth**. Normally a rather stout creature, they inhabit coastal swales and roadside ditches in natural areas abundantly and other wet habitats such as swamps and floodplains regularly. They will stray into yards in either very high

SNAKE

or low water, and are seen crossing roads, especially in fall. They are not the ones we see lying on limbs over lakes and rivers, as they rarely do this.

Cottonmouths are identified by several things. They have broad, flat, large heads with a lateral dark stripe down the side of the face, like a mask. This covers the eye, hiding it from predators and prey alike, as eyes are conspicuous in wild animals. They have broken hourglass patterns against a mostly brown ground color. When cornered they will open their mouth in readiness to bite, exposing their "cotton mouth," which leaves little doubt as to their identification. Cornered they will vibrate their tails like a nervous shake, which Water Snakes do not do. Some land snake species that shouldn't be confused with Cottonmouths do vibrate their tails, like rat, king and pine snakes, coachwhips and racers.

This coiled Cottonmouth seems ready for any intruder

The word "moccasin" is used by many for various snakes seen in the wild, but technically it does not apply to any particular snake. The poisonous snake found around the water is a Cottonmouth but many use "moccasin" when spotting Water Snakes and Lord knows what else. But the species likely to be confused with Cottonmouths are Water Snakes, particularly Browns and Bandeds. The former has no black with dark brown squares, and the latter has only a thin, diagonal line down the face, if any mark at all. On dead specimens, Cottonmouths will separate themselves from Water Snakes by having a single anal plate, facial pit, elliptical pupils and, of course, fangs. But remember, freshly killed snakes have reflexes and have been known to bite!

Cottonmouths prefer dark, dense areas where they can hide and surprise their quarry of birds, frogs, mammals and even other snakes and lizards. The young have a yellowish tail tip (a good field mark) that they wiggle and lure unsuspecting prey with. They generally will not bite unless stepped on, but sturdy shoes or boots are recommended when walking in wet areas. Cottonmouths sometimes forage in shallow water, especially in the early morning, for fish easily caught.

Water Snakes are in direct competition with Cottonmouths, with the fewer of the former making the latter more abundant. In addition, Water Snakes eat mostly sick and diseased fish, making them valuable to fishermen. The wanton killing of Water Snakes is unwise, bad for fishing and of questionable ethics.

Rattlesnakes of three kinds are found regularly in North Florida. Massive **Eastern Diamondback Rattlers** are still found in the pine woods and occasionally in hardwoods as well. Their yellow ground color and grayish diamonds are unmistakable. but finding yourself in close proximity to the compact coils and deafening buzz will leave little doubt as to the snake's identity or the direction you wish to move. And by the way, whoever started the old wive's tail about standing still when seeing a poisonous snake by your feet must have been a doctor getting kickbacks from snakebites. They only get madder as seconds tick by, so move quickly !

Diamondbacks eat only warm-blooded prey like birds and mammals and adults can actually eat half-grown rabbits. They survive best where gopher holes or stumps are found as winter requires a hibernation location. Wearing boots (though not necessarily hundred dollar "snake-proof" boots) is recommended for hiking in areas rattlesnakes may be found, and one should always keep his eyes primarily on the ground in any natural area.

In some areas such as the Palm Hydric community **Dusky Pigmy Rattlers** are found commonly. A nasty-tempered little viper with a light-gray ground color with black spots, they camouflage in sandy soil quite well. They also have the black mask of a Cottonmouth and the faint buzz of their rattle aids in identification. Eating almost entirely small rodents they are found over much of North Florida.

Two species of vipers, the **Canebrake Rattler** and **Southern Copperhead**, are found only rarely in our area. Canebrakes are virtually absent in the Panhandle but regular around the Lake City area between Tallahassee and Jacksonville. Copperheads are known to occur in the bluffs region near Bristol but are scarce and seldom seen. However, locals across North Florida misuse the term "copperhead" like they do "moccasin" to name Corn Snakes, Banded Water Snakes, young Cottonmouths and any other snake with yellowish near their head. It seems the southern male would far rather tell of an encounter with a venomous variety, especially when the snake was killed. Saying, "I blew that kingsnake's fool head clean off" lacks a certain testosterone content.

The only member of the cobra family in the New World are Coral Snakes, and our **Eastern Coral** is uncommon and local throughout North Florida. A stunningly beautiful creature with a black nose and red, yellow and black rings, it looks like a reptilian candy cane. Sadly, children have played with these and suffered the consequences. Their neurotoxic venom is just as seductive, causing only numbness and paralysis until the victim is in critical condition.

Coral Snakes seem to prefer reptilian prey and their venom is especially potent on lizards and small snakes. They are active in early morning and after dark and seem more drawn to pine woods than hardwoods. They are not ill-tempered creatures but the price for a nip is too high to be careless with these deadly snakes.

Lastly, a plug for civility. It is time we as a species move to a mentality of respect for our fellow animals on this rock. This includes snakes, sharks, spiders and others we cringe at, or fear. There is honestly no excuse for the wanton destruction of species that we simply don't like, or for trying to display our manhood by blasting innocent creatures. Snakes are fascinating, and they have to fight an uphill battle on this planet. Aiding them in their struggle against cars, cats, and the intentional weapons of man would say much for our compassion and appreciation of all God's creation.

A Key to Shed Skins of North Florida Snakes

Snakes shed their skin several times a year, depending on how fast they grow. These skins may be used to identify the snake and this is especially valuable if the shed was found around human habitations. The following is a key to distinguishing various groups and species, using different taxonomic (structural) features. In order to identify the snake that left the shed, the entire shed is helpful, as three different parts of the snake's body reveal clues about its identity. They are:

1) The head.
2) Any portion of the main part of the body.
3) The entire tail.

To proceed, examine the snake for two very important characteristics, taken from numbers 2 and 3 above. You need to find out whether the back scales are keeled or smooth, and whether the anal plate is divided or single. This is very easy. This procedure will also work with a live snake, but do NOT hold a snake until you know that it is harmless. Plus, don't forget that some nonpoisonous snakes, such as Water Snakes, can bite very painfully.

Hold the scales up to the light (any non-belly scales will do) and see if there appears to be a line running down each scale. This is a slight ridge that gives the snake a rough feeling, especially if felt across the scales. These are called keeled scales. It is detectable on just the shed as well, although it is not as rough. No keels means it's smooth. Remember, the skin is inside-out.

Second, look on the snake's belly and find the base of the tail where belly scales end and the obvious beginning of the tail is found. The belly scales will stretch all the way across the belly, and in all snakes but pit vipers, they immediately become paired underneath the tail. If they are single at the beginning of the tail the snake is either a Cottonmouth, some kind of rattlesnake or a Copperhead.

Right between the belly scales and the tail scales is an opening where snakes mate, release musk and release waste material. This is called the cloaca, and you will see an opening. Now, look closely and examine the large scale (anal plate) covering the cloaca. In some snakes it has a diagonal line running through the middle of it (divided) and in others it is one scale (single).

So now you know what kind of anal plate the snake has, single or divided. You also know whether the body scales are smooth or rough. You are now able to put the snake into one of four categories, based on the taxonomy of these two characteristics. In this key, we will only deal with snakes that attain a length of two feet, to keep it simple. There are many small, harmless snakes that pose no threat and seldom leave sheds out to be found, anyway. Here are the species or groups that fall into the four categories, all discussed following the four divisions below:

1) Smooth and single	Indigo Snake, all kingsnakes, Scarlet Snake
2) Smooth and divided	Mud and Rainbow Snakes, Ringneck Snake, Black Racer and Coachwhip, Coral Snake
3) Keeled and single	Garter and Ribbon Snakes, Pine Snake, all pit vipers
4) Keeled and divided	Water snakes, Hognosed Snakes, Rough Green Snake, both rat snake species

Snakes with **smooth scales** and **single anal plates** are usually kingsnakes. The massive Indigo is rare, even in the few parts of North Florida they may occur. But unlike our kingsnakes, the shed skin of the Indigo is patternless when held up to the light. No speckles, bands or anything. The Scarlet Snake, usually short and pencil thin, will also have pattern and a pointed nose. So if you have a kingsnake (or Indigo) in your yard, rejoice! Not only are they harmless, but they will eat any poisonous varieties that come your way.

Species having **smooth scales** but **<u>divided</u> anal plates** are usually long and slender and almost always either a Coachwhip or Black Racer. Telling them apart requires a careful count of the rows of scales diagonally running over the back. Start from the edge of a belly scale just in front of the anal plate, go over the top and end when you reach a belly scale on the other side. Racers have fifteen rows of scales and Coachwhips have thirteen. Neither presents a threat to people and are normally merely a streak in the grass.

To identify a skin belonging to a Mud or Rainbow Snake, check to see if there are a few keeled scales on the back, above the anal plate. If so, it's one of these two. If the very front scale on the nose is divided, it is a Rainbow Snake. This pair also has the thickest skin of all North Florida snakes, so there might well be pattern showing when held up to the light.

The two remaining possibilities are pencil thin and almost never more than two feet long. Coral Snakes will have the hint of rings on the shed skin while Ringneck Snakes are solid colored on the back, with only one light ring behind the head. The chances of a Coral Snake showing up in your yard are about that of winning the Lottery, or of Lottery money actually going to education.

If the skin's scales are **keeled** and **single**, first check to see if it has facial pits. These are small indentations about half way between the eye and nostril on either side of the snake's head. For the vast part of the state, if it has these pits (making it a pit viper) and a pointed tip on the tail, it is a Cottonmouth. If the tail ends abruptly, it's probably a rattlesnake, although on rare occasions a Cottonmouth's tail tip may break off during shedding. Pattern can be seen lightly on shed skins of rattlers, so identifying them to species is quite possible if you look for diamonds, spots or squares. Pigmies also differ from the larger rattlers in having proportionately large scales between the eyes.

If it has no pits, and it's a large snake, it's a lock to be a pointed-nosed Pine Snake. However, a smaller, thinner snake is likely the abundant Garter or Ribbon Snake. If you wish to tell these harmless ones apart, measure the tail (up to the anal plate) and then the total length. If the tail is greater than 29% of the total length it is a Ribbon Snake; less than 26% makes it a Garter.

Here's where it gets really hard, with **keeled scales** and a **divided anal plate**. See if the scales on the side are quite keeled all the way to the belly, or if they are only weakly keeled, with some not keeled at all. The latter are rat snakes; either a Corn Snake or the Gray/Yellow Rat species. They, of course, are no threat to people and are quite beneficial in rodent control.

If the scales are all quite keeled, you have some choices. A pencil thin snake with no pattern is a Rough

Green Snake, with a very delicate skin. A thick snake with an upturned nose is a Hognose Snake, which never, ever, bites people. If it is neither of these, you have a Water Snake of some species. Browns almost always shed their skins on the river, as do Redbellies. The likely Water Snake that will leave you a shed is the harmless and widespread Banded. If you should find a Green

SUMMER SWIM

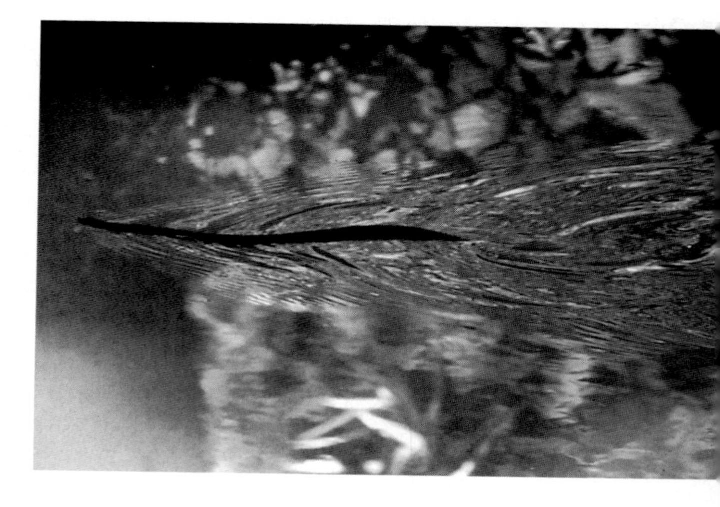

This Banded Water Snake eases across a North Florida slough with head held lower than Cottonmouths

Water Snake shed, you will notice an extra row of scales along the upper lip. This means that other Water Snakes have a scale that borders on the mouth and touches the eye, but Greens do not. Despite their ferocious personalities, Greens are no threat as they almost never go in yards.

The Magnificent Frigatebird sails overhead in the warm season on some parts of North Florida's Coast

Waterbird Wisdom and Landbird Lore

With all its coastline and fresh water bodies North Florida is loaded with waterbirds. A great many, such as waterfowl and gulls, winter along the coast and in the large Karrst lakes. Others, like shorebirds, are abundant in the rush of migration and some even arrive in late spring to nest here. We will survey the water bird orders and families, mentioning key groups and species found at various seasons and locations.

Common Loons, throwbacks to the time of dinosaurs, make their long trek from the far North to our waters in late October along with **Horned Grebes**. They are found in inshore waters and large lakes and begin disappearing for their northern nesting grounds in March. **Pied-billed Grebes** are residents in ponds and lakes but shy away from most salt water.

Brown Pelicans have returned to our coastline in big numbers since the DDT fiasco of the 60's, and are joined in modest numbers by monstrous White Pelicans in winter. On fall cold fronts, sometimes a huge flock of **White Pelicans** (well, all flocks of these are huge) sails overhead in a beautiful display of grace and symmetry. Their cousin, the **Magnificent Frigatebird**, is mostly a fall migrant, sailing along our coastline in association with cloudy, rainy weather. By the arrival of the cold front, they will be long gone, as their jellyfish quarry have disappeared. **Northern Gannets** may be seen from

November through mid-spring out in the deeper parts of the gulf, such as St. George Island and Cape San Blas and on the Atlantic Ocean. Long streams of them may be observed at Cape San Blas around April 1 as they follow the coastline all the way around Florida and up the Atlantic coast to their Canadian nesting grounds.

Double-crested **Cormorants** are residents, but their numbers are profoundly augmented in winter. **Anhingas** seem confined to fresh water lentic and lotic habitats, spearing fish with their dagger bills instead of grabbing them with hooked beaks as the cormorants do.

Most species of waders (Plates 6 and 7) are common and easily found in fresh and salt water through North Florida. **Reddish Egrets** are found occasionally around the St. Joe Peninsula area and St. Mark's Refuge. **Little Blue Herons** are uncommon coastally but breed in the great swamps inland such as Tate's Hell. **Least Bitterns**, which breed locally in marshes and large Karrst lakes are replaced by a few **American Bitterns** from fall through spring. Found commonly all over North Florida are **Green**, **Great Blue** and **Tri-colored Herons** and **Great**, **Cattle** and **Snowy Egrets**.

White **Ibis** are abundant in North Florida and are being joined by **Glossies** from the peninsula in small numbers. Storks nest in scattered localities with great swamps but are most commonly seen as early fall migrants. **Roseate Spoonbills** are wandering up our way like the Glossies and may continue to do so as the earth warms.

Introduced **Canada Geese** have become residents and almost domestic in many areas such as Tallahassee but late fall wild flocks still excite the crisp morning air with their honking overhead. **Snow Geese** occasionally visit North Florida as well, with both dark and light morphs.

Large numbers of ducks (Plate 8) abound in various areas of North Florida from November through early spring. In the marine environment **Lesser Scaup**, **Red-breasted Merganser** and **Redhead** boast high populations while several species of puddle ducks occupy the lakes and marshes. The **Ring-necked Ducks** are abundant in large Karrst lakes in winter and are taken frequently by hunters. North Florida is replete with freshwater ducks in winter (see Plate 8).

Sandhill Cranes are occasionally seen (or heard) on late fall cold fronts as our peninsular birds are augmented in winter by those from the North. Their cousin the **Limpkin** inhabits rivers and swamps where **Apple Snails** abound, such as the Wacissa and Wakulla systems.

Rails are small, secretive relatives of cranes and Limpkins that creep through our marshes for invertebrate cuisine. **Clapper Rails** are residents of salt marshes, famous for their loud kik kik kik calls while the similar **King Rail** prefers fresh water marshes with both being found on occasions in brackish water. Smaller winter residents include the short-billed **Sora** and ubiquitous **American Coots**. The latter are often thought of as large rafts of ducks and even eaten by hunters when they can't shoot "blue-bills" (Ring-necked Ducks and scaup). The recipe for coot is to boil them in vegetables, throw away the coot and eat the vegetables.

Fairly common breeding birds, augmented in winter, are **Common Moorhens** (formerly "gallinules"). They resemble coots but have a red, candy-corn bill and a brownish hue. The exquisite **Purple Gallinule** arrives in April from the tropics and breeds on lily pad-laden Karrst lakes before their departure in late summer.

FAMILIAR SIGHT

The Killdeer scurries along on lawns and pastures all over our area

Plovers are chunky little shorebirds with big heads and short bills. They feed on the substrate, picking up small invertebrates and other bits of food off the beach or mud flats. They are fewer in number than the monstrous family of sandpipers but are by no means rare. Most are found in close association with water. An exception is the **Killdeer**, who are as much at home in pastures and fields as on shorelines. They have two rings on the chest and are somewhat slender for plovers.

On shores, our most numerous "ringed" plover is the **Semipalmated**. Its dark back separates it from the **Piping** and **Snowies**, while it is considerably smaller than the **Wilson's**, which summers and breeds on our beaches. The Semipalmated and **Piping** (with orange legs) are here from fall to spring while the ghostly-white Snowy (with black legs) is a resident on sandy beaches (Plate 10).

The **Black-bellied Plover** is one of Florida's three abundant shorebirds on beaches and is a permanent resident. From fall to spring it lacks the black belly but can be separated from the **Golden Plover** (a rare migrant in fields) by the black "wing pit" (axillaries), larger head and bill. In late spring, Black-bellieds begin attaining their black undersides and disappear for the Arctic. Some that never turn plumages stay as non-breeding summer residents.

Two sandpipers dominate the beaches with the above plover. The large and noisy **Willet** feeds along our marine shoreline from fall to spring in gray plumage. Late spring most of their kind heads North to breed but some brown up and nest in the salt marshes. Most easily identified at all seasons by the black and white wings stripe, Willets have long bills and legs.

Sanderlings scurry all over the beach and are quite territorial, despite their diminutive size. They are very whitish but they also brown up in late spring before they migrate to the Arctic. Like the plovers, a few stay all summer and neither breed nor attain the brownish nuptial plumage.

Dunlins and ubiquitous **Short-billed Dowitchers** may be very abundant in loose flocks on mud flats from fall through spring and also change into breeding garb before migrating North for the summer. Sort through the dowitchers, especially inland, for **Long-billeds**.

American Oystercatchers (Plate 9), may be found on oyster bars or resting along places like the causeway to St. George Island. Look for the abundant **Ruddy Turnstones** in association with them or on beaches. **Black-necked Stilts** are moving (and breeding) northward from southern Florida and nesting at St. Mark's Refuge and on the Atlantic coast. **American Avocets** are occasional winter residents.

Greater **Yellowlegs** are regular winter residents with large numbers of **Lessers** migrating through in spring and fall with a few **Solitary Sandpipers**. **Spotted Sandpipers** are found on bulkheads and other shorelines most of the year, identified by the bobbing of their rear ends. **Upland Sandpipers** join Golden Plovers as "grasspipers" in fields and pastures spring and fall with a rare chance of **Buff-breasted** or **Baird's Sandpipers** in early fall.

HIDDEN IN THE GRASS

This Common Snipe hides along a North Florida ditch, and is frequently seen from October through April

Whimbrels may be seen with **Marbled Godwits** about any month (seldom in summer) with the occasional sensational **Long-billed Curlew** mixed in. Other winter resident sandpipers include the **Red Knot** on beaches, and in the migration, **Pectoral Sandpipers** in wet, grassy areas, the **Stilt** and **White-rumped Sandpipers** and **Wilson's Phalarope** in late spring and early fall along shores.

Peeps are tiny sandpipers told apart by leg color and bills, and provide a challenge for even top birders. **Least** and **Western Sandpipers** are winter residents with the former being brownish with yellow to greenish legs (be careful about black mud on the legs!). Westerns have black legs and a longish bill that droops slightly, not unlike a small Dunlin. **Semipalmated Sandpipers** are very common in late spring and early fall on shorelines but absent in winter.

Common **Snipes** are winter residents, probing marshes and even roadside ditches with their long bills. Built similarly, **American Woodcocks** inhabit moist forests and swamps, unearthing worms with bills as long as snipe. Both have brains which are upside down as a result of the way they feed. Both are game birds with tremendous bursts of speed and dark, tasty meat. Woodcocks are permanent residents and breeders with their population increased in winter by northern visitors.

Three species of gulls are very common in North Florida. **Laughing Gulls** are present all year and breed on desolate beaches in spring, after they have developed their black heads. In any plumage the dark back separates them from other gulls in our area. Their characteristic laughing calls are familiar noises at the beach, which they prefer over inland locations.

Herring and **Ring-billed Gull** adults can look pretty similar, though the larger Herring lacks the bill ring. Ring-bills are the frequent inland species in parking lots and lakes. Young Herrings are quite dark brown all over and easily recognized. Uncommon in winter is the **Bonaparte's Gull**, a tiny but beautiful northern bird with a conspicuous dark spot on the side of the head and unique black and white patterns on the wings.

North Florida coasts are replete with terns. Most common are the **Royal** and **Forster's Terns**, which both get scarce in summer. The former feeds out to sea but the latter is abundant right along the shore of the gulf. Slightly larger but similar to the Royal is the **Caspian**, with a bulky body and a red bill. They feed along side Forster's but stay through the summer. Very similar to Forster's are **Common Terns** which arrive in late spring and may be seen through September, though they do not breed very often. Spring birds may be recognized by their dusky undersides and young birds by the dark carpel bar running parallel to the back.

Intermediate in size between the four terns above is the ubiquitous **Sandwich Tern**. Identified by a black bill with a yellow tip, this shaggy-crested sea bird joins the Royals out deep where they dive for various species of top water marine fishes. Of a similar size is the **Gull-billed Tern** that nests on beaches but feeds in salt marshes (just the opposite of Forster's, actually). Summering birds, they have thick, black bills and a grayish tinge to their top side.

Two very small terns are the **Least** and **Black Terns**. Leasts nest on some of our beaches and are very vocal with their *klee klee klee* notes. Blacks migrate through in late spring and again in early fall, and are seen especially on days with cloudy, foreboding weather.

The clown of the sea birds is the **Black Skimmer**, a resident nesting on many beaches and the causeway to St. George Island. The only bird whose lower mandible is longer than its upper, they skim the water surface for tiny fish, which they involuntarily flip up into their mouths. Skimmer populations have suffered recently and care should be taken to ensure their reproductive success.

When one includes the fabulous bird migration, North Florida may be considered an excellent place for land birds as well as water birds. First there are those found year round, like cardinals, jays and thrashers. Many other birds fly to our area in winter because Florida is at the bottom of the continent. Some species borrow our woodlands in summer just to nest and then leave for their home in the tropics in late summer. Lastly, a fourth group is the exciting migrants which invade our area twice a year on their way north or south.

Raptors (Plate 11) are large, primitive hunters with hooked beaks and sharp, strong talons. They have been worshipped almost since the beginning but hated by many farmers throughout this century. Now, though, the image of them as "bad" seems to be fading into the realization of their pest control value, although it is sad that a creature's existence must be justified by its value to humans.

Hawks are a huge family and are often found in North Florida's open fields and animal-filled forests. Buteos are the most common and familiar hawks, with their long wings and wide tails for soaring. The huge **Red-tailed Hawk** occupies open areas and eats a wide ranging diet from snakes to mammals. Becoming scarce in summer, a few stick around to nest in tall trees near fields and pastures.

Occupying the moist forests is the **Red-shouldered Hawk**, a thinned-down version of the Red-tail. With frequent calls and an abiding nature, it is familiar to many in our area. From spring to fall it is joined in the hardwood forests by the smaller **Broad-winged Hawk**, who somehow escapes the wrath of the larger bird. A confirmed lizard eater, the **Mississippi Kite** completes the trifecta in summer, being especially conspicuous very late in the afternoon. Watch for splendid **Swallow-tailed Kites** near cypress swamps and other woodlands near the coast.

The accipiters have short, rounded wings, a long tail, rapid flight, and the habit of chasing songbirds through the forest canopy, matching them move for move. **Sharp-shinned Hawks** are tiny accipiters that are regular in the migration and winter. The larger **Cooper's** nests at our latitude and is told by their rounded tail (plus, check the field guide).

Essentially a huge buteo, the **Bald Eagle** has returned from endangerment to breed in many localities in North Florida. Locally common at St. Mark's Refuge, they scoop fish off the surface and in winter make life miserable for brainless coots. **Golden Eagles** are rare winter visitors in the open areas of North Florida, looking much like immature Bald Eagles.

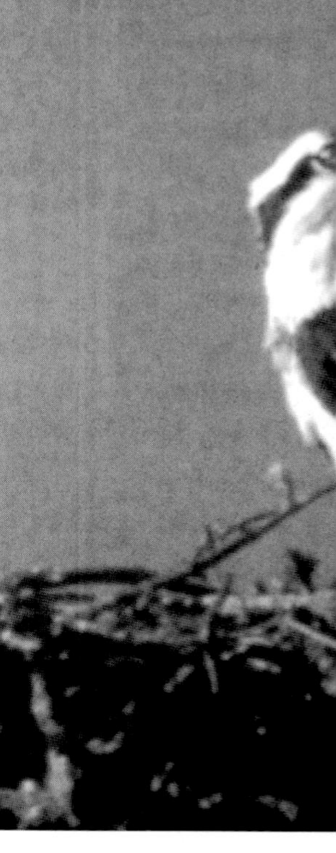

LORD O

Ospreys are often confused with eagles and are even called fish eagle or fish hawk. They are best distinguished by their white bellies and dark eye stripe. Ospreys plunge feet first into the water for surface-feeding fish and breed in spring along areas with large shorelines. They have joined eagles in recovering from DDT.

Northern Harriers tilt and sail low over fields and marshes after rats from September to May. Most are brown, being females and immatures, with the gray males being more common out west. Watch for the raised (dihedral) wings and white rump patch.

HER REALM

Falcons are speedy raptors with pointed wings for diving and relatively frail bodies. **American Kestrels** winter in good numbers in our inland open areas but become scarce in summer while feeding on grasshoppers and other insects. **Merlins** swish through in spring and fall like dark bullets along the coast. Watch for a dark kestrel with a big chest and direct flight.

Peregrines, the most efficient predator on earth, become bewilderingly common between about the twentieth of September and the tenth of October along the coast. Winter birds are scarce and in spring they return farther west, like so many birds, mostly missing Florida. Speaking of returning, it is great to see how their population has rebounded from near extinction!

This mother Osprey watches over her territory for danger and good fishing grounds

Vultures may or may not be raptors, but there is no controversy over whether they are abundant in North Florida. The **Turkey Vulture** is a widespread resident, being identified by its red head, brown coloration, and dihedral, two-toned wings. **Black Vultures** are often in sizable flocks over dead cows, etc., and may be as numerous as their brown cousins. Some authorities place vultures with storks, which goes to show everyone is entitled to their opinion.

PROUD AND BEAUTIFUL

Upland game birds are comprised of two families, and most individuals are fast flying birds with light meat and smallish size. The exception to that is the **Wild Turkey** which has a disjunct range over most of the Eastern United States. They are very secretive, though, and found throughout North Florida. Suspicious individuals near roads, etc., may be told from domestic turkeys by their brown (instead of white) tail tips.

Wild Turkeys are still fairly common over the drier woodlands of North Florida, bringing a real challenge to hunters

SAYING ITS NAME

A male Bobwhite struts near his female, singing the familiar "bob-white" that gave them their designation

Greatly reduced from past decades is the **Northern Bobwhite** (Quail). Along with fire ants, feral cats and blatant deforestation, lack of proper forest and much-needed prescribed burning has diminished their numbers. Though hunting never helps, it is not considered to be a huge threat to this species. The efforts of organizations like Tall Timbers has gone a long way towards an understanding of the needs of many pine-forest species.

Mourning Dove

Eurasian Collared Dove

Three species of doves are found in North Florida, with another becoming well established. The ubiquitous **Mourning Dove** nests in our area and reinforcements arrive in October just in time for the fall dove hunts. The number of "MoDos" on cold-front days over fields is staggering, and the fact that their population never seems dented is amazing.

Common Ground Dove

The tiny **Common Ground-Dove**, with a squared-off tail and reddish wings, still survives (barely) in sandy soil and agricultural lands. On the horizon, and already abundant in some places, is the **Eurasian Collared-Dove**. Looking much like the

Ringed Turtle-Doves in field guides, this species is thundering across the Deep South like a virus. At least the **Rock Doves** (city pigeons) stay in the cities.

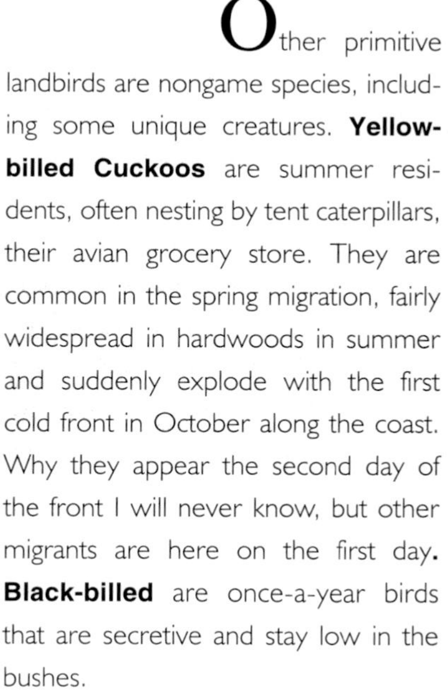

Other primitive landbirds are nongame species, including some unique creatures. **Yellow-billed Cuckoos** are summer residents, often nesting by tent caterpillars, their avian grocery store. They are common in the spring migration, fairly widespread in hardwoods in summer and suddenly explode with the first cold front in October along the coast. Why they appear the second day of the front I will never know, but other migrants are here on the first day. **Black-billed** are once-a-year birds that are secretive and stay low in the bushes.

Rock Doves

WEB FULL OF WORMS

Looking like a shopping cart full of groceries to a cuckoo, this tent caterpillar nest will feed little cuckoos for weeks

Owls are well represented in North Florida with several species occupying several habitats. The huge **Great Horned Owl** prefers open woodlands and may be seen around dusk sitting atop trees near fields. Feasting on skunks, they are plenty common near the coast, as well as inland. **Barred Owls** inhabit moist woodlands and are most appreciative of river bottoms and swamps**. Eastern Screech Owls** like open pine woods best but also winter in stands of oaks (middens?) coastally. **Barn Owls** are scarce but occasionally seen in farming country. Watch for the light underside and legs that hang down in flight.

Members of the Goatsucker (Plate 13) family fill the night air with strange sounds and probably lessen the number of beetles considerably. The derivation of their bizarre name comes from their habit of hanging out in goat stalls and apparently scaring poor "Billie" so much that she gives little or no milk. Farmers began thinking that the birds were milking the goats, which we now know is utterly impossible.

Common Nighthawks, so elegantly erratic in the air, buzz into North Florida in spring off the gulf and find nesting places in fields, on buildings and other dry, flat surfaces. Their nasal *kent* can be heard from April to midsummer and their white wing bar will seal the identification. They are often seen over sporting events at night, hawking for bugs over the lit fields.

The **Whip-poor-will** is a very uncommon goatsucker in the winter months (some migrate through in early fall) and is best seen before dawn on dirt roads through heavy woodlands. Many hear the song of the **Chuck-will's-widow** and call it a "whip," but these summer songs are chucks. Listen to the syllables and compare to the name. Chucks are partial to pine woods and a drive through any piney area on a summer night reveals their golden eye shine while you drive.

The **Chimney Swift** roars in off the gulf in early spring and nests all over Eastern North America in chimneys and burned-out trees. Looking like a "cigar on wings" they zip across the sky at speeds virtually unrivaled in the bird world. Their shallow wing beats and all dark bodies separate them from swallows. The good news that no predator can catch them is somewhat compromised by the bad news that they occasionally have fatal crashes with each other in flight around roosts, causing at least this observer to wonder just how "swift" they really are.

Hummingbirds are related to swifts and have tremendous powers of flight. The three hundred species, all confined to the Americas, can hover at a food source or blaze across the Gulf of Mexico and arrive hours before most songbirds. They are essentially nectivorous with straw-like bills and tiny feet.

Our species is the **Ruby-throated**, greenish on top, off-white underneath, with males having red gorgets that glow like neon. These bright throat patches settle confrontations, supposedly, but several hummingbirds all trippin' on sugar get pretty feisty at feeders. In my opinion, these feeders should be removed after October to encourage Ruby-throats to head south. Both **Rufous** and **Black-chinned Hummingbirds** occasionally come east instead of south in winter and are normally the two species seen from November to February when Ruby-throats are absent.

WATCH-ING FOR DINNER

A male Belted Kingfisher sits on a phone wire above his favorite ditch watching for just the right minnow

The **Belted Kingfisher** is a well known picivore feeding on surface fish and splashing headlong into shallow water. Their blue colors and distinctive shape render them unmistakable, and they are a favorite among bird lovers. Occasional breeders in summer with their latitudinal burrows in embankments, they pile up here in winter, especially along the coast.

Woodpeckers (Plate 12) are marvelously adapted for a life hammering on trees, and with all its timber, our area is replete with many species. All share the chisel beak, thick hard head, long, strong toes (two in front, two in back) and stiff tail for bracing on bark, and many have "ladder" backs to blend with tree bark. They are a neat group in and of themselves but their holes also aid many other species of animals needing a home.

Our most common species is the **Red-bellied Woodpecker**, familiar from neighborhoods to hardwood forests. The zebra back and red cap identify it, but the red belly (only on adults) is barely visible in the field. True **Red-headed Woodpeckers** are uncommon and are found in open oak tree plantations and Longleaf communities.

Smaller than these species are the **Hairy** and the sparrow-sized **Downy**, found in both hardwoods and pine forests. The endangered **Red-cockaded Woodpecker** (the Spotted Owl of the South) is still found in pristine Longleaf communities, often having their dry rattle heard before they are seen. Visually, the white cheek patch separates it from other "ladder-backed" species. Many resources are going into saving this species and the outlook is bright.

The hefty **Pileated Woodpecker** thrives from urban hardwoods to swamps and floodplains, with its ringing *yik yik yik* call blaring all year. Still called "Ivory-billed" by locals, their larger cousin appears to have joined the dinosaurs as no credible evidence of their existence has been found for decades. A victim of our encroachment and short-sightedness, North Florida was one of their last strongholds. With any luck, the fate of Ivory-bills will ensure the fortune of Red-cockadeds this coming century.

Two woodpeckers with other names are the **Yellow-bellied Sapsucker** and the **Northern Flicker**. The former arrives in October and spends a quiet, retiring winter in hardwoods, leaving holes all over the forest. Eating insects along with sap, they normally forage on the opposite side of where we stand. At rest or in flight they can be identified by the white wing stripe.

Flickers breed in Longleafs in small numbers and are sometimes detected by their very long call issued only in the breeding season. They pass through in droves on October cold fronts and may be heard issuing their *kee-yah* call. They thin out in winter and are curiously scarce in spring.

Songbirds are a tremendous order, comprising almost two-thirds of the birds in the world. Their cries are heard all over North Florida from field to forest and their colors decorate coastal trees in spring with unimaginable beauty. From April to July, walking outside in our forests is like hitting a wall of sound that reminds us how great it is to be alive.

BEWARE OF THE BUTCHERBIRD

Somewhat anticlimactic to that thought is the first family of songbirds, the flycatchers (Plate 12). They do not sing but their insect-eating ways is cause for forgiveness. Handsome birds, they sit erect and watch for hapless bugs sailing past, unceremoniously snapping them dead with heavy, wide, hooked bills. They are easy to spot, flying off, banking and returning to the same limb.

Eastern King-birds are striking predators with their black top, white underside and even whiter tail tip. They live up to their name, bullying much larger birds like crows and hawks, protected by a flycatcher's almost miraculous ability to fly. This species still nests sparingly in North Florida in open areas and may be abundant in early fall. **Grays** are found sparingly on the coast in the breeding season.

Great-crested Flycatchers are here for the same time period but inhabit moist forests. Their habit of taking flies of the family Tabanidae (Dog, Horse, Deer and Yellow Flies) has certainly endeared them to me, and using shed snake skins for nest material is as interesting as it is fascinating. In the upper canopy they are not easily seen but their *WEEP!* call or dry rattle belies their haunt.

In more moist situations the small, greenish **Acadian Flycatcher** chips sharply and loudly while spending summers in North Florida. More slender birds of Longleaf communities are **Eastern Wood-Pewees**. More slender, elongate

and less green than Acadians, they make long, aerial swoops through open areas for insects and have subdued chips to accompany their pee-wee call.

Our only wintering flycatcher is the handsome **Eastern Phoebe**. With a large, dark head and stocky body, it sits in the open near water bobbing its tail and watching for low-flying bugs. The phoebe also has a loud chip but enunciates its name *fee-o-bee* for all to hear.

Loggerhead Shrikes often leave grasshoppers behind and pursue mice, small birds and lizards, pinning them on thorns

There are other species of flycatchers that are scarce and rarely seen, including **Scissor-tailed**, **Vermilion** and **Least Flycatchers** (possibly other *Empidonax)* and **Western Kingbird**. Always check out extralimital possibilities when unsure and especially when an ordinary bird seems out of place. Upon finding a "rare" bird, be sure to report it to experts so you contribute to science.

North Florida has a fair number of **Loggerhead Shrikes**, despite their lowered population in the United States. This "butcher bird" inhabits open country, eating grasshoppers in summer and warm-blooded vertebrates like mice and sparrows in winter. The black mask allows them to hunt by looking into the sun without a bad glare, so they can see the shiny grasshopper exoskeleton. Shrikes got their nickname by virtue of pinning their leftover meals on thorns and barbed wire to save for another day.

Vireos are built much like flycatchers but forage by moving through the canopy lethargically in search of insects like caterpillars, which they pull out with their hooked bills. They are somewhat plain birds, although they may be confused with warblers if the bills are not carefully observed. The **Red-eyed**, **White-eyed** and **Yellow-throated** all nest in our area, while the **Blue-headed** (Solitary) is a winter resident in flocks of other small songbirds.

The family Corvidae is among the smartest, most adaptable birds on earth. The familiar **Blue Jay** is in everyone's yard and, as a generalist, eats about anything one puts on the feeders. Their note gives them the name "jay" but they also mimic certain buteos, especially **Red-shouldered Hawks**. Crows are also abundant in North Florida with the **American** found in the country everywhere and the **Fish Crow** congregating along shorelines, rivers and in towns. The former's young birds can sound like Fish Crows, and the adults, for some reason, imitate turkeys!

Swallows have long, pointed wings and tails and are the masters of songbird flight. Feeding on insects on the wing, they prefer open areas and are highly migratory. **Barns** nest in our area under bridges and similar structures while **Rough-wingeds** prefer sandy embankments where they burrow a latitudinal nest like a kingfisher. **Banks** and **Cliffs** nest to the north, along with **Trees**, which spend the winter in huge flocks along the gulf coast, eating sand gnats.

BUG EATERS

Purple Martins often live right in Floridians' yards, bringing cheer to the neighborhood

P**urple Martins** are large swallows which are drawn to gourds and martin houses erected on lawns around North Florida residences. They are our first "spring" migrant, arriving in early February to set up shop. Amazingly, many leave for their "fall" migration south in late May! Martins are reputed to reduce the population of biting insects in neighborhoods, but there is little evidence of this. Wooden houses are likely to be healthier than aluminum ones for young birds.

C**arolina Chickadees** and **Tufted Titmice** are familiar favorites among back yard birders. They are nonmigratory and tame, frequenting feeders and raising young within small areas. They both have conical bills for cracking seeds and devour suet in winter. Their high-pitched notes create problems for identification and they are often the first to fuss at snakes and cats in the yard.

Nuthatches (Plate 13) are not well known by many but three species may be found in North Florida. **White-breasteds** are in the Peidmont north of Tallahassee near Tall Timbers and the Georgia State Line. **Red-breasteds** are uncommon winter residents throughout North Florida and are found along the coast after late fall cold fronts and in the spring migration. **Brown-headed Nuthatches**, endemic to the Longleaf community, are fairly common in places like the Apalachicola National Forest.

Four species of wrens regularly inhabit Florida with the **Carolina** being a common resident in neighborhoods and forests through the state. They are famous for nesting in mail boxes, old cars, garages, and potted plants. Their loud song, sung in triplets, is familiar to many who listen to birds. The abundant winter resident **House Wren** actually shies away from houses in the South, preferring fields and scrubby areas with a vengeance.

Two wrens of wet, marshy areas are the **Sedge Wren** and the **Marsh Wren**. The former is a winter resident which prefers slightly drier areas than the latter, which is abundant in salt marshes the entire year. Wrens keep their tails cocked and are very vocal with chatters and fusses.

Kinglets are noisy, tiny, greenish winter residents from the North. **Ruby-crowneds** are virtually everywhere in winter, wherever trees and shrubs grow. Listen for their constant chatter before you look for their ruby crown, as the crown is sometimes inconspicuous and is seen only on males. **Golden-crowneds** are irruptive, being common one winter and nearly absent others. Their crown stripe is much easier to see and their high-pitched calls are barely audible and easily confused with wintering **Brown Creepers**.

The **Blue-gray Gnatcatcher** is a tiny insectivore with a cocked, long tail and a thin bill. Their song is a high-pitched jumble of notes, sounding like a sped-up Alvin the Chipmunk. The fact that they also imitate other species makes their song even more interesting. Their nests, built with lichen like hummingbird nests, camouflage themselves on hardwood branches.

Thrushes (Plate 17) are chunky, strong fliers and great songsters. The most abundant member of this family is the **American Robin**, a familiar bird to us all. An abundant winter resident, robin redbreast has been nesting in North Florida increasingly the past few decades. Also increasing is the **Eastern Bluebird**, whose numbers plummeted in the 1960's due to DDT. Robins prefer hardwood forests with bluebirds choosing open fields and Longleaf communities.

Five species of transit thrushes inhabit our state with their brown backs and spotted chests. The **Wood Thrush** arrives from the tropics in April and fills our moist hardwood forests with flute-like songs to die for. Around the time they leave in fall the **Hermit Thrush** takes their place as a winter resident, leaving in April. Three other species, **Gray-cheeked** and **Swainson's Thrushes** and the **Veery** all pass through in fall, less commonly in spring, and pose tough identification problems for birders. Consult the field guide, get a good look, and pray.

Related to the preceding are the Mimic Thrushes, longer and more slender than Thrushes, with a penchant for the songs of others. The **Northern Mockingbird** is abundant throughout in varied habitat, imitating an amazing assortment of songbirds and other avian notes. Not quite the mimic is the **Brown Thrasher**, lurking in thick undergrowth and hedges. Their similar song seems to be in syllables and their mimicry gets a B–.

Gray Catbirds, formerly a winter resident, now breed locally over much of North Florida. Their slate coloration hides them well in thickets and brush, and the chestnut color under the often-cocked tail seals the identification.

They are poor mimics but their most frequent call really sounds like a cat's meow. A dizzying assortment of "catbird" calls comes forth in the fall migration.

Starlings from Europe are largely found in our cities, living off our scraps

DESPISED CITY DWELLER

The **European Starling** has spread its filth all over the country and inhabits all our cities with messiness and disease. In winter they join other real blackbirds in pastures and fields, trying to make an honest living. Like the **House Sparrow**, city pigeon and various rats they make us not so proud of our accomplished ability to introduce animals where they don't belong.

American Pipits are common winter birds not well known by the rank and file. They seem to prefer wet areas where they walk along shorelines and forage in fields for insects and seeds. The **Cedar Waxwing** is a tame, favorite yard bird, also visiting Florida in the winter. In late winter they congregate in large flocks eating hordes of berries and sometimes staying into late spring.

Warblers (Plates 15 and 16) are the crown jewel of the bird world. About three dozen species pass through Florida annually, lending their greens, yellows, blue and reds to our canopies. Marvelous songsters, they fill our coastal scrub with sound in fall and spring with some breeding in North Florida. In all, thirteen species breed in some part of North Florida:

Prothonotary Warbler	Common along rivers and floodplains
Northern Parula	Common in moist forests to floodplains
Yellow-throated Warbler[1,2]	Uncommon in pine and oak woodlands of North Florida
Prairie Warbler[1,2]	Scarce in fields of Panhandle
Pine Warbler[1,2]	Abundant in the pine woods
Kentucky Warbler	Uncommon in moist forests of North Florida
Hooded Warbler	Fairly common in moist woodlands of North Florida
Worm-eating Warbler[2]	Rare and local on extreme West Florida rivers
Swainson's Warbler	Scarce and local in wet areas of central North Florida
Louisiana Waterthrush	Rare and local on eastern Panhandle rivers
Common Yellowthroat[1]	Abundant in marshes throughout North Florida
Yellow-breasted Chat	Common in brush, fields, cut-over forests
American Redstart[2]	Rare and local on extreme West Florida rivers

---

[1] Permanent resident (others are spring through fall birds)

[2] Scarce in summer but easily found in the migration

Four other species are winter residents, arriving in fall and leaving in spring:

Orange-crowned Warbler	Fairly common in swamps and open thickets
Yellow-rumped Warbler	Abundant in most semi-open areas, especially coastal
Black-and-white Warbler	Uncommon in oak and Beech/Magnolia forests
Palm Warbler	Regular in pine woods and coastally

Many species are strictly seen in the migration and neither in winter nor summer:

Golden-winged Warbler	Rare in spring and fall; seriously decreasing
Blue-winged Warbler	Uncommon in spring and fall; increasing
Tennessee Warbler	Regular spring and especially fall
Bachman's Warbler	Formerly bred; now probably extinct
Nashville Warbler	Rare in spring; uncommon in fall
Chestnut-sided Warbler	Uncommon in spring, common early fall
Cape May Warbler	Abundant late spring, rare in fall
Magnolia Warbler	Uncommon late spring, regular late fall
Black-throated Blue Warbler	Regular spring and fall

Cerulean Warbler	Rare in spring and fall; decreasing
Blackburnian Warbler	Uncommon late spring and fall
Black-throated Green Warbler	Regular spring and fall
Bay-breasted Warbler	Uncommon late spring, common in October
Blackpoll Warbler	Abundant late spring, rare in fall
Yellow Warbler	Regular late spring, common throughout fall
Connecticut Warbler	Rare in May
Canada Warbler	Rare late spring, regular around September 20
Wilson's Warbler	Rare spring and fall
Ovenbird	Regular in spring, common in fall
Northern Waterthrush	Common spring and fall
Mourning Warbler	Rare in early fall

Tanagers are beautiful fruit eaters with much red on males and yellow on females. They have thick bills, chunky bodies and are excellent fliers. The **Summer Tanager** breeds in hardwood and pine forests from spring through fall while the **Scarlet** passes through in modest numbers both migration seasons. Summer males maintain red year-round while Scarlet males appear like females with blackish wings. Scarlets are abundant at times in the spring migration on the coast.

The unique **Eastern Towhee** scratches the undergrowth from Jacksonville to Pensacola issuing their *to-hee* year-round. Though occasionally taken for a robin, towhees are familiar and prized by many yard-birders, as they faithfully come to feeders, and liven up yards with color and song. **Dark-eyed Juncos** are irregular winter residents in open areas around hardwoods in Florida.

Closely related to the above pair are the sparrows (Plate 13), a huge group of rather plain seed-eaters which largely winter in Florida. The familiar **House Sparrow**, seen so often in our cities, is actually an Old World Sparrow from Eurasia, and not a sparrow at all. We only have four true sparrows that breed in North Florida, and they aren't that easy to find.

The **Bachman's Sparrow** is a resident of the Longleaf community that is far easier to hear than see. Its song is a sustained whistle followed by a lower trilling whistle like someone calling his dog. Though common in their narrow niche, this species is closely watched for population problems.

Seaside Sparrows are common residents in some salt marshes but absent in many. This doesn't make them any easier to find than Bachman's, as a trudge through needlerush is required for results. Then you must differentiate this fleeting large, dark sparrow from possible sharp-tails or wrens. **Field Sparrows** nest in small numbers near the State Line in central North Florida, while **Chipping Sparrows** nest in extreme West Florida.

Winter resident sparrows include the Chipping, very common in fields and roadsides; **Nelson's** and **Salt Marsh Sharp-tailed**, in salt marshes; **Savannahs**, abundantly covering fields and grassy roads; **Song Sparrows**, usually in hedges near water; **Swamps**, in marshes and other wet areas; **Vespers**, uncommon near roads in late fall; **White-crowned**, uncommon in late fall along the coast; and **White-throated**, abundant in hardwood forests and neighborhoods.

Finches are like colorful sparrows that feed more in trees than on the ground. Most are northern and either migrate through Florida or winter here. Most are sparrow-sized but some, the grosbeaks, are larger and capable of cracking huge seeds and eating big chunks of fruit in the migration. The **Rose-breasted Grosbeak** is a regular migrant through North Florida. **Blue Grosbeaks** nest throughout Eastern North America, but some utilize our fields and other of our open areas for nesting. Their song somewhat resembles that of a **Summer Tanager**.

There are three sparrow-sized finches in North Florida, including the wintering **American Goldfinch**, usually seen in drab plumage. About the time they leave in April, **Indigo Buntings** arrive in huge numbers, and some nest in our fields. Along certain sections of the eastern and Panhandle coast, **Painted Buntings** spend the summer and nest in dense thickets. Considered the most beautiful bird in North America, these sing like Indigos and are amazingly secretive for their brilliant colors. Greenish females are often misidentified if the conical bill is not seen.

Eastern Meadowlarks are fairly common breeders in open areas of North Florida and abundant winter residents. Their brown backs, yellow chests and black bib are common to many birds of the grasslands like larks and Dickcissels worldwide (convergence). Their clear whistle is well known to outdoors people, many of whom call them "field larks."

Bobolinks love grasslands of the north central United States in summer and those of Argentina in winter. But in the migration they visit North Florida localities. Found more on the east coast in fall and the gulf coast in spring, they are

BLACKBIRDS ABOUND

one of several birds that follow this loop in migration. Fall birds are all like females but spring males are beautiful, with their white and buffy patches against a black background. They call a bit like **Orchard Orioles** or **Barn Swallows** and may be seen in the Panhandle in fall with east winds and commonly farther east.

Red-winged Blackbirds may be the most abundant bird in Florida, with some wintering flocks numbering in the tens of thousands. Less common in summer, they breed in marshes and grassy Karrst lakes where one male assembles a harem. His job is stud, singing and protecting nests from intrusion. Females are brown-streaked and not readily identifiable by many.

Blackbirds the size of redwings without any wing patches occur in winter. Usually found in swampy areas and riverbottoms are **Rusty Blackbirds**, named for the brownish immatures. The **Brewer's Blackbird** is fairly common in West Florida where it flocks in fields and pastures with other blackbirds.

This Red-wing keeps watch for enemies while his harem raises his kids

Various species of this group are found abundantly all over North Florida (opposite page)

Brewer's Blackbird

Boat-tailed Grackle

Common Grackle

Brown-headed Cowbird

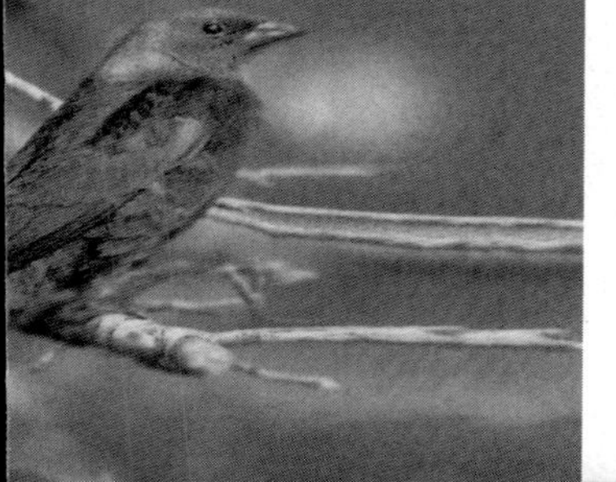

Florida also has two species of grackles. The **Boat-tailed Grackle** is mostly a coastal species but does inhabit some large Karrst lakes. **Common Grackles** are abundant in cities, farmland and other areas touched by human hands. Boat-tail males, which also accumulate harems, have a huge tail and females are brown, unlike Commons.

The low-rent **Brown-headed Cowbird** is abundant in North Florida, especially in the breeding season, unfortunately. A brood parasite, they lay their eggs in other species' nests where the young often displace and kill the mother's own chicks. Despite being a native bird, cowbirds are a menace because we have increased their populations dramatically through our use of agricultural fields which provide huge food sources. They are easily told from other blackbirds by their conical bill.

Orioles are as orange as tanagers are red (Plate 14). The summering **Orchard Oriole** male is burnt orange and black with the females a fairly plain yellow (often mistaken for Pine Warblers, etc.). They make their sock-like woven nests in hardwoods and leave our parts by Labor Day. The **Baltimore Oriole** passes through in spring and fall, occasionally wintering. Orioles are fruit-eaters like the tanagers, their diet providing the energy to support their bright colors.

The bird migration is a great time to be in the field. Not only can observers see

birds that only occur during certain windows in spring and fall, the weather is pleasant and many other interesting animals are active. Landbird families such as flycatchers, vireos, buntings, tanagers, grosbeaks, thrushes, orioles and especially warblers are found in many places. The coast, often the first or last place a bird stops en route, is usually the best place to observe migrants. Some water birds are also found coastally in the migration, although freshwater mud flats and marshes can really be productive.

Bad weather has forced these swallows down for the afternoon in the migration

Weather plays a large part in how many migrants are seen on any given day. Amazingly, for opposite reasons, cold front days are best in spring or fall, and the weather is usually exquisite for doing field work as well. In spring, the north winds ground migrating birds that would normally pass over us, creating huge "fall-outs" with dozens of bird species. In fall, these same fronts bring the birds to us, instead of them lingering to the north, waiting for favorable winds. Rain also downs birds in either season but most rain is associated with fronts in spring or fall.

The spring migration peak is late April, but good numbers of migrants may be seen from late March to early May. In fall, which is more spread out, September and October are excellent, but some birds virtually finish migrating by Labor Day while some wintering birds, like geese and finches, may not arrive in force until November.

SWALLOWS GALORE

If you wish to observe bird migrants, pick a natural area with water and woods along the coast. Along the Panhandle you will notice peninsular migrants flying east along the shoreline in fall, heading around the gulf, although the opposite in spring is not so noticable. Other birds are trans-gulf and wait along the coast feeding in trees until dawn or dusk when they strike out across the trackless waters. On the Atlantic coast, they will be flying south down the coast in fall and back north in spring.

There are other differences between spring and fall. Spring birds are in a hurry, driven by their desire to reproduce. Fall birds are often leisurely, although cold-front days have them moving more briskly. Spring birds are in their breeding plumages, while most fall species are wearing their winter colors following their post-nuptial moult. Spring birds are quite vocal and many males are singing, while fall birds are often silent and less conspicuous.

Winter birding has fewer variables, with activity all day and little bird movement. Summer birds are most easily found in the "cool" of the morning; you can reserve your afternoons for air conditioners and lemonade. But if you are a birder, there is nothing like being in the field on a great day for bird migration. The surprises, the color and the beauty are almost too much to behold.

The Magic of Mammals

Mammals have none of the bright colors of their fellow warm-blooded friends, the birds. They also lack the musical songs, and calling isn't even done by most of their ranks. The vast majority can't fly, so migration is pretty much out of the question. They lack the specialized bills of birds, and their feet are pretty plain. So what do they have that's so special?

Brains. Mammals are so far ahead of bird (brains) they are the gifted compared to the profoundly retarded. With these brains come an adaptability that few birds can match. This class of hairy creatures has come to dominate our planet since the great meteor 65,000,000 years ago and this ruling of the roost caused our species to (somewhat immodestly) dub the Cenozoic the "Age of Mammals."

Mammals have traded bright colors for great camouflage, as their browns and grays blend with the forest floor with unmatched success. This is good for mammals because they cannot fly and some are pretty slow afoot. Their cunning supplements their ability to hide and I have often found myself in very close proximity without knowing of their presence for quite some time. They may be viewed on Plate 5.

Our furry friends also have the best teeth in the animal kingdom. They are heterodontic, with various purposes for different types. Canines kill, incisors cut and molars chew and grind. We have first hand knowledge of teeth, of course, and can see the value of this arrangement. But what you may not know is just how important these teeth are historically.

In the earlier part of the Cenozoic, long after the dinosaurs were nothing but a bad dream to mammals, birds were the dominant predator. Huge, flightless birds six to eight feet tall stomped along the trails eating anything that moved. Their massive hooked beaks tore through mammal flesh like we eat candy bars. Being warm-blooded was a big advantage for birds over reptiles, but it was their size and great bill that placed them over the developing mammals. It was actually a subtle advance in mammalian structure that eventually tipped the scales in their favor.

The carnivores developed teeth for cutting, so they could slice meat easily—live or dead. Their new fangled dontic scissors ripped large bird necks with brutal gashes, and many massive avian predators fell dead as a species. Mammals quickly flourished as a group and radiated into many niches previously held by birds. They were the new kings.

The translation of this today is that across North Florida, mammals are the dominant creatures. Eagles are big and fierce (and rare) and rattlesnakes are poisonous, but they are hardly a brief match for a coyote, bobcat or bear. And that is not to mention man himself. But even the small, subtle mammals are doing well and clearly reign over North Florida and the world.

The most primitive mammal is a success story if ever there was one. The **Opossum**, our only marsupial, traversed more miles than any migrant ever. Originally in Australia, they crossed the Antarctic when it was warmer and farther north, winding up in southern South America. With time, they radiated and became many tropical species to our south and when South and Central America articulated in the Eocene, they began another long trek toward our continent. One kind made it to North America and is abundant throughout our state and beyond.

Something like a small mouse, shrews are seldom out in the open for us to see

Possums give birth to the tiniest of young which make an amazing journey of their own up the mother's belly and into a pouch. Here they develop until they can move around on their own and discover the world. The claims about them playing dead are true, but beware—wild 'possum will bite savagely when provoked. Frankly, this is true of most wild mammals. So admire these sojourners from a distance and watch for them while driving on country roads.

A TAME SHREW

Shrews have a metabolism only rivaled by hummingbirds. The amazing thing is, they live on meat and not sugar! They are tiny mammals normally encountered while turning over trash like boards, but have the appetite of a horse. No arthropod is safe around them and they will soon starve to death if kept in captivity. I'm just glad they aren't the size of horses! Our species are the **Least**, **Southeastern** and **Short-tailed Shrew**.

Related to shrews are moles. These insectivores are subterranean and have velvet fur, huge front feet for digging and useless, vestigial eyes. Not a favorite of many with lawns and gardens, moles are amazing animals and highly adapted for life underground. The tunnels can often be detected from above and usually belong to the **Eastern Mole**.

Bats are specialized beetle-eating mice with more tales and folklore than snakes. Their front limbs have linings to give the creature lift and radar for tracking bugs in the air. Their tiny eyes tell them when it is getting dark, but they are not nearly as blind as myth claims. They basically fly silently, but, when close, high-pitched squeaking noises may be heard. They hide in dark places during the day and sometimes emerge in great numbers around dusk.

Our two common species are the **Red Bat**, which occupies the pine forest, and the **Seminole Bat**, found in hardwoods like oaks. They are medium-sized bats, with the former flying higher and having a redder hue than the mahogany of the latter. Neither species migrates, and it takes cold weather to cause them to hibernate.

Other bats in our area include the smallish **Eastern Pipistrel**, found in open areas regularly. The diverse genus *Miotis* are mostly cave-dwelling bats and different ones of these diminutive animals are found throughout North Florida. One other small bat, the **Mexican Free-tailed**, is locally abundant under certain bridges and in old buildings.

The large **Yellow Bat** migrates through North Florida and can be ridiculously common at times. Its larger cousin, the **Hoary Bat**, seems to be a winter resident near the Georgia state line (I have collected three of the six Florida records north of Tallahassee). Their silver fur-tips give them a "hoary" (meaning silver) appearance, looking almost like frost.

The **Evening Bat** and **Eastern Big-eared Bat** supposedly live in North Florida, but I've never recorded them. Identification of bats is difficult in the dim light of dusk, though, and much is not known about the status and life histories of these elusive critters.

Black Bears are fairly common in North Florida where sizable forests still grow. As omnivores, they find much to eat, needing to support their great weight. These are shy creatures, almost never having attacked humans. They can be a nuisance in yards, and at least some caution seems prudent with such a large, powerful animal. They are most easily seen in May along forest roads when berries are strewn along the roadside. The other color morphs are virtually absent here.

The **Raccoon** is about as adaptable as they come. These omnivores range throughout Eastern North America and always seem to find ways to profit from human presence. They are basically shy but become tame in places like parks and camping areas. However, very tame 'coons should be given a wide berth, as incidents of rabies do occur. Raccoons are easily recognised by their ringed tail and black facial mask.

River Otters are cute creatures, seen playing in our rivers and savage carnivores when cornered or attacking dogs in water. Their diet is fish and crayfish with occasional mollusks thrown in. Otters have disappeared from many of their historical playgrounds but still survive in small numbers on some of our more pristine rivers and other fresh water bodies. Their terrestrial cousins **Mink** and **Long-tailed Weasel** occur in North Florida but seem virtually invisible.

Striped Skunks are common in North Florida, especially in sandy soil such as the coast where they can burrow. Omnivores, they eat small animals, plant tubers, berries and are killed on roads at times while eating carrion. The rare **Spotted Skunk** is small with white squiggles on a black body. Both have the ability to spew out musk and pollute the air for miles.

A clever creature making more and more inroads into North Florida, the coyote is not altogether welcomed by many people

The **Coyote** has made its way to Florida and is living right under many peoples' noses, feeding on garbage, small animals and, sadly, cats. In natural areas they bring with them their ecology from the west and probably have a deleterious effect on many native animals' populations. The highly adaptable Coyote is a hard animal not to admire, but its presence in North Florida represents a "clear and present danger" to native species that desperately need our help. There are no wolves living wild in Florida, or even close.

G**ray Foxes** are common throughout North Florida and are often seen crossing country roads, especially after dark. Watch for the long, bushy, straight tail. They have reddish on their coats and are often called **Red Foxes**, but this species lives naturally only in extreme West Florida. They are, however, occasionally turned loose on fox hunts and earn their freedom. Reds may be separated from Grays by their black legs. Foxes are carnivores, eating mostly birds and rodents.

B**obcats** are extremely shy and adept at hiding but are actually fairly common in wilder areas of North Florida. They may be identified crossing roads by their short tail and hunched appearance. Other wild cats are mostly peoples' imaginations, as there are no **Florida Panthers** in North Florida. Ted Turner did learn a lesson about the government's resolve to restrict introductions to their releases, and remnants of his pumas may still be seen East of Tallahassee.

One mammal, not completely wild or domestic, is the huge population of feral cats that have escaped or been turned loose throughout North Florida (and about everywhere else). These are incredibly destructive creatures, eating lizards, small snakes and especially birds, none of which have any knowledge of what cats are.

This doesn't work out too well for the cats, either, who soon die of starvation or excruciating disease. Even domestic cats with owners are frequently run over (or worse) but kill many small animals during their lifetime. Bells don't work to prevent this unnatural predation, and neither does declawing the cat, as cats bat birds and other prey with their paws. The only solution is to get rid of these half-wild "feral" cats and somehow convince owners that cats should be kept indoors, and that the vast majority of these pets are destroying our natural resources.

The **Gray Squirrel** is abundant and living happily with people all over the East. They are largely responsible for unwittingly planting many oak trees, an interesting mutualistic relationship. The **Fox Squirrel**, a native of both Longleafs and oak forests, survives in some areas despite pressures on them from deforestation, predators and other human interference. A polymorphic species, they may be black, gray or almost white, often with a black nose. The **Southern Flying Squirrel** is a resident in pine and oak forests in the South and may be identified by its high-pitched whistles at night. Nothing is more exciting than seeing one swoop over open areas and land softly on trees without effort. The **Eastern Chipmunk** is found in the Marianna area locally in hardwoods with geophysical relief.

The **Southeastern Pocket Gopher** is the mammalian counterpart to the **Gopher Tortoise**, both of whom make burrows in sandy soil. Rather than providing homes for snakes, though, these are the principal food of the **Florida Pine Snake**. Pines are where they live and may be seen in many places across North Florida. They are named for the cheek pouches in their faces for food storage.

The **Beaver** is still found in certain parts of North Florida (absent in the peninsula) and has been reintroduced into other parts. Some landowners don't appreciate their "improvements" on fresh water ecosystems, and many are killed for their transgressions. It is true that they warn other Beavers of danger by slapping their flat tails on the water, but they have few if any natural enemies in this part of the world. By the way, by any assessment, cooked Beaver is terrible.

FOOD FOR ALL

There are four species of mice in North Florida which are confusing both in identification as well as ecologically. They are the **Oldfield**, **Cotton**, **Eastern Harvest** and **Golden Mouse**. Some are distinguishable only with an examination of the incisors by experts, so calling them "mice" seems understandable.

Abundant Cotton Rats are preyed upon by everything from rattlesnakes to hawks

The **Eastern Wood-rat** is larger than mice, and told from other species, including our introduced (European) ones by soft fur and a short, hairy tail. These "packrats" are common in hardwood areas and sometimes do damage to our property left unattended. The somewhat similar **Hispid Cotton Rat** has grizzled fur and a bare tail and is abundant in fields across North Florida. It forms a tremendous food source for creatures such as rattlesnakes and hawks and seems to not be a threat to humans like the species described in the next paragraph.

Black and **Norway Rats** are European imports that carry diseases (sometimes carrying the fleas that carry the diseases, such as the Bubonic Plague) and infest our cities and ruin our wiring. Blacks are very common in sea ports but come far inland as well. Their tails are longer than their head and body, unlike the Norway Rat. Blacks seem to prefer tops of buildings while Norways stay in rubbish piles and floors.

Two species of rats are semiaquatic and natural to our North Florida ecosystem. The **Florida Water Rat** makes huge grassy nests in swamps and Karrst lakes throughout North Florida and provide a food source for predators like Northern Harriers and Eastern Kingsnakes. **Rice Rats** are more a shoreline species which may invade rice fields and do modest amounts of damage.

Two species of rabbits live across North Florida. The **Eastern Cottontail** is a widespread species of the grasslands and open areas, employing its expendable white tail as a flash color for bobcats and other predators to aim at. They are very fast and hide exceptionally well. The large ears are for heat regulation; broadside to the sun heats blood in capillaries and parallel to the sun's rays allows for heat loss.

The **Marsh Rabbit** is an inhabitant of damp, dark areas, where its smaller ears need less of a function in heat regulation. They lack the "cotton" tail and are generally a smaller, darker rabbit. In extreme Northwest Florida, in Escambia County, the **Swamp Rabbit** lives in cane and other wet areas, with its range extending west to Texas.

The pigs that run wild across various parts of North Florida are from **European Wild Boar** stock. In many areas they have become an extreme environmental problem and many game managers are taking strong steps to eliminate them. They rip fragile habitat to shreds and eat many small animals such as salamanders and frogs. This is one of the most serious and damaging human introductions of all time and all possible steps should be taken to eliminate it.

The **White-tailed Deer** is a popular Floridian, both as a game animal and an interesting wildlife subject to watch. They are browsers, with slanted teeth for ripping leaves off bushes (as opposed to grazers like horses and cows, whose molars are flat). Deer are rich brown in summer but turn gray in the cool season. Like the Cottontail, their white tail causes would-be predators to go for the expendable portion of the body, allowing the creature to escape.

Of course, there aren't many predators left. Panthers no longer roam North Florida, **Red Wolves** have been gone for years, and humans continue to create more and more deer habitat by clearing portions of deep woods. The fact is, deer are, in many places, starving and dying of diseases because of overpopulation, and man's hunting ironically is keeping the problem from getting worse.

Armadillos are unique "possums on the half shell" that burrow for roots, berries and gobs of insects. They have a horny material covering their back for protection but certain predators have learned to neutralize this defense. Armadillos will also bite hard, scoot through the woods at a pretty good clip and even roll into a ball like a giant pillbug.

This is a tropical family of mammals, having little hair and homodontic peg-like teeth. In the past, one race lived in the peninsula and another in West Florida, but in the 1970's the two met in Leon County and should be forever merged. Primitive creatures, armadillos have been found in fossils fifty million years old.

Few mammals have gotten the attention **Manatee** have. These gentle giants roam the warm gulf and Atlantic waters from North Carolina to the Florida Keys and along the Upper Gulf Coast. In winter they find warm water sources such as power plant discharge or rivers with somewhat constant temperatures. Confirmed vegetarians, Manatee eat a variety of river and bay grasses, and probably a few small animals that are inadvertently ingested with the salad.

Everyone loves dolphins

Speaking of the Atlantic and Gulf, the **Bottle-nosed Dolphin** is by far our most abundant marine mammal. A friendly and approachable creature, they are intelligent and playful. In some places, such as off Panama City, there are pods that become very chummy with people and allow close swims. Though not all officials are happy with this, many folks experience great joy being with these remarkable animals.

Dolphins are fish eaters with homodontic teeth, almost like Armadillo. Porpoises, which are not synonymous with dolphins, have spade-shaped teeth, while 'Flipper' and his ilk have conical teeth. Dolphins (and porpoises) have flat tails for pushing them to the surface (on porpoise) for periodic breaths of air. Sharks, which some confuse with dolphins, have longitudinal tails, with a long top tail fin to push down and force the heavy head to move straight through the water. Dolphins have their blow hole on top of their head for convenient breathing, which takes place every minute or two. As warm-blooded animals, they have tremendous endurance, which helps when one chases fish for a living.

Life arose from the sea in the Paleozoic, over 350,000,000 years ago. It is interesting that many animals since have returned, trading their terrestrial adaptations for flippers and fins. Joining the dolphins, porpoises, whales, seals and sea lions are sea snakes, sea turtles, sea otters and a host of birds, all realizing the ocean is teeming with life and food. Let's hope the last creature to develop doesn't ruin our seas for everyone else.

Major Area Descriptions and Field Trips

Across North Florida, most people live in several of the major cities or their outskirts. In this chapter we will look at the general ecosystems of these major cities and talk about what is special to each area. In addition, we will outline several field trips for those who wish to explore the natural areas of their home. It also might serve as a guide for anyone wanting to travel across North Florida to see what creatures lie across the Sunshine State's northern edge.

We will start with the sprawling city of **Jacksonville** on the eastern edge of North Florida, near the Atlantic Ocean. Located near the mouth of the St. John's River, many waterbirds may be seen right in the city, as well as the usual landbirds. But to discover what lies in the former ecosystem, trips to the northeast and northwest are suggested.

Nestled in the bosom of downtown Jacksonville are two natural areas that are nice to visit and offer birds and other animals for nature enthusiasts. Take University Blvd. north and then get on Ft. Caroline Road to the Ft. Caroline National Monument. Next to it is the Theodore Roosevelt Preserve, which offers excellent birding and the spotting of other wild animals. This preserve was owned by a Jacksonville native and hermit, Willie Brown, who saved it while all lands around it were being sacrificed for "development." Donated to the Nature Conservancy, this and the National Monument offer a respite for

naturalists, not far from the maddi crowd. While there, don't miss Spani Pond, which offers many interesting fre water creatures and a lovely view.

Theodore Roosevelt Preserve lies within Jacksonville and provides beauty and animals for visitors

There is a route up the coast that is exce lent for birds, migrating butterflies and other creatures and whole day is required to make it. You begin by heading up H 17 and taking HW 105 east to the Kingsley Plantation on t southwest end of Ft. George Island. The loop road is excelle for migrant songbirds, Painted Buntings in summer, and there a many animals throughout the woodland. Working this ro slowly in the morning will yield good results before heading the ocean.

Stay on 105 to A1A and discover the wo derland of the Mayport Jetties. Once called "Woods Bank" it no has the official name and designation of Hugenot Park, manag by the City of Jacksonville. The wintering population of sea bir is astounding, and the bushes and scrub are super places woodland migrants in spring and fall. There are other animals here such as snakes, lizards, frogs and butterflies. The mighty Johns runs along the south edge of the property offering go views of loons, grebes, mergansers and many gulls and terns e tering and leaving the river. In my little tir here as a youth, I have personally se Ipswich Sparrow, Snow Buntings, Lapla Longspur and Horned Lark within t dunes, as well as Glaucous and Iceland Gu on the shores, scoters, shearwaters a jaegers over the ocean, and Purp Sandpipers on the jetties, Wow!

The Purple Sandpiper barely eases into Florida from the North in winter

If you can tear yourself away, head north on A1A and enjoy Little and Big Talbot Islands. They have lots of migrating birds in spring and fall and the swales and ponds are loaded with snakes, frogs, interesting fish and LOTS of insects (at times). Before leaving Talbot, be sure to stop at the marsh on the right just before the bridge. Once a worthless cattail marsh, nature flooded it with salt water, killing the cattails, and created a wonderful area for birds and small critters. I have seen Mink in this area and never in the Panhandle. Big and Little Talbot State Parks are on this island, and camping arrangements may be made at (904) 251-2320.

Ft. Clinch State Park has beautiful hardwoods and many interesting animals in the woods and open areas

BEAUTIFUL SANCTUARY

Continuing up A1A the scenery is outstanding and many large water birds such as herons, egrets, ibis, Osprey and others are easily seen. Stop wherever you see congregations of birds and get away from the road. Be sure to make time to stop at the Ft. Clinch Pier at the mouth of the St. Mary's River for a walk out onto the Atlantic. This is one of the premier spots for pelagic birds, with opportunities for jaegers, shearwaters, petrels, and much more. Bring a telescope or strong binoculars and a field guide. Afternoon, with the sun at your back, is your best bet. Return home taking A1A west to I-95 and back into Jacksonville.

On another day, a lovely place to visit is Crooked River State Park, just north of the mouth of the St.

Mary's River. Easiest access is up I-95, taking HW 40 east just four miles past the Georgia State Line. Essentially a marine habitat, it offers quiet waters, many birds and some natural habitat to explore.

PATH TO

Admittedly, there is a paucity of natural areas around Jacksonville, so to really see some good inland locations, I suggest you take 301 northwest to Folkston. Here you head south to find six miles or so of Longleaf Pine Forest, called the Cornelia County Recreation Area. Many of the Longleaf species described in Chapter 2 are present here, including Red-cockaded Woodpecker and other pine forest birds.

This is also an excellent entrance to the mammoth Okefenokee Swamp, fabled with its huge alligators and snake-filled trees. This is no fable. There are not only big 'gators and snakes out the wazoo, there is a plethora of freshwater species of frogs, salamanders and fishes, plus various mammals and birds that love the deep wetlands. An interesting geophysical structure, this great swamp is the world's largest peat bog, spanning fifty miles across at any point.

This is a marvelous area to camp with good facilities and safe supervision. There are amazing boardwalks for night viewing, where a strong flashlight will open up the swamp world safely to whole (quiet) families. Barred Owls hoot, fish float right on the surface and the rare Carpenter Frog klinks off in the distance. This species has only been found in Florida at the southern end of this great swamp, by my father, Bruce Means and myself one steamy night.

THE DEPTHS

This opening leads to the Okefenokee and all the dark mysteries of this great wilderness

An alternate route to the Okefenokee might be to take I-10 west to HW 125, which merges with HW 127 north. Turn left on HW 2 and you will border along the swamp to your right. You can then enter Georgia on HW 94 and take HW 177 straight into the swamp. This is a wild area with amazing numbers of animals!

Running south from the Okefenokee, then east, then north and finally east again, as if drawn up by the state's highway department, is the beautiful St. Mary's River. Not the easiest river to access, it forms the border with Florida and Georgia for well over a hundred miles before emptying into the Atlantic Ocean north of Fernandina Beach.

This river emanates from the Okefenokee and is therefore extremely blackwater. Its banks in Georgia are low and surrounded with pine flatwoods. As it continues, it builds a higher and higher bank, shrouded in oak forest. The river is wild, with snakes and 'gators, and excellent fishing. With much of

SIZE IS RELATIVE

the bank privately owned, it has maintained its natural beauty and is well worth a canoe trip. Further information, such as public landings, may be received from the St. John's Water Management District in Palatka (904) 329-4401.

This east end of North Florida has many unique creatures. The Atlantic shore quite naturally has a lot of marine animals not found on the Panhandle coastline, including gobs of deep water species. Many of these kinds die and wash in, making the East Coast a terribly interesting place to drive and look for specimens. Some of the marine fishes that only occur on this "side" of Florida and not the gulf waters are Short-nosed Sturgeon, Blueback Herring, American and Hickory Shad and Sea Lamprey, to name a few.

The Great Black-backed Gull, peculiar in Florida to the North-eastern section, is huge for a gull, but is dwarfed by the Brown Pelican

There are also several Atlantic birds commonly spotted that are seldom seen on the gulf coast. Among these are Great Black-backed Gull and Purple Sandpiper, found from October through April. Other sea birds found much more commonly here than in the Panhandle include loons, grebes, scoters, Oldsquaw, gannet, jaegers and shearwaters.

The bird migration is quite different along the Atlantic coast, as opposed to the Panhandle. There are some birds which migrate right down the Atlantic coast essentially north to south, following the coastline. Huge numbers of Sharp-shinned Hawks stream down like a predatorial river in September and October, making a living nightmare for migrating songbirds. Not all songbirds follow Panhandle patterns, either.

HALFWAY THERE

Bobolinks, which fly out over the Atlantic in fall, and abundantly through Florida in spring, are halfway between their destinations of Canada and Argentina when visiting our state

In fall, when Bobolinks and Cape May, Black-throated Blue and Blackpoll Warblers are virtually absent on the gulf coast, they may be amazingly abundant on the Atlantic coast, depending on wind direction. Many species , such as the hawks that were mentioned earler, are also far more common, because they are landmark migrants and use the shoreline to navigate. However, in spring, the Panhandle probably gets more migrants as a result of many birds such as the above migrating in a loop, where they are displaced to the East in fall and return in spring more to the West. This explains the tremendous spring days here in my present home state of Texas, and the relative paucity of fall migrants.

In the salt marshes there is the usual cast of characters from Panhandle shorelines, but the newly described Salt Marsh Sharp-tailed Sparrow joins the fray along our Atlantic seashore. There also seems to be a tendency for northern birds to be more regular in this area than the Panhandle (see the fourth paragraph of this chapter).

Moving inland, let's check the vertebrate species unique to the Jacksonville area. Among fish, this ecosystem specializes in the Eastern Mud Minnow, Lined Top Minnow, Mud Sunfish and the rare Black-banded Sunfish. These fish hardly, if ever, make it to the Panhandle and give the Jacksonville area unique species richness and identity.

Reptiles found in northeast Florida that seldom occur further west are Striped Mud Turtle, Spotted Turtle, Florida Box Turtle, the introduced Brown Anole, Island Glass Lizard, Striped Crayfish Snake, Peninsula Ribbon Snake, Pine Woods Snake, Florida Brown Snake, Yellow Rat Snake, Florida Kingsnake and the beautiful Canebrake (Timber) Rattlesnake.

Osceola ranges from beautiful Longleaf to deep swamp with plenty of convenient access roads

Three amphibians in northeast Florida are also absent (or nearly so) in the Panhandle: the Striped Newt, Carpenter Frog and Many-lined Salamander. But the part of the Okefenokee Swamp west of Jacksonville is an excellent place for amphibians, fresh water fishes and reptiles. There are also many wetland birds that cannot readily be found around the concrete and asphalt jungle of Jacksonville.

GEM OF A NATIONAL FOREST

L**ake City** lies near I-10, and more importantly, near the Osceola National Forest. This sprawling pine forest forms the southern end of the Okefenokee Swamp and encompasses such beautiful natural areas as Ocean Pond. There are numerous paved roads through the forest such as State Road 250, and too many dirt roads to count. These make exploring this oasis easy and the camp sites scattered through the forest beg us to examine it further. One plan when headed west from Jacksonville might be to take HW 125 to Taylor and the long stretch of SR 250 right through the forest diagonally to Lake City.

The northern half of the Osceola National Forest is, according to the National Forestry Service, naturally occurring Slash Pines, although I thought it interesting they were growing in rows. Logging has taken its toll on much of the forest earlier this century, but current efforts by the service to convert planted and clear-cut areas to their original state should be applauded, and there are certainly some fine areas developing along SR 250 and some side roads.

This is also true of the southern half of the forest where officials are restoring Longleaf Pine areas, which stood for many square miles before our timber activities. Already replete with Longleafs, the future looks bright for the forest and its creatures—such as Red-cockaded Woodpeckers—in the new century.

WAY DOWN SUWANE

Flowing through the Okefenokee Swamp, far to the north is the famous Suwanee River, with all its folklore and magic. It winds its way, in no special hurry, south near Lake City before taking an improbable turn to the northwest, southeast and straight south to the gulf. This is a beautiful river, which combines characteristics of spring-fed and alluvial systems into a majestic lotic body. It is easily accessible from Lake City by heading north on HW's 41 or 47 (441). Tubing and fishing is excellent, but wildlife viewing, both on the river and through the adjacent woodlands, is a treat. The Suwannee and the national forest is a far cry from the planted slash pines, pastures and fields, so worthless for wild animals, that lie southwest and southeast of Lake City.

Just down HW 47 from Lake City is Ichetucknee State Park, with about the coldest water one can imagine! This is a popular tubing destination, but many wild animals may be seen in the park and along the river (including Redbelly Water Snakes). There is no tubing after Labor Day until Memorial Day, so the park is more peaceful and closer to nature (904) 497-2511.

On the south end of our focus is the university town of **Gainesville**, half way across the upper reaches of the Florida peninsula. There is a sprawling wetland called Paine's Prairie just south of the city with tremendous populations of fishes, aquatic reptiles, amphibians and water birds. It is sad that both I-75 and HW 441 transect this wonderful ecosystem and somewhat miraculous that so many creatures may still be found, despite eight lanes of speeding traffic. Swamp Snakes, Water Snakes, turtles, various frogs, interesting sunfish and killifish and wading birds are but a sample of what this reservoir holds. Fed occasionally by the Alachua Sink, water levels fluctuate and at high water, untold numbers of creatures attempt the gauntlet across the merciless asphalt. In 1968 I walked 441 early in the morning for two miles and counted 976 (!) dead snakes along that particular stretch. Amazingly, huge kills like that still occur. While in Gainesville, the State Museum on the campus of the University of Florida provides wonder and education for the whole family.

UPON THE RIVER

Stephen Foster's lovely song was inspired by this mystical river

Two fine forested areas may be found along the northern reaches of the city as well. For Pine Upland habitat, Loblollies and some Longleaf, try Morningside Nature Center on HW 222. Not terribly far from Morningside is San Felasco, a hardwood forest with Beech/Magnolia species and mesic soil. Beautiful damp soil oaks such as Laurel and Water Oaks provide cool shade and many songbirds are easily found.

Between these two contrasting forests and Paine's Prairie, Gainesville residents may be treated to fine wildlife and lovely scenery.

Between Gainesville and Tallahassee there are at least three natural areas that are worth a visit. Thirteen miles west of Live Oak is the Suwanee River State Park, where this famous river joins the Withlacoochee to provide scenic beauty and plenty of animals. Plant communities include sand hills, river swamps and hardwood hammocks with many native species of animals quite tame and easily seen. Make reservations to camp at (904) 362-2746.

Due west of Gainesville is Manatee Springs, located near Chiefland, Florida. There are swamps with cypress, gum, ash and maple surrounding the springs, but the main attraction is the famous Manatee. Over a hundred million gallons of water flow from Manatee Springs daily to join the Suwanee downstream, and many birds, amphibians and reptiles are drawn to this water world. Camping and hiking trails enable the nature lover to revel at this pristine park (352) 493-6072.

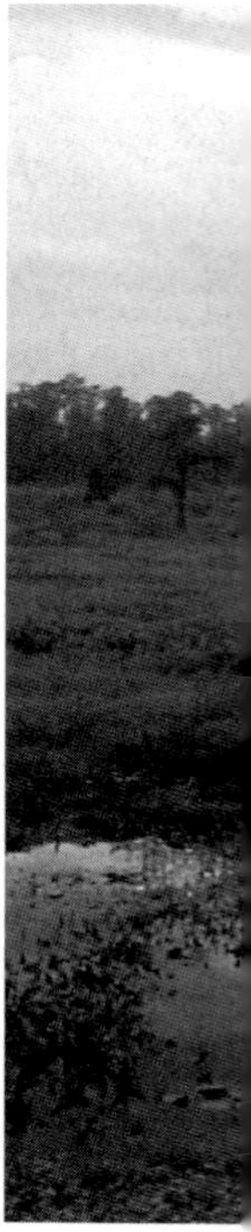

A MARSH

While taking the less traveled road from Gainesville to Tallahassee (HW 27), try a canoe trip on the wild side on the Econfina River. Take HW 98, about half way between Perry and St. Mark's Lighthouse south of Tallahassee, and the Econfina crosses the road with a convenient landing for canoes. This is one wild trip, with swamp birds, Brown Water Snakes on the limbs, and exciting near misses with limbs. But with all the nature it offers, this is not a trip for the inexperienced. Canoers may be picked up downstream by taking HW 14 south.

TO DIE FOR

Tallahassee is not only the capital city, it is the gateway to the best natural areas for animals and unique ecosystems in the State. It truly has it all: huge Karrst lakes, all three types of rivers, pristine Longleaf Pine Forests, untouched grass beds, savannahs, and much more — all within an hour's drive from this lovely, oak-shrouded modern city.

Lake Miccosukee's highly productive wetlands span miles and are only a few minutes east of Tallahassee

East and north of Tallahassee are two Karrst lakes that deserve a visit. Out HW 90 east a few minutes is Lake Miccosukee, with its lily pad covering, marshy areas and open water in winter. It is hard to list what is found there, but its strength may be what lies below the surface. Slender Dwarf Siren are easily caught with a pool net in the weeds, huge Greater Siren amble along the shore and spillway under HW 90 at night; gar, bass and mudfish stand ready to tear the rod right out of your hand, and a neat collection of *Fundulus* and other small "minnow" species zip across the surface and hide in the weeds.

There is now a catwalk built for people to observe wildlife overlooking the spillway by the highway. This is a short but exciting walk during the day and the opportunity of a lifetime at night with a strong flashlight. Well supervised kids will see nature like few have, with mammoth siren, behemoth frogs and menacing gar within easy sight.

On the surface, huge Green Water Snakes laze in the morning sun, dreaming of tearing some intruder's hand off at the wrist. Bandeds are very common as well, with gargantuan Mud Snakes coming up for air periodically. Leopard, Bronze and Southern Cricket Frogs dot the bank with large flocks of woodland birds like titmice and chickadees fussing at Barred Owls and Gray Rat Snakes. It is as healthy a lake as Florida has to offer, with rafts of coots and Ring-necked Ducks thick as thieves in winter and wading birds lining the shallows. Out the Centerville Road you will enjoy the canopy drive to the sleepy town of Miccosukee, where public access to the lake is easy and rental boats are offered. From alligators to Red-winged Blackbirds and inland Boat-tailed Grackles, this is a paradise for those who want to experience nature at work.

North of Tallahassee, mighty Lake Jackson spreads its acreage east of HW 27 and north of I-10. Not the same lake it was twenty-five years ago, it still offers excellent wildlife viewing, but a lack of environmental regulations controlling growth and urban sprawl has damaged this great ecosystem, possibly beyond recovery. It does have the interesting habit of disappearing every few years (though not the exact twenty-five that some people claim) when the mud plugging the hole to the aquifer gives way under pressure like pulling the stopper in a bathroom tub. Further to the north, however, is Lake Iamonia, which is on par with Lake Miccosukee as a healthy, productive, animal laden lake.

The Orchard Pond Road, which runs across the northern limit of Lake Jackson, is part of the red hills ecosystem, making one wonder what state they are actually in! Towering pines and deep gullies through the clay house everything from White-breasted Nuthatches and Red-headed Woodpeckers to Eastern Tiger Salamanders and Smooth Earth Snakes. A singularly bad road, it has excellent wildlife opportunities on both ends, as well as along its few miles.

LIGHTING THE NIGHT

At the west end, at Old Baimbridge Road, is the Old Iron Bridge (recently improved) where the lovely floodplains house Southern Dusky and Three-lined Salamanders, Bronze Frogs, snakes of several species, Five-lined and Ground Skinks, and many other herptiles. Typical river bottom birds are abundant, with fall migrants in evidence August to October. Prothonotary Warblers and Acadian Flycatchers breed, filling the air with clear, sharp calls and songs.

At the east end of Orchard Pond Road, take a left and head a couple of miles out Meridian Road to the "twin bridges" and park anywhere. This is a marvelous ecosystem with the swamps to the west giving way to the marshes to the east. Many allopatric species meet here and the species diversity is staggering. Dwarf Salamanders lie in wait under rotting logs to the east, where excellent swamps and marshes both reside.

The St. Marks Lighthouse also serves as a beacon to birders looking for water birds

One of the truly neat experiences is walking under the second bridge at night with a good flashlight and observing the herps. There are River, Bronze, Bull and Leopard Frogs hopping hither and yon, with the poorly known Two-toed Amphiuma slithering through the shallow water. Many interesting fishes such as Pirate Perch and madtoms cut through the pools as the rare Northern Cricket Frog chirps in the distance. Remember restraint when tempted to slay the golden goose; many of us have known of this place for years and not collected it heavily.

South of Tallahassee lies a wonderland of natural areas. Taking HW 363 through the town of Woodville, and taking HW 267 over to HW 98, one finds the road to the St. Mark's Wildlife Refuge on their right just after crossing the beautiful St. Mark's River (great trout fishing in winter). The refuge is heavily laden with birds and large alligators, and also has an excellent visitor's center, and there are other abiding creatures such as armadillo, deer, Marsh Rabbit, Dwarf Salamander and even the rare Flatwoods Salamander. Snakes abound, including the now uncommon Eastern Kingsnake around the Lighthouse area. There is no camping on this refuge.

This is a bountiful refuge for wintering birds, with thousands of waterfowl from November through March. At the Lighthouse Pool, Greater Scaup and Canvasback join many other species to create a mosaic of color and variety not found anywhere else in North Florida. Walking the dikes leads to many species of rails, shorebirds, sparrows and frequent glimpses of Bald Eagles sailing overhead to and from their nests. The dikes are solitary places to truly "get away."

The fishing off the lighthouse is renowned, as is the scalloping in the grass beds out the mouth of the Wakulla and St. Mark's River. In winter this serves as an excellent boat trip for loons, ducks, grebes, shorebirds, and much more. In this cool season, trout and reds move upriver to deep holes and are caught at times ridiculously easy. Take it easy, though, as Manatee love these waters and terrible accidents have happened with speeding motor boats.

Zipping back to HW 98 and taking HW 267 over to HW 61, Wakulla Springs is a truly beautiful State Park with a fantastic appeal for nature enthusiasts. The springs itself offers rare views of Limpkin and many other aquatic species. The Beech/Magnolia Forests around the springs affords us all the typical moist forest birds in summer, many visitors in the migration and uncommon winter species such as Red-headed Woodpecker, Purple Finch, Pine Siskin and much more.

Mammals are common and tame, with herps being frequently encountered on the park's trails and grounds. This experience is well worth the small entrance fee and supporting Florida's State Parks makes sense for those of us who wish to show our grandchildren our natural heritage. There is no camping here but hotel and restaurant facilities are available (850) 224-5950.

WILD AND

A small caveat about this area: The two largest Cottonmouths I ever saw came from Wakulla Springs and nearby McBride's Slough. They were over six feet (!) and one had twelve mullet inside. It seems there is a gene pool in Central Wakulla County of enormous Cottonmouths, as I have seen others, including one I caught and measured that was 5' 7", of Biblical proportion. Whether it's the cold waters of these springs or some other factor of which I am unaware, those leviathans that ease their way through the shallow, weed-infested sloughs, looking for fish trapped in shallow water, are both massive and of great length. They also exhibit sexual dimorphism, with the males

WONDERFUL

being a sharply defined black with bands and the larger females tan-brown with bands.

Many people who visit the gulf coast wish to conduct cuisine research on various species of mollusks, crustaceans and our piscine friends. One laboratory which conducts excellent preparations on these delicate creatures is the Spring Creek Restaurant in the tiny town of Spring Creek. Perhaps creating the finest seafood ever tasted, it is right at the end of HW 375 in a lovely little building complete with limestone walls and interesting natural artifacts. After consuming massive amounts of marine invertebrates, resist the temptation to curl up and nap, and walk to the dock where the surface boils with one of dozens of springs in front of you. This is the world's largest spring (not Wakulla) albeit underwater and subtle. For the fisherman, winter is a great time to take your boat out and sit over the small "springlets" catching unlimited numbers of sheephead with dead shrimp and a small hook. Their light, flaky meat is delicious.

The spring and river of Wakulla are among the most beautiful in the world

Heading southwest and then south on HW 98, you must stop at the Gulf Specimen Marine Laboratories in Panacea. Author Jack Rudloe and his marine-biologist wife Ann provide all kinds of invertebrates for (real) research all over the country. Their tanks are chock full of all the sensational critters we discussed in Chapter 7, complete with informative signs and a staff who will conduct tours by calling (850) 984-5297 for prior arrangements. You may simply show up seven days a week (not Sunday mornings) to guide yourself, and the fees are nominal. This fabulous live collection is great for all ages, as small kids are gog-eyed and high school pupils can easily learn marine taxonomy from these instructive tanks. For fifteen years I took my students here and they always had great fun and learned tremendously.

Heading south on HW 98 you will immediately cross the Ochlockonee River mouth — for sure the epicenter of Sand Sharks. See if you and your kids can hold their breath all the way across the bridge! If nothing else, it will keep them quiet for a few treasured moments. Not long after arriving on the Franklin County side is a road off to the left to Alligator Point, which is a terrific area for bird migration. Famous for western stuff like Scissor-tailed Flycatchers, Western Kingbirds, Yellow-headed Blackbirds and White-winged Doves, the west end has a Loblolly forest that is excellent for migrants. The protected land beyond becomes sandy and welcomes Snowy Plovers and Least Terns nesting while the bar is the only location I know for Lamp Shells of the rare phylum Brachiopoda.

Farther west, back on HW 90, you will see the Florida State University Turkey Point Marine Lab. On the far (west) side there is a walk out to a point, where some of the oldest fossils in Florida may be found just lying around like trash. These are probably imported from Goose Pasture and seem to be Miocene. There are also Pliocene fossils, probably dredged up from the intracoastal waterway. This is a great area for shore-

birds, with Marbled Godwits, Whimbrel and American Oystercatchers commonly seen. The hammock in the woods, probably a midden, is often a nice spot for transgulf migrants, and harmless Gulf Salt Marsh Snakes abound in the pools, rippling with killifish.

The "Marine Lab Point" at Florida State University's Turkey Point is loaded with ancient sea creatures in the rock, as well as great plovers and sandpipers

Continuing on west, you must be hungry! Just across the bridge in Carrabelle, where the police station consists of a cop parked at a phone booth (I'm serious), treat yourself to a seafood platter at Julia Mae's you will carry with you the rest of your life. The small platter may only be measured in metric tons, while the "platter for two" (countries) could end world hunger.

Just between Julia Mae's and the bridge is a paved road to the west that curves around, forks (take the left) and heads into the famed Tate's Hell Swamp. This area received its name from the old story of a guy named Tate who met "Tate's fate," lost in the swamp (actually a huge shrub bog). The story alleges that he went in after a panther with a dozen Airedales, or a half-dozen hounds, or maybe one big lab. Depends on who you listen to. Anyway, the dogs were killed by snake bite and Tate got struck, too. Finally, he wandered out to the road and was taken to the Carabelle hospital. They asked him what happened, to which he replied, "I've been through Tate's (his own) Hell." Truth be told, my hypothesis is he found a copy of the waterbird exam I used to administer to my students, and died of hydroornithophobia.

This area has been ditched and planted with Slash Pines eons ago by Buckeye Cellulose, Inc., but has never lost its wildness. Now owned by the State of Florida, it is being restored and has become part of an extensive wildlife corridor. A nice loop is to take the first big fork to the right, turn right just over the small bridge, head north up the west side of the Carabelle River, turn right at the "T" to cross the river again and rest in the facilities at Gully Branch. Try the water at the artesian well so you can appreciate city water again, and continue east. Then, take River Road south, cross the river at the large bridge, turn left, and you'll come back out the way you entered. There are a million neat places you can get out and swat flies, but remember, there are three species of pit vipers fairly common in this area, so watch your step.

Continuing down the coast on HW 98 is a beautiful drive with tiny towns and gorgeous beaches. In a few minutes you will come to East Point, where Carl and Eunice Ard at the Fina station are some of the finest people there ever were. From gas and car repair to a clean grocery store, they will stop and help you any way they can. And they love the Seminoles!

In East Point you may cross the causeway to St. George Island (in summer, drive slowly to miss the skimmers) if you like beautiful beaches. But Rattlesnake Hammock in the State Park is the top location for migrant birds in this entire area, and birders should always go here spring and fall. There is excellent fishing for whiting and trout in the surf, many interesting animals on the trails, and the elusive Island Glass Lizard lives on the extreme east end. Facilities for those who wish to camp are available by calling (850) 927-2111.

A TREAT TO NORTH FLORIDA

Returning to East Point, you may then cross the mighty Apalachicola River and drive through historic Apalachicola. The old houses are beautiful and John Gorrie, inventor of refrigeration, hailed from this tiny town. Painted Buntings once nested here and should be watched (listened) for by visiting birders from late April through July.

Off the coast from Apalachicola is Little St. George Island and St. Vincent Island, both lying between Big St. George and Indian Pass. These were all formed from sand from the Appalachian Mountains flowing out the mouth of rivers and being carried westward by longshore currents (see Chapter 1). Neither is accessible by car, but trips may be arranged through the State Parks (Little St. George) and the U.S. Fish and Wildlife Service (St. Vincent). The State Parks are great folks to work with, and they'll take school groups by boat to their large cabin and allow them to stay for educational purposes. It is a great deal!

Reddish Egrets are regular at Cape San Blas, except in midwinter

Heading out of Apalachicola on HW 98 west you have only the best ahead of you! Be sure to take the left fork about four miles out of Apalach. If you wish to drive the beach to fish or look for great shorebirds, get a permit and drive from the tip of Indian Pass (across from St. Vincent Island) all the way to Cape San Blas. I have seen terrific birds on this beach, including all three species of jaegers. The cape is a truly spectacular place, with clouds of shorebirds and a lagoon with many fascinating marine animals. The red fishing off the cape is excellent and big sharks are often caught. Keep an eye on the gulf as gannets are regular in the cool season, and I have seen Masked Boobies, many frigatebirds, and Oldsquaw over the water. Reddish Egrets are often in the lagoon and the marsh is full of sparrows and wrens.

The cape may be accessed, with a good walk, by taking the left turn immediately after the road makes a right (north) curve. There is a nice wayside park with facilities and showers on your left immediately after you take the left turn to go out to St. Joe Peninsula. Head west and as the road curves right (after the military station) take the left fork and you will wind up in a parking lot with a pleasant half-mile beach walk to the cape.

But by not taking this left fork, you automatically head north out the St. Joe Peninsula, a real spectacle in the fall migration. Don't miss the nature trail just inside the State Park on the right and never miss the opportunity to work the turtle grass beds in Eagle Bay. In the warm season, snorkel with a dive flag and in the cool season, wade out on low tides and see the diversity! (Chapters 6 and 7.) Camping and housing are available by calling (850) 227-1327.

Anyone visiting the town of Pt. St. Joe can enter the grass beds from the north side, but the beds are in poor shape with much less diversity. The entire stretch from this town all the way to Panama City has lovely beaches but not much exciting biofaunistically. Much of it, also, is Tyndall Air Force Base land, and they are real funny about citizens wandering around their forests. Traveling north, though, up the Apalachicola River, can be very exciting, indeed!

To experience a wonderful Longleaf Pine forest, exit Tallahassee southeast on the Springhill Highway (373). Upon crossing Capital Circle, birders should check the Sewage Treatment Plant immediately on the left for excellent shorebirds, especially in late spring and early fall. Right after that, on the left, is a typical "perched" pond where many species of amphibians breed in the ephemeral (temporary) water.

LOOKING PRETTY GOOD

This is where the Longleafs begin, and there are many places where one can leave the highway on dirt roads and be among this fire disclimax community (Chapter 2). My favorite road is reached by taking the wide, paved road just before the Bloxam Cutoff, called Helen Guard Station Road that turns right and actually crosses Bloxam Cutoff, where it becomes dirt and is labeled "309." This graded road not only transects terrific Longleafs, it also crosses some wonderful dark, deep sloughs. These are home to river bottom birds, Brown Water Snakes, amphiuma, flier, Dollar Sunfish, River Frogs and much more. It eventually comes out on HW 375 where you can take a left, go south for about five miles, and turn right on the only paved turn. Just ahead on the left is a nice portion of the Florida Trail and then a bridge over the Ochlockonee River. Continuing on will take you to HW 67, which goes northwest to Telogia and south to Carabelle.

A portion of the Apalachicola National Forest, burned regularly, depicts the open ground of a healthy Longleaf forest

You may reach exquisite Bradwell Bay by taking 348 south after several miles of road 309, then turning right on the nice, wide, national forest road. You will see the signs for Bradwell Bay on your left, and a drive around this mammoth shrub bog offers excellent opportunities for looks at various wild animals and insectivorous bogs.

After circling Bradwell Bay you may head south to the coast by taking the road out on the south side, which intersects HW 375 to Sopchoppy, where you pick up HW 319 to the coast. You can also take the main grade road around the north side of Bradwell Bay straight east, which will take you out to Crawfordville and back up to Tallahassee.

Clearly, the most beautiful country in the area are the bluffs overlooking the Apalachicola River. For this, you need to take HW 20 either straight out of Tallahassee (Pensacola Street) or from the point two paragraphs back where 375 meets HW 20. But there is much to see on the way, so don't be in too much of a hurry!

One of the best floodplains in the area, studded with steepheads, is found by taking HW 375 south off HW 20, for 3.1 miles. You will see a decent dirt road off to the right, and it eventually dead ends into the Ochlockonee River. Follow the trails straight ahead and you will pass into a floodplain that will conjure up thought of jungle movies and deep, dark forests. Stay near the valley sidewall on the left and soon you will see small steepheads forming in the wall. Within 200 yards there will appear out in the floodplain the biggest tree you have probably ever seen. It is a cypress, logged in the 1930's (see its chopped top). After you finish standing in amazement, continue on another 100 yards to see a fine steephead stream enter the floodplain. This entire area is great (in cool, damp weather) for Two-lined, Three-lined, Mud, Red and Apalachicola Dusky Salamanders, as well as the rare One-toed Amphiuma. Winter birding is excellent, snakes abound, and chorus frogs hop to and fro.

STRANGE FOSSILS

This quarry has the most delicate mollusk remains you'll ever see

Back to HW 20, there is an interesting deposit of aragonite just before the Ochlockonee that is reached by taking the last paved road on the left before the bridge and stopping at the dead end by the river. Walk into the tiny forested area on the trail to the right, and you will find a wall of dirt in the back of the clearing. These marine fossils are aragonite and, though delicate, may be removed with any small tool.

After you pass the booming metropolis of Hosford, there is a depression on the right a couple of miles west where an insectivorous bog resides. In the warm season, Hat Pins will alert you to this habitat (as they always do), and just park on the right and get ready for muddy shoes. You will immediately see White-capped Pitcher Plants, the protected species in the bog, sticking up in many places. On the mud, just across the ditch, there are Red and Thread Sun Dews glistening away. Walking just uphill, there are loads of Venus Flytrap with their red and green colors. Just down the ditch from the crossing are gobs of Bladderwort, the underwater insectivore. This is a fragile little community which is still here because folks have respected it and left it alone. Please allow future visitors to experience and enjoy this tiny patch of paradise.

Resisting the temptation to put your muddy shoes on the floor of your nice, clean car, take off toward Bristol, and the Garden of Eden. Upon arriving, go ahead and cross the bridge over the Apalachicola. The view is spectacular, and I'll guarantee you it'll be earlier than you think when you reach the Chattahoochee side (since it's

GREAT RIVER

Central time there). Huge floodplains line the river and a tromp through it (with boots) will not disappoint you.

But eventually return to Bristol and up S-12. Soon, you will see the "Garden of Eden Road" (see Preface) on the left. Take it and park in the lot at the road's curve. Put those muddy shoes back on, bring some water and snacks, and take off on a hike that'll make you feel young again. In the cool season, wear layered clothing as you will get plenty warmed up on the first steephead.

Even at low water the Apalachicola is an impressive sight

Very soon you will see a path to the left that will take you to paradise. You are surrounded by Longleafs, but soon they will give way to hardwoods a little downhill. You know something's up . . . . Then, off to your right, the land suddenly disappears and a canyon—right here in Florida—sits out there like you're in the Appalachians. You honestly won't believe what you see!

Continue "down" the trail and you come to a wooden walkway crossing a large steephead stream. A huge Spruce Pine towers out of the evergreen shrubs—you'll see it. The smell of Star anise is in the air and birds of the moist forest like vireos and warblers are singing everywhere. The canopy effect cools your brow and you submit to the temptation to drink the cool, clear water drifting under you. Welcome to Eden.

Time's up. You can trudge up the far bank's trail for a long walk to Alum Bluff or return the way you came. If you do so, turn left when you get back to the sand road for a two hour walk to Alum Bluff or right to go home. I promise you, if you make this hike, you will not be sorry. Alum Bluff is the most beautiful place I have ever seen in Florida, and was the Mecca for my high school program for fifteen years. We did research there on the new species of salamander in the steepheads, but it also gave us an emotional chip that activated every time we approached the edge of the bluff and saw the mighty Apalachicola down below and the sprawling floodplain as far as the eye could see.

Once you finish gawking at the scenery, try hiking down to Little Sweetwater Creek. Simply follow the sand roads around to the north (left, on the way out) and keep peeling around to the left. You will go downhill and soon arrive at the creek. If time permits, try walking up Little Sweetwater, watching for harmless Queen Snakes on the limbs. There are sphagnum bogs with larval Mud Salamanders and steephead streams that enter from the south. You can even take one of those to its source and see the steephead, so typical of this geophysical structure and so unlike gully erosion, with its gradual slant. And don't get lost, or you will be "up the creek."

Upon returning to the departure point, which hopefully you marked, you might wish to ease into the floodplain just below. It gets a little mucky, but it's beautiful and so pristine. This is the home of the rare One-toed Amphiuma, several lungless salamanders of the floodplain, and all kinds of unique fish, insects and reptiles. How lucky we are that The Nature Conservancy owns the Alum Bluff area and has preserved it for all generations!

Teachers and researchers may ask permission to enter the locked gate on S-12 to drive to the Bluff by calling The Nature Conservancy in Tallahassee at (850) 222-0199. The road is sandy and often impassible in dry weather with conventional cars. But in a school bus full of teenagers, it's a scream (they called it "Road from Hell").

A little to the north of the Alum Bluff property is Torreya State Park, home of the disappearing Torreya Tree. With a red clay base, the foundation is radically different from Alum Bluff, and has some interesting creatures. Red Crayfish are common in the streams, with many typical floodplain and Beech/Magnolia creatures found along the nature trail. The view from the bluff is remarkable, and there are actually restrooms and water fountains! The view overlooking the bluff, sitting on the lawn, is surreal, and a great place to picnic or take a group. Camping is nice in the forests and reservations may be made by calling (850) 643-2674.

Leaving the Tallahassee area, we head out HW 20 toward Panama City. Unfortunately, what we see are Slash Pines (and in some cases, Sand Pines) planted in place of the Longleafs we have clear cut years ago. In some places, our intelligence is insulted where the logging industry has left a thin row of trees along the highway to hide the unnecessary deed of clear cutting. Put the pedal to the metal and head west.

The bad news of the Panhandle is the thousands of acres of planted pines. The good news is that there are simply stupendous rivers flowing south to the gulf. One such river is the Chipola, a spring-fed system with clear water and great canoeing. One of the last places Ivory-billed Woodpeckers were seen, the Chipola offers unique fishes, some good steepheads, harmless water snakes to keep boaters awake, and terrific fossil formations during low water.

For the best fossiling, though, go back to the Apalachicola River on HW 20 and take a boat up to Alum Bluff when the water is low. The river level is the Chipola Formation with calcareous sands, between forty and fifty feet above sea level and fifteen to twenty million years old. Above that layer is the Hawthorn Formation, largely sand. The exciting Jackson Bluff layer from seventy to eighty-five feet above sea level is around ten million years old and heavily laden with mollusk shells. The clay above it represents the continent before the sand eroded down the rivers and then about fifty feet of sand lies atop the clay. Sitting in a boat, experts could lay out half of the Cenozoic Era by pointing, and others could teach a fair amount of marine biology with a fossil hammer.

Another excellent fossiling location easily reached off HW 20 is just north of Clarksville on HW 73. There is a nice park at Four-mile Creek for picnics but continue on to the next creek, lying in an ancient dry estuary. Leave the highway 100 yards past the bridge and bounce along down to the dirt road, which takes you back to the bridge. Set your parking brake and take a fossil tool under the bridge and carefully ease down to the stream. This clay deposit is early Pliocene and yields some beautifully preserved mollusks, and sometimes manatee ribs.

Upon arriving in nearby **Panama City**, you will see some amazing Karrst lakes with white sand shores. These unique ecosystems have interesting creatures, such as many partially melanistic mosquitofish. Pitcher plant bogs are along the road and dirt roads leading off into the pine forest are not uncommon. These roads are unfortunately used by inconsiderate people to dump trash, but the occasional refrigerators and stoves are excellent places for many creatures. Scorpions, Black Widow Spiders, various lizards and snakes and certain dry land amphibians all may be found.

Pitt Springs provides a sure way to beat the summer heat, as well as a good area for unique animals

Another wonderful river is the Econfina Creek, in Bay County (not to be confused with the beautiful Econfina River in Jefferson County). It may be reached on either HW 20 or HW 388, where a canoe could take people into paradise. Much of the land, though, is owned by the Water Management District and is closed off. But for Panama City people looking for a nice river to canoe, it is a terrific choice. It lacks the high bluffs of the Chipola but has dense bottom lands with many of the species mentioned that inhabit floodplain forests.

FROZEN FUN

On HW 20 there is the Pitt Spring Recreation Area on the Econfina, located in beautiful woods of Beech/Magnolia. There are trails to walk and safe spots for children to swim. On the branches of the river are Queen Snakes and Midland Water Snakes, in this lovely example of blackwater. No more than 100 yards down stream, off to the west, is another spring, which is as beautiful as it is secluded. It is reached by walking the shallows or canoeing. Camping is allowed on the east side of the road by calling the Northwest Florida Water Management Office at (850) 772-9919.

When HW 20 hits HW 79, it is time to head south. There are pretty nice pine forests along the way, although "Pine Log State Forest" has few Longleafs and is mostly show. The poor paved road off to the west, about half way from HW 20 to Panama City Beach, has some good dirt roads to the side with many pine forest animals such as Fence Lizards, Cricket and Little Grass Frogs, Black Racers, various grasshoppers and many other species.

For birders in the migration, either side of Phillip's Inlet can be productive, especially in frontal conditions. The east side has long been a nice, though primitive, spot but the new park on the west side is well kept. Birders could bring their families, uninterested in birds, and have options for the whole family. This is also true of St. Andrews State Recreation Area, which shelters St. Andrews Bay and is mostly pine trees. There is camping available by calling (850) 233-5140.

Snorkeling is nice by the jetties out into the gulf. Many species of interesting gamefish are seen milling around the rocks, including barracuda, as well as echinoderms like sea urchins. The beach is right there, so alternatives for nonswimmers exist. But for those into marine animals, the real treat is the Turtle Grass beds on the bay side. Though perhaps not as great as St. Joe Bay, many creatures do abound in these calm waters, and a good low tide in the cool season can be a thrilling morning of walking on the low tide flat. Be sure to check regulations about what can or cannot be taken.

For the stout hearted, try getting to Shell Island, just southeast of the recreation area. Pristine and lovely, it makes great primitive camping and is loaded with animals (among which are rattlers). The Turtle Grass beds on the bay side are untouched, and the high dunes on the island cut the strong south wind. Winds in places like this could be a nuisance or a godsend, depending on the temperature and bug population.

Inhabitants of **Ft. Walton Beach**, **Crestview** and **Defuniak Springs** have their own little inland playgrounds in mammoth Eglin Air Force Base property and Blackwater River State Park. Spanning from Defuniak Springs to Pensacola Bay and I-10 to the coast, Eglin must be given credit for keeping many thousand acres from being developed. It is a conglomerate of planted Slash Pine, decent Longleaf and oaks that have gotten too large to burn. Nevertheless, it is an expansive forest with many interesting animals and places to get away from our species.

A "grass stage" young Longleaf on Eglin land demonstrates these adolescents and shows why they are fire-tolerant

BURN ME, I DARE YOU!

In two of the most exciting discoveries in Florida herpetology this century, two incredible frogs were found to reside on Eglin property. The Florida Bog Frog, a new species to science, was discovered in the early 1980's in seepage bogs and sphagnum near small streams. And if that wasn't enough, the Pine Barrens Treefrog, a species long thought confined to a limited range in the Carolinas was discovered right in this area. More than anything, it is a testament to Florida's biodiversity, not to mention what a poor working knowledge we have had on Panhandle species (don't forget the One-toed Amphiuma and the Apalachicola Dusky Salamander).

There are many roads through Eglin that cover a variety of habitats. Be sure to call the Eglin Air Force Base

Natural Resources Office and see what permits currently are needed, and check in at the office when arriving. It seemed easy to gain access at one point when my students and I successfully found the Bog Frog in the late 1980's.

Blackwater River State Park is a lovely Longleaf Pine forest with the beautiful Blackwater River flowing through it. The park has a large herpetological presence and many freshwater fishes are unique to Florida as inhabitants of the extreme northwest corner (see Chapter 9). Birds are plentiful as most Longleaf species are easily found in the well-managed pine forest. Camping is to be found in the park, whose number is (850) 983-5363.

Blackwater River State Park provides all the beauty of the river as well as terrific Longleaf stands and great camping areas

Near the park are ravines of the Blackwater River where unique herps may be uncovered. The Northern Dusky Salamander is only found in this location in Florida, along with Midland Water Snake, Upland Chorus Frog and Dusky Gopher Frog in this general location. Mud Salamanders may also be surprisingly abundant in the seepage of West Florida.

There is a tremendous birding location in Ft. Walton Beach for many kinds of birds (especially shorebirds) and sometimes other interesting kinds of animals as well. The Ft. Walton Beach Sprayfields are reached by taking HW 189 (Beal Parkway) 4.5 miles north to the Tom Thumb on the left and taking the first road north of that intersection (Green Acres) to the left. Turn left and go north on the Beal Street extension to the end. The sprayfields are on the right, and don't forget to check the bird log upon arriving. You may drive out to the left to the sprayfields, but not on the lawn around the holding ponds. My

The lovely sea oats along the road into Ft. Pickins charms the coldest heart

suggestion is to delay arriving until late morning, as earlier the sun is quite blinding off to the east. Don't be shocked to see the resident gator snatch up some unaware sandpiper feeding along the edge.

Extreme West Florida around **Pensacola** concludes our North Florida summary with several outstanding locations for birds and other animals. Ft. Pickins on the extreme west end of Santa Rosa Island is about as good a spot for avian migrants as it gets. Get there early in the fall and late morning in spring. You will see transgulf migrants foraging in the hardwoods and peninsular migrants flying east along the coastline. Cold-front days are the best shot at a great list of birds, spring or fall. Also marvel at the beautiful sea oats lining the dunes on this federal land, but don't pick them, as they are protected by law. Fair Point in Gulf Breeze has produced some great bird records through the years as well, and the entire barrier island string along West Florida is capable of big birding days in spring and fall with the right weather.

For great inland locations in extreme West Florida take HW 29 north out of Pensacola and pass Barth and Molina. Two locations—Pine Barrons Creek and Cotton Lake—are wild and beautiful for many kinds of animals. Certain creatures like Swamp Rabbits are only found in Florida right in this area and observers should always be watching for new species (such as the Diamond-backed Water Snake) to our state. Nature lovers with a willingness to seine may very well catch new fishes or salamanders, and Lord knows what new insects could be added here. This is true for any natural area from HW 29 to the Perdido River, at the Alabama state line. You can add to the body of knowledge of science and subsequently help the animals by reporting your findings to the proper authorities and rightfully feel the accomplishment you deserve.

HW 4, which runs from Century to near Crestview, has many nice stands of Longleafs on it, including the Blackwater River State Forest (as opposed to Blackwater River State Park).

One personal note. Many of you readers know that my father, Dr. Henry Stevenson of Florida State University, literally "wrote the book" on Florida birds, and my work certainly pales in comparison to his life and legacy. As a father, he gave many things I will always cherish, including and especially an example of integrity and courage few will ever match. But it was the love for the outdoors he instilled in me that has most profoundly affected my life, as field zoology has been the epicenter of my forty-six years in this Garden of Eden. I just wanted to suggest that you parents give your child the opportunity to know nature and love the outdoors. The balance and perspective it teaches us is only exceeded by the amazing secrets and miracles its inhabitants share.

BIRDING BOND

Father and son Henry and Jim logged countless hours in nature for over thirty-five years

Index

A

B

C

D

E

H

I

J

K

L

M

N

O

P

I N D E X

BIBLIOGRAPHY

The following books will prove valuable in field identifications of animals covered in this book:

For Marine Invertebrates: *Peterson Field Guide: Southeastern and Caribbean Shores*, by Eugene Kaplan; Houghton Mifflin Company, Boston 1988

For Terrestrial Invertebrates: *Peterson Field Guide: Insects,* by Donald J. Borror and Richard E. White; Houghton Mifflin Company, Boston 1970

For Fishes: *Peterson Field Guide: Freshwater Fishes*, by Lawrence Page and Brooks M. Burr; Houghton Mifflin Company, Boston 1991

For Reptiles and Amphibians: *Peterson Field Guide: Reptiles and Amphibians (Eastern and Central North America)*, by Roger Conant; Houghton Mifflin Company, Boston 1991

For Mammals: *Mammals*, by William H. Burt and Richard P. Grossenheider; Houghton Mifflin Comapny, Boston 1976

For Birds: Any field guide which includes Eastern Birds.